Adjudication under the NEC

Richard N. M. Anderson
Barrister

Thomas Telford

Published by Thomas Telford Publishing, Thomas Telford Ltd, 1 Heron Quay, London E14 4JD.
URL: http://www.thomastelford.com

Distributors for Thomas Telford books are
USA: ASCE Press, 1801 Alexander Bell Drive, Reston, VA 20191-4400, USA
Japan: Maruzen Co. Ltd, Book Department, 3–10 Nihonbashi 2-chome, Chuo-ku, Tokyo 103
Australia: DA Books and Journals, 648 Whitehorse Road, Mitcham 3132, Victoria

First published 2001

Also available from Thomas Telford Books
The New Engineering Contract: A Legal Commentary. Arthur T. McInnis ISBN: 0 7277 2961 6
NEC and Partnering. John Bennett and Andrew Baird. ISBN: 0 7277 2955 1

A catalogue record for this book is available from the British Library

ISBN: 0 7277 2997 7

© Richard N M Anderson and Thomas Telford Limited 2001

Designed and typeset by Bookcraft Ltd, Stroud, Gloucestershire.
Printed and bound in Great Britain by MPG Books Ltd, Bodmin, Cornwall.

Disclaimers

Generally

The Publishers and Author expressly disclaim all and any liability and responsibility to any person, whether a purchaser of this work or otherwise, in respect of anything done or omitted to be done by any such person in reliance, in whole or in part, upon the contents of this work.

Worldwide

The above general disclaimer applies but, in addition, the attention of users worldwide is specifically drawn to the fact that either the law of the contract and/or the law of the country may have an impact upon the process of adjudication being used there and readers adjudicating there should accordingly seek the advice of a competent professional adviser.

United Kingdom

The above general disclaimer applies but, in addition, the attention of users in the United Kingdom is specifically drawn to the fact that the legislation applying to adjudication is new. It has yet to be fully tested, drawn, and developed. Accordingly, although references to decisions of first instance are made in this book, those decisions might later be changed. In relation to any specific transactions readers should seek the advice of a competent professional.

Dedication

This book is dedicated to Veronica Baker.

Acknowledgements

Adjudication as a concept has been in existence for some time, but the spread of the concept worldwide and its development as a statutory entitlement in the United Kingdom is new.

A great deal of shared research and tuition has gone into keeping pace with these changes, and in that respect the author is grateful to the following: Len Bunton, Andrew Burr, Guy Cottam, Brian Eggleston, Reziya Hamson and Eric Mouzer. Special mention must be made of Gordon Bathgate, Tony Bingham, Chris Dancaster (also an adjudication author), John Campbell, Gordon Coutts, and Brian Totterdill (also an adjudication author) who will know the contribution that they have made. In particular, my genuine thanks go to Jeremy Brinton at Thomas Telford for his tireless support and to Drick Vernon, Technical Adviser at the ICE, who read over the first part of this book and made a number of valuable suggestions.

Any remaining errors of fact or interpretation are those of the author alone.

Preface

Construction contracts have been with us for some time, and have gradually become standardised. For some this has been a comforting development in that it has introduced an element of certainty, but for others, as a recent survey suggests, it has been a discomforting development which has encouraged rather than discouraged disputes.

In the 1990s the apparent development of adversarial culture and the feeling that something was 'just not quite right' led the construction industry to re-examine itself. That process appears to have been initiated by the Institution of Civil Engineers, the Legal Affairs Committee of which recommended a wide-ranging review. They concluded that standard forms had become so complex, so rigid and so unwieldy that they no longer best met the needs of their users, and recommended the introduction of a new contract strategy for their members. This resulted in the introduction of the New Engineering Contract, and over time the family of New Engineering and Construction Contracts was developed that are in use today.

The process was continued when the construction industry and the government of the day jointly requested Sir Michael Latham to undertake a review of the construction industry as a whole. As part of that review the desirable features of a modern construction contract were considered, and Sir Michael found that the provisions of the then newly-introduced New Engineering Contracts very nearly met those conditions. Also as part of the review, the most desirable means of providing for the independent, speedy and inexpensive interim determination of disputes as works progressed was considered, and Sir Michael recommended the adoption of the process of adjudication. In the family of New Engineering and Construction Contracts, the procedure designed for the resolution of disputes is adjudication. The procedure is not, however, automatic, and some care is required in the setting up of the adjudication procedures in the NEC contracts, an issue we consider in the first part of this book.

Although initially developed in the UK, the New Engineering and Construction Contracts are intended for use worldwide, and are regularly to be found employed internationally. In these circumstances, the concept of adjudication may be used in its purest form, and we consider that use in the second section of this book.

Where, however, the contracts in the New Engineering and Construction family of contracts are being used for works within the United Kingdom – in circumstances where they are 'construction contracts' – then different considerations may arise. Here the contractual concept of adjudication must be read side by side with the statutory concept of adjudication. Furthermore, each of the territories making up the United Kingdom – England, Wales, Scotland and Northern Ireland – is entitled to its own rules.

The early indications appear to be that the NEC Engineering and Construction family of contracts is working well in operation, with few disputes arising. Even with the best will in the world, however, some disputes – often arising from a genuinely-held difference of opinion – will arise. It is hoped that this book will assist in helping the process of adjudication operate as it should. All law covered in the book is stated as at 1st July 2001.

About the author

Richard N. M. Anderson is a specialist in construction law. He is a trained and accredited Mediator, Adjudicator and Arbitrator. He has in the past been seconded to a large international construction company and is now in practice as a Barrister. His interest in adjudication in particular has developed from over ten years' experience of sitting as Chairman of a Panel in one of the Government Adjudication Schemes.

Richard N. M. Anderson has advised, lectured and written widely on construction matters and published work includes the following:

'Building Contracts', *The Stair Memorial Encyclopaedia* (assistance)

'Keeping Construction disputes under control', *Construction Law* Vol 9, Issue 3

'The Route to Adjudication', *Construction Law* Vol 9, Issue 7

'The Route to Adjudication in England and Wales', *Construction Law Journal*

'Jurisdiction in adjudications', *Construction and Engineering Law* Vol 5, Issue 2

'Jurisdiction Issues', *Adjudication Construction Law*, Vol 11, Issue 6

He is also a frequent case editor in the *Construction Law Journal*.

Richard N. M. Anderson has also previously published a book on adjudication, namely:

A Practical Guide to Adjudication in Construction Matters. W. Green/ Sweet & Maxwell, London, 2000.

Richard N. M. Anderson
Barrister
Pepys' Chambers
17 Fleet Street
London
EC4Y 1AA
Tel: (020) 7936 2710
Fax: (020) 7936 2501
E-mail: anderson@cqm.co.uk

The scheme of the book

Most developed countries have a construction industry. Originally, these industries served their own domestic needs but increasingly they are in competition with each other in what is now a 'global' industry.

In order to succeed in such a global industry it is necessary to be competitive. Evidence of competitiveness is difficult to come by and, even where it can be obtained, difficult to compare. Nevertheless, such evidence as is available suggests that the cost of producing a typical structure varies enormously between, for example, the USA, Japan, Asia, South Africa and the various countries which make up the EC.

There are a number of reasons why this might be so, but one of the factors can be the damaging cost of resolving disputes arising from an adversarial culture. Such a culture has no place in modern working conditions. Wherever it might be in the world, a major project is likely to be made up of a number of contractors from a number of countries taking part. Managing such a project is an increasingly complex business and what is required is a culture not of adversity but of partnership and co-operation.

It is into this brave new world that the NEC Engineering and Construction family of contracts has embarked. It offers this service both within the United Kingdom and on a worldwide basis. Its new form of approach is aimed at fostering co-operation and partnership and its new form of contract is aimed at preventing disputes arising in the first place and resolving those disputes which do arise swiftly and effectively by way of adjudication.

Adjudication, as a means of resolving disputes, is of considerable antiquity. Under both civil law systems and common law systems the original and preferred method of resolving disputes appears to have been what we would now call Arbitration (from which 'adjudication' might be said to also derive) and indeed, historians tell us that in Greece, Rome, Scotland, England, and in many other countries, the process which we now know as 'arbitration' pre-dates the process which we now know as 'litigation'.

Litigation is, however, complex, time-consuming and expensive and in recent years Arbitration appears to have followed a similar path. While recognising their merits (along with other methods) as an ultimate means of finally determining disputes, what was sought was an intermediate means for the speedy and inexpensive resolution of disputes which would allow the Works to keep moving. Adjudication offers that promise and adjudication is offered (it is not compulsory) in the NEC family of contracts.

For those Parties who wish to incorporate adjudication into their NEC contract, we consider in Book I what may be required in that respect. In Book II we consider adjudication itself. In Part I we consider what is involved in adjudication worldwide and in Part II we consider what is involved in adjudication for those Works which are undertaken within the United Kingdom and which fall within the definition of 'construction contracts'. For both Parts we consider what may precede an adjudication (Section I), the process of adjudication (Section II) and what may follow an adjudication (Section III).

Note that throughout this book [.....] represents blanks to be filled in on forms.

Foreword

Professor Sir Michael Latham

**DL, MA, (Hon) FRIBA, FRIAS, FR.Eng, FLCE,
FCIOB, RLCS
Chairman, Willmott Dixon Ltd
and Knowles Management Ltd.
Author, *Constructing the Team***

In 2000 I was glad to be able to write a foreword for Richard Anderson's *Practical Guide to Adjudication in Construction Matters*. He has now produced a further detailed guide to adjudication under the Engineering and Construction Contract (NEC) family of documents, and I am glad to be able to welcome this new book as well. I am sure that it will be a most helpful document for practitioners working with the NEC.

When I undertook my enquiry in 1993/94 which resulted in *Constructing the Team*, I was indeed impressed by the NEC, as the book points out. Because of the NEC's emphasis on efficient management of the project, clear delineation of roles and provision of a matrix of interlocking documents throughout the supply chain, I felt that it had the potential to become a standard document for all types of construction. While I would have wished for still more uptake of it since 1994, especially for UK Government contracts, its use has spread quite widely. Willmott Dixon are now using it on a variety of building projects, and it has become the normal procurement route for one of our social housing partner clients.

Adjudication was already a part of the NEC when I produced my report, and that was one of the reasons why I recommended that the adjudication process should become the normal method of dispute resolution in construction. That has increasingly become the case since the introduction of the Construction Act in 1998. Those who were sceptical about the practicality of the whole reform process – and there were many such doubters – could see that adjudication was a system already in being, not some fanciful idea of mine. Some have since accepted that it has been a powerful instrument for change.

No doubt the whole adjudication process will continue to be refined by experience, but the strongly supportive attitude of the Courts has reinforced the determination of the industry to make it work well. Adjudication is a right, not a duty, and is a backstop for dispute resolution, not the first port of call. No one wants disputes, and the best practice is to follow the procedures of the NEC, by which problems are spotted and avoided before they arise, in a spirit of mutual co-operation. However, if they do reach the status of a dispute, despite everybody's best endeavours, there is now a practical and increasingly well-rehearsed system available to resolve them quickly.

I commend this book to the attention of all involved in the construction process.

Chronological index of adjudication cases

Contents

Section III   What may follow the process of adjudication

Part II   Adjudication under the NEC (in relation to 'Construction Contracts' within the UK)

Section I   What may precede the process of adjudication

Section II   The process of adjudication

Section III   *What may follow the process of adjudication*

Book I

The constitution of the NEC family of contracts

Introduction

The process known as 'adjudication', used as a means of resolving construction disputes, is and remains essentially consensual. The process remains consensual throughout in that provided all of the Parties are agreed as to a particular course of action in an adjudication, then by and large that is the course of action which will be followed. The process is consensual in that the Parties usually make provision for adjudication in their contract. The new form of contract with which we are here concerned, known as the NEC Engineering and Construction family of contracts, makes provision for adjudication as an intermediate means of resolving disputes. Book I is concerned with an examination of the NEC contracts which make up the family of contracts and in particular the provision which they make as regards adjudication.

1. The approach of the NEC Engineering and Construction family of contracts

It appears to have been a generalised concern within the profession as a whole which led the Institution of Civil Engineers, in 1985, to initiate its fundamental review of contract strategies in their industry. The conclusion arrived at was that the traditional and existing forms of standard contract no longer adequately met the needs of the users generally, particularly (in relation to the matters with which we are here concerned) as regards the proliferation of disputes and the resources wasted in resolving them. It was for that reason that the Institution of Civil Engineers set out to develop a new form of contract, the New Engineering Contract, aimed at better reflecting the current and future needs of a modern construction industry.

That same generalised concern within the United Kingdom appears to have led the Government of the day together with the construction industry to commission, in July 1993, a joint review of the UK construction industry. That task was entrusted to Sir Michael Latham, who produced interim (*Trust and Money*) and then final (*Constructing the Team*) reports. Sir Michael Latham was clearly impressed by the New Engineering Contract, which he recommended as a model for the industry, and also by the process of adjudication as a means of resolving disputes. Although wide-ranging, those recommendations were later converted into UK legislation only in relation to two particular respects – payments and adjudication.

Against a background that the construction industry in the United Kingdom was still under-achieving, the then Government of the day set up, in 1987, a Construction Task Force under the Chairmanship of Sir John Egan. This was asked to report and advise on the scope for improving the quality and efficiency of the construction industry. Their shorter report (*Rethinking Construction*) identified five key drivers of change: committed leadership; a focus on the customer; integrated processes and teams; a quality driven agenda and commitment to people. Sir John Egan also recommended that in order to achieve its full, worldwide potential, substantial changes in the culture of the construction industry would be required. These included the replacement of competitive tendering with partnering in the form of long-term relationships based on clear measurement of performance and sustained improvements in quality and efficiency. It is not yet clear what progress has been made in these areas.

That approach is to a large extent reflected in the related contracts which now go to make up what is known as the NEC Engineering and Construction family of contracts. The procedures in these contracts are aimed at providing a stimulus to good management. By providing a modern method for participants to work collaboratively it is hoped that this will lead to a much-reduced risk of poor performance and an increased likelihood of good performance. In this way, it is hoped that disputes can be avoided altogether but, recognising that some disputes will be inevitable, it is hoped that any disputes may be more easily resolved by the intermediate process of adjudication.

The NEC Engineering and Construction family of contracts is intended to be used either standing alone or as an interlocking group of contracts. It is also intended to be used not only within the United Kingdom but on a world-wide basis.

Background to the NEC Engineering and Construction family of contracts

Following upon identified concern in the industry, the Legal Affairs Committee of the ICE recommended to its Council in September 1985 that there be undertaken a 'fundamental review of alternative contract strategies for civil engineering design and construction with the objective of identifying the needs of good practice.'

That review duly took place. In December 1986, a specification was submitted which in June 1988 led to the development of a new style of contract under the heading of the 'New Engineering Contract' (NEC) which was released in a consultative version in January 1991 and in a working version (the First Edition), together with its associated Subcontract, in March 1993.

The New Engineering Contract was followed in 1994 by the first editions of the Professional Services Contract and the Adjudicator's Contract.

A further review of the working of the New Engineering Contract then took place. Amongst other things, it was decided to expand the ambit of the new contract to cover both engineering and construction works and that this fact should be reflected in the renaming of the contract as the 'NEC Engineering and Construction Contract'.

A second edition of the contract, entitled the NEC Engineering and Construction Contract and its associated Subcontract, was published in November 1995. In addition, a number of amendments were introduced, with the designation of the country which they represent, as options (e.g. Option Y(UK) 1; Option Y(UK) 2). There are also Products and Maintenance contracts available.

A second edition of the Adjudicator's Contract was published in April 1998 and a second edition of the Professional Services Contract was published in June 1998.

The first edition of an NEC Engineering Construction Short Contract was published in July 1999 .

Most recently, a draft Partnering Agreement, for use as an option, was issued for consultation in September 2000. That draft has now been confirmed, and the NEC Partnering Agreement is now issued as an option (Option X12).

Project Chart

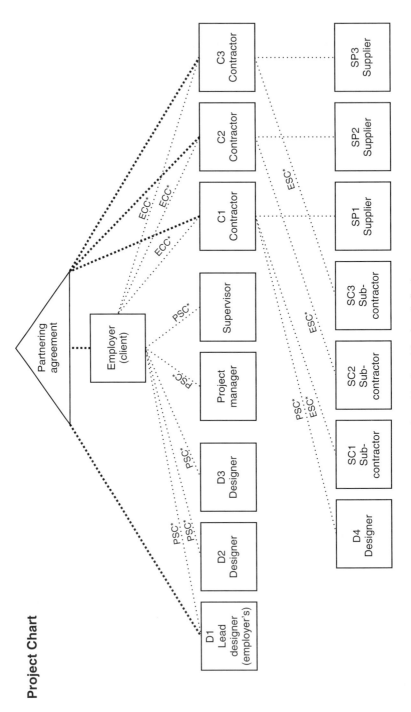

* capable of providing for adjudication

Using the NEC Engineering and Construction family of contracts as the contract strategy for a project

Project Chart

At present, therefore, the 'family' of NEC Engineering and Construction Contracts consists of the following contracts:

- The Professional Services Contract (PSC)
- The Engineering and Construction Contract (ECC)
- The Engineering and Construction Subcontract (ECS)
- The NEC Partnering Agreement (PA)
- The Engineering and Construction Short Contract
- The Adjudicator's Contract

and the *dramatis personae*, or essential persons, in such a Project might include the following:

- The Employer
- The Designer
- The Project Manager
- The Supervisor
- The Contractor
- The Sub-contractor
- The Adjudicator.

It is proposed to consider how these persons and contracts might interrelate in relation to a major Project before considering each of these contracts in turn and then going on to concentrate upon those provisions relevant to adjudication.

The NEC Professional Services Contract (PSC)

The dramatis personae

The Employer
The NEC family of contracts is essentially client-led and the Employer is effectively that Client.

The Employer and the Designer(s) Designers might appear in such projects in a number of ways. Designers engaged by Employers are generally given the role of developing a design to meet the Employer's objectives to the point where tenders can be invited and thereafter this might result in a Professional Services Contract (PSC) between the Employer and the Designer in that respect. That contract might make provision for adjudication.

The Employer and the Project Manager The Project Manager is likely to be central to any such project.

Following on from the design of the project, it is likely that the Project Manager will carry matters forward to the feasibility stage of the project.

The Guidance Notes suggest that the Employer engage the Project Manager at the earliest possible (feasibility) stage of a project. The brief given to the Project Manager at that stage might include advising the Employer on design, on cost and time estimates, on the merits of alternative schemes and on choosing the most appropriate contract strategy. This might result in a PSC between the Employer and the Project Manager in that respect. That contract might make provision for adjudication.

For the implementation stage of the project, the Project Manager will be appointed by the Employer (either in-house or brought in) to represent the Employer's interests and to manage the contract on behalf of the Employer and to achieve the objectives which the Employer has for the completed project.

Considerable authority is placed in the hands of the Project Manager whom it is assumed has the Employer's authority to carry out the actions and make any decisions which are required. That authority can, of course, be limited by the Employer, in which case it will be the responsibility of the Project Manager to comply with those limitations.

The Guidance Notes point out that the Project Manager is free to seek the Employer's views as much or as little as his relationship and contract with the Employer requires. He will normally maintain close contact with the Employer so that his decisions reflect the Employer's business objectives but has the authority to change the work, instruct the Contractor and generally apply his managerial skills and judgement. The Project Manager is constrained from acting unreasonably in this role by statements of the basis upon which each type of action is to be taken, but not in relation to what decision is actually taken. Much of the stimulus for good management operates through the management of the project by the Project Manager, whose role is therefore perhaps that much greater than a similar role under traditional contracts.

As the designs are completed, the work put out for tender and the individual contracts placed, the Guidance Notes recommend that the person already appointed as Project Manager to oversee the whole project be appointed as the Project Manager of these individual contracts also. The Guidance Notes suggest, however, it is essential that for a particular project the Project Manager is sufficiently close to the work and has the time and authority to carry out the duties effectively. Some delegation may be necessary in that respect. This could result in a number of different PSCs between the Employer and various Project Managers. Those contracts might make provision for adjudication.

The Project Manager and the Designer(s) In carrying the project forward from the feasibility stage to the implementation stage, it is recommended that the Project Manager's brief includes the management of designer's activities so that the Project Manager can exercise some control over the implementation of designs and any changes to design. In particular, this would allow the Project Manager to evaluate, on behalf of the Employer, the time and cost effects of any proposed changes to design before authorising the Contractor to proceed. A number of designers may be required and, if so, it is recommended that a Lead Designer be appointed.

There may not, therefore, be a direct contract between the Employer and the Designer at this stage, with such matters being regulated under the PSC between the Employer and the Project Manager. That contract might make provision for adjudication.

The Employer and the Supervisor The Supervisor is appointed (in-house or brought in) by the Employer for a particular project. Essentially, his role (similar to that of a Clerk of Works or Inspector assisting a resident engineer or architect) is to check that the works are constructed in accordance with the contract. The arrangement between the Employer and the Supervisor is likely to be through a PSC. That contract might make provision for adjudication.

The Parties generally According to the Guidance Notes, the basis upon which an Employer might use the PSC can clearly vary but will normally involve the following:

- Some intimation of willingness to treat from the Consultant.
- The Employer will then be the master of the contract strategy and by completing and submitting to the Consultant the Contract Data, Part One will identify the professional services to be provided, the basis of payment, the balance of risk between the Employer and the Consultant, the options selected and any other provision thought necessary.
- The Employer will also provide some of the material to appear in the section (one of the most important in the PSC) dealing with the detailed requirements of the Employer under the heading of 'Scope'. Various options may be selected matching the provisions of the PSC to the provisions of any other NEC contracts involved in the project.
- The Consultant will then, if so advised, complete Part Two of the Contract Data.
- Where selected, an Activity Schedule may be completed (Options A and C).
- Where selected, a Task Schedule may be completed (Option G).
- It is important in relation to the PSC that the section headed 'Scope' is fully and properly completed as this contains the detailed requirements of the Employer and is frequently referred to throughout the PSC.
- A letter of acceptance may then be issued by the Employer.
- The Employer and the Contractor, as Parties, may then enter into a Form of Agreement or some alternative form of agreement to comply with the laws of the country concerned.

The contract

The purpose of the PSC is to provide a standard contract for the appointment of consultants providing professional services generally in the engineering and construction industry. The PSC can be used in a number of ways: for example, for the appointment of a Project Manager at the feasibility stage; for the appointment of a Lead Designer at the development stage; for the Project Manager in relation to a particular contract; for the Designer in relation to a particular contract; or for the Supervisor in relation to a particular contract.

The PSC was created for the purpose of entering into agreements with these professionals (such as Designers, Project Managers, Supervisors and the like) and regulating their relationships as they carry out the various roles ascribed to them. Following upon a consultative document in 1992, the First Edition was published in September 1994 and the Second Edition in June 1998.

It was always intended that the PSC would have a wide role allowing professionals to enter into agreements even where an NEC contract was not being used and even when no construction work at all was involved. It is also, of course, designed to operate 'back-to-back' with other contracts from the NEC family of contracts. Clearly, the PSC closely follows the layout, language and the standard style of the NEC family of contracts.

It was also considered that the incorporation into the PSC of established management procedures and its non-adversarial approach would be of considerable benefit, particularly in relation to the increasing use of partnering arrangements where employers were seeking conditions of contract compatible with partnering. It should, therefore, interrelate well with the draft NEC Partnering Agreement.

The PSC will often involve the Employer as a Party but the PSC can also be used one stage removed as where, for example, a Contractor or a Sub-contractor wishes to employ the services of a Designer. In these circumstances, adaptation is possible to make the PSC effectively a sub-contract with, in relation to the PSC, the Contractor or Sub-contractor in the role of the Employer and the Designer in the role of Consultant.

The NEC Engineering and Construction Contract (ECC)

The dramatis personae

The Employer
The NEC family of contracts is essentially client-led and the Employer is effectively that Client.

The Contractor
The main contract in any major project is likely to be that between the Employer (guided by the Project Manager and perhaps after having been advised on design) and the Contractor. This contract is likely to be the NEC Engineering and Construction Contract (ECC). This contract is likely to make provision for adjudication.

The Contractor and the Designer Designers engaged by Contractors are generally given the role of helping the Contractor to meet the specification. The Contractor in turn may wish to enter into a contract with the Designers advising them. The contract between the Contractor and the Designer could take the form of either an NEC Professional Services Contract or an NEC Engineering and Construction Subcontract. Clearly, it would assist if all such contracts being used 'back-to-back' were compatible as a result of their all being members of the NEC family of contracts. Whichever contract is used may make provision for adjudication.

The Parties generally According to the Guidance Notes, the basis upon which an Employer might use the ECC can clearly vary but will normally involve the following:

- The Employer will make a selection from the six main options as to which type of pricing mechanism to apply.
- The Employer will incorporate the nine core clauses.
- The Employer will incorporate such of the fourteen secondary options as are required.
- The Employer will include under the fifteenth option any additional provisions relating to the contract which are required.

The contract

For the purposes of allowing the Employer to enter into agreements with Contractors, the Engineering and Construction Contract was created and following upon a consultative document in 1991, the First Edition (as the NEC) was published in March 1993. As a result of experience in the use of the ECC and the publication of the Latham Report, a number of amendments were made, the name was changed to the Engineering and Construction Contract and a Second Edition of the ECC was published in November 1995.

Clearly, at that time the ECC was a stand-alone contract and although it can still be used in that way, it was always intended that other contracts would be created to interlock with it.

The ECC is intended:

- to be used for engineering and construction work containing any or all of the traditional disciplines such as civil, electrical, mechanical and building work
- to be used whether the Contractor has some design responsibility, full design responsibility, or no design responsibility
- to provide all the normal current options for types of contract such as competitive tender (where the Contractor is committed to his offered prices), target contracts, cost reimbursable contracts and management contracts.

The NEC Engineering and Construction Subcontract (ECS)

The dramatis personae

Since no provision is made under the NEC family of contracts for Sub-contractors to be nominated, most sub-contract arrangements are likely to be directly between the Contractor and the Sub-contractor. Such projects are likely to involve a number of contracts between the Contractor and various Sub-contractors. These are likely to take the form of the NEC Engineering and Construction Subcontract (ECS). This contract is likely to make provision for adjudication.

The Contractor

The Contractor, who is likely to have already entered into an NEC Engineering and Construction Contract with the Employer, may then enter into any necessary subcontracts with essential Sub-contractor using this NEC contract.

The Sub-contractor

The Sub-contractor's relationship in such a contract will be a direct relationship with the Contractor.

The Parties generally The basis upon which an Contractor might use the ECS can clearly vary but will normally involve the following:

- The Contractor will make a selection from the six main options as to which type of pricing mechanism to apply.
- The Contractor will incorporate the nine core clauses.
- The Contractor will incorporate such of the fourteen secondary options as are required.
- The Contractor will include under the fifteenth option any additional provisions relating to the contract which are required.

The contract

For the purposes of allowing the Contractor to enter into agreements with Sub-contractors, the Engineering and Construction Subcontract was created and following upon a consultative document in 1991, the First Edition of the Subcontract (as the NEC) was published along with the Main Contract in March 1993. As a result of experience in the use of the ECS and the publication of the Latham Report, a number of amendments were made, the name was changed to the Engineering and Construction Subcontract and a Second Edition of the ECS was published in November 1995.

There was no obligation, when using an NEC Main Contract, to also use an NEC Sub-contract although certainly they were always intended to interlock (and are, in fact, almost identical). It was also always intended that other contracts would be created to interlock with them.

The ECS is also intended:

- to be used for engineering and construction work containing any or all of the traditional disciplines such as civil, electrical, mechanical and building work
- to be used whether the Sub-Contractor has some design responsibility, full design responsibility, or no design responsibility
- to provide all the normal current options for types of contract such as competitive tender (where the Sub-Contractor is committed to his offered prices), target contracts, cost reimbursable contracts and management contracts.

The NEC Partnering Agreement (PA)

Released as a draft and apparently well received the NEC Partnering Agreement has now been confirmed as Option X12.

The NEC envisage in the future bringing out further contracts to be integrated into the NEC family of contracts such as a products contract and a maintenance contract.

The NEC Engineering and Construction Short Contract

Unlikely to be found as part of such a project (unless the Employer was laying off a certain section of the Works to a desired Contractor alongside the main project) this contract nevertheless forms part of the NEC family of contracts. It is presumably envisaged that this contract will largely be used on a stand-alone basis.

The NEC Adjudicator's Contract

Where provision is made for adjudication in any of the above contracts, then the framers of the NEC family of contracts envisage that the NEC Adjudicator's Contract will at the same time be entered into between the Adjudicator and the Parties and this contract is provided for that purpose. On this, however, see Book II, Section II.

2. Making provision in the NEC family of contracts for the resolution of disputes

Introduction

It will be appreciated from the foregoing review of the NEC family of contracts that (with the exception of the truncated version of the termination and disputes clause used in the NEC Engineering and Construction Short Contract) each of the contracts in the NEC family of contracts has an identical disputes and termination clause as Core Clause 9 of the contract.

It should also be appreciated, however, that that Core Clause will, of itself, not (in the absence of the agreement of all the Parties) be sufficient to operate the procedures for the resolution of disputes. For those procedures to work effectively it is essential that further particulars are added in the information sections of the contracts.

The purpose of this chapter is to consider the provision which requires to be made to allow for the resolution of disputes and it is proposed to do so under the following headings:

- Selecting the Adjudicator
- Selecting the Law of the Contract
- Selecting the Nominee
- Selecting the Tribunal

Selecting the Adjudicator

Introduction

According to the Guidance Notes it is envisaged that the Adjudicator will be appointed jointly by the Parties.

Experience has apparently shown that if no Adjudicator is suggested in the first place then the likelihood is reduced of an Adjudicator being appointed at all. It appears to be, therefore, for that reason that the section where the name and address of the Adjudicator is to be inserted in the Contract Data is to be found in Part One which, in the case of the NEC Engineering and Construction Contract, for example, is information to be provided by the Employer.

Notwithstanding that fact, the Guidance Notes indicate that the insertion of the name and address of an Adjudicator there is only a suggestion and that the selection of a suitable Adjudicator should be a matter of discussion and agreement between the Parties.

The Guidance Notes go on to suggest that one possible method might be for one Party to propose a list of acceptable names from which the Other Party can make a selection, or that the Other Party might be asked to propose a list of suitable names for the Adjudicator.

Whatever method is adopted by the Parties, there seems little doubt that under the NEC family of contracts the selection of the Adjudicator is a matter to be jointly agreed between the Parties.

We consider below the considerations which might affect the selection of an Adjudicator by the Parties.

The nature of adjudication

In selecting an Adjudicator, the Parties should bear in mind the nature of adjudication.

The process of 'adjudication' is fundamentally of some antiquity. Indeed, many historians now consider that in Greece, Rome, England, Scotland and much of Continental Europe, the processes which we now call 'adjudication' or 'arbitration' in fact preceded the creation of the Courts and the process which we now call 'litigation'.

The attraction of these ancient processes was, of course, the involvement of a wise old man with experience in the area in which the dispute has arisen. There was not seen to be any particular need for representation. Parties would, of course, put their own cases as 'amateurs' and indeed one definition of the word 'adjudication' is 'to act as a judge in a competition between amateurs'.

Upon closer examination, however, the concept of 'adjudication' might be interpreted as going deeper than that. The person whom the Parties jointly approached to determine their dispute was selected not only because he was old and had many years' experience in the field, but because he was also considered to be wise. The Parties therefore expected – as well as a lifetime's experience in the field – that the person selected would act fairly. What the Parties were seeking, therefore, was not simply the determination of their dispute through experience but also the determination of the dispute *judicially*. The word 'adjudication' derives from the Latin word *judex* and can also be interpreted as meaning 'to determine judicially'.

It is suggested, therefore, that the essence of adjudication in the person appointed to act as Adjudicator to determine judicially the competition between amateurs is a blend of both substantial practical experience in the particular field to which the dispute relates *together with* the ability to act judicially.

Some fortunate people are blessed with both of these essential qualities. Experience has shown, however, that in practice it is often necessary to create such a blend. In Arbitration, for example, the trend in England appears to have been for the Arbitrator to be a Lawyer (to provide the judicial aspect) who is assisted by an Expert (to provide the practical experience), whereas the trend in Scotland appears to have been for the Arbiter to be an Expert (to provide the practical experience) who is assisted by a Solicitor acting as Clerk (to provide the judicial aspect). Adjudication appears to be following the same path as Arbitration in that respect.

By whatever means it is arrived at, however, it is suggested that the essence or the nature of adjudication is to be found in this blend of acting with experience and acting judicially.

The qualifications for an Adjudicator

The NEC family of contracts does not specify any specific qualifications which must be possessed by the person selected to act as an Adjudicator under their contracts. The Guidance Notes suggest that the relevant experience, qualifications and general ability of any prospective Adjudicator must be carefully considered and also suggest that the qualities of an Adjudicator should, at a minimum, include the following:

- knowledge of the procedures used in the [NEC family of contracts]
- a full understanding of the roles of the Project Manager and the Supervisor
- a full understanding of how construction costs arise and how they are affected by changes
- knowledge of construction planning and of how plans are affected by changes
- the ability to obtain technical assistance when his own technical knowledge is insufficient
- the ability to obtain up-to-date information about construction costs when no data is there
- an appreciation of construction risks and how allowances should be made for them.

Clearly, the Parties will want to select a person who alone, or together with others, makes up that essential blend of acting with experience and acting judicially. In practice, some Parties approach this matter by selecting as Adjudicator a Lawyer (clearly able to act judicially) experienced in construction matters to whom they give the power to obtain the assistance of specific Experts where required. Other Parties approach the matter by selecting as Adjudicator an Expert (clearly able to act with experience) to whom they give the power to obtain the assistance of a Lawyer where required.

Whichever method is selected, from the point of view of all concerned, the key to a successful adjudication is clearly, at least in part, dependent upon the selection of an Adjudicator best suited to the dispute in question.

In relation to a large project, however, such as the one which we have used as an example in the preceding chapter, there are practical difficulties in selecting an appropriate Adjudicator capable of covering every eventuality so far as potential disputes are concerned. The difficulties can be illustrated as below.

On a complete basis

Employer/Lead Designer 1	PSC Adjudicator inserted and Adjudicator's Contract agreed
Employer/ Designer 2	PSC Adjudicator inserted and Adjudicator's Contract agreed
Employer/ Designer 3	PSC Adjudicator inserted and Adjudicator's Contract agreed
Employer/ Project Manager	PSC Adjudicator inserted and Adjudicator's Contract agreed
Employer/ Supervisor	PSC Adjudicator inserted and Adjudicator's Contract agreed
Employer/ Contractor 1	ECC Adjudicator inserted and Adjudicator's Contract agreed
Employer/ Contractor 2	ECC Adjudicator inserted and Adjudicator's Contract agreed
Employer/ Contractor 3	ECC Adjudicator inserted and Adjudicator's Contract agreed
Main/Designer	PSC Adjudicator inserted and Adjudicator's Contract agreed
Main/ Subcontractor 1	ECS Adjudicator inserted and Adjudicator's Contract agreed
Main/ Subcontractor 2	ECS Adjudicator inserted and Adjudicator's Contract agreed
Main/ Subcontractor 3	ECS Adjudicator inserted and Adjudicator's Contract agreed

On a truncated basis

The above arrangement, on a complete basis, would involve the appointment at the outset of the project of twelve Adjudicators (although it would not, in theory, be anticipated that the Adjudicators would require to be paid anything unless and until a dispute arose).

In practice, however, the process can – possibly at the expense or risk of some overlap or some loss of objectivity – be truncated so that the same Adjudicator was agreed for various categories of agreement, viz.:

Employer/ Lead Designer 1	PSC Adjudicator inserted	Adjudicator's Contract agreed
Employer/Designer 2	PSC Adjudicator inserted	
Employer/Designer 3	PSC Adjudicator inserted	

Employer/ *Project Manager*	PSC Adjudicator inserted	Adjudicator's Contract agreed
Employer/Supervisor	PSC Adjudicator inserted	
Employer/Contractor 1	ECC Adjudicator inserted	
Employer/Contractor 2	ECC Adjudicator inserted	
Employer/Contractor 3	ECC Adjudicator inserted	Adjudicator's Contract agreed
Main/Subcontractor 1	ECS Adjudicator inserted	
Main/Subcontractor 2	ECS Adjudicator inserted	
Main/Subcontractor 3	ECS Adjudicator inserted	
Main/Designer	PSC Adjudicator inserted	Adjudicator's Contract agreed

This would involve the appointment of only four Adjudicators. The process could be contracted even further if it was thought that a single Adjudicator was capable of adjudicating upon all of these potentially diverse disputes, viz.:

Employer/Lead Designer 1	PSC Adjudicator inserted	
Employer/Designer 2	PSC Adjudicator inserted	
Employer/Designer 3	PSC Adjudicator inserted	
Employer/Project Manager	PSC Adjudicator inserted	
Employer/Supervisor	PSC Adjudicator inserted	
Employer/Contractor 1	ECC Adjudicator inserted	
Employer/Contractor 2	ECC Adjudicator inserted	
Employer/Contractor 3	ECC Adjudicator inserted	Adjudicator's Contract agreed
Main/Subcontractor 1	ECS Adjudicator inserted	
Main/Subcontractor 2	ECS Adjudicator inserted	
Main/Subcontractor 3	ECS Adjudicator inserted	
Main/Designer	PSC Adjudicator inserted	

Alternative arrangements

As discussed earlier, it is in theory possible – although perhaps a difficult pleading task to create and co-ordinate – for the Parties to agree to the adjustment of the NEC family of contracts so that, although adjudication is agreed as the means of resolving any disputes, the actual appointment of an Adjudicator skilled in the field of the particular dispute which has arisen is to await the arising of the dispute (if any) when the precise nature of the dispute can be identified.

Methods of naming/appointing the Adjudicator

As well as considering the qualifications which they wish their Adjudicator to have, the Parties will require to consider what method they wish to use for the selection of the Adjudicator. In relation to adjudication generally there are essentially two main methods of selecting an Adjudicator, which we can describe here as 'Naming' and 'Appointing'. It is proposed to consider here the merits of each method before going on to consider the options open to the Parties under the NEC family of contracts.

Naming the Adjudicator

Some adjudication procedures allow the Parties to name the Adjudicator in advance in the contract which the Parties are entering into.

The advantage of this method is that with the Adjudicator already appointed, all that remains when a dispute arises is to submit the dispute to the Adjudicator.

The disadvantage of this method is that the Adjudicator named will require to deal with all disputes which arise, whether or not they relate to that Adjudicator's particular area of expertise.

A subsidiary disadvantage is that the named Adjudicator, available at the time when the dispute was entered into, may no longer be available at the time when the dispute arises.

Appointing the Adjudicator

Some adjudication procedures allow for the appointment of the Adjudicator once a dispute has arisen.

The advantage of this method is that an Adjudicator can be appointed whose skills exactly match the dispute which has arisen.

The disadvantage of this method is that if the Parties cannot agree upon the appointment of an Adjudicator then resort would have to be had to any provisions made for the compulsory appointment of an Adjudicator.

Naming the Adjudicator under the NEC family of contracts

If this is the preferred method of the Parties then, as this is the preferred method of the drafters of the NEC family of contracts, it is only necessary to follow the procedures set out in the NEC family of contracts. The Guidance Notes suggest that:

> The Adjudicator is appointed jointly by the [Parties to] the contract. [One Party] should insert his choice of Adjudicator in Part One of the Contract Data. If the [Other Party] does not agree with his choice, a suitable person will be the subject of discussion and agreement before the Contract Date. Alternatively, [One Party] may propose a list of acceptable names, and the [Other Party] may be asked to select one of them to be Adjudicator. Some Parties may prefer the Other Party to propose suitable names.

The Guidance Notes go on to specifically point out that the Adjudicator becomes involved only when a dispute is referred to him.

Naming the Adjudicator in the contract is achieved simply by naming the person agreed to be Adjudicator in the Contract Data.

The Guidance Notes also point out that normally at the same time the Adjudicator will be appointed jointly by the Parties using the NEC Adjudicator's Contract (although presumably it would be possible to use some other form of contract).

Appointing the Adjudicator under the NEC family of contracts

If this is the preferred method of the Parties then it will be necessary for the Parties to amend (using Option Z) the terms of the NEC contract involved as follows:

A specific clause should be incorporated into the contract providing for the appointment of an Adjudicator once the dispute has arisen. This clause can be of a cascading nature so that it would be possible to provide that in the first instance the Adjudicator may be appointed jointly by the agreement of the Parties to the contract. What is essential, however, is that the clause provides for some method of appointment (usually using an independent Adjudicator Nominating Body) where the Parties are unable to agree upon the appointment of a suitable Adjudicator.

Appointing the Adjudicator in the contract is achieved simply by the Parties agreeing who is to be the Adjudicator or, failing which, the Adjudicator being independently appointed.

Normally the Adjudicator will be appointed jointly by the Parties at that stage under the NEC Adjudicator's Contract.

Selecting the law of the contract

The NEC family of contracts contains provision for the law of the contract to be specified.

There does not appear to be any indication as to who is to choose the law of the contract. The section where the information is to be inserted is contained in the Contract Data, Part One – Data provided by the Employer, where under 1. General it is provided 'The *law of the contract* is the law of [.....]'.

It is not clear, therefore, whether the choice of law is intended to be a matter for the Employer to choose or whether, like the identity of the Adjudicator, this is intended to be a suggestion by the Employer which is open to negotiation by the Other Party. At the end of the day, presumably, if the Other Party does not care to enter into a contract under that law then they will decline to do so.

Where the law applicable to the contract is a matter of negotiation, however, then it is a matter upon which legal advice should be taken and to which careful consideration should be given. For example, to select for the contract a law which comes from a legal system based on the civil law is likely to produce one set of practical remedies if needed, while to select for the contract a law which comes from a legal system based on the common law is likely to produce another set of practical remedies if needed.

In many instances, the law applicable to the contract will sit in the background and the provisions of the contract will be sufficient to regulate matters between the Parties. It is where the contract proves to be insufficient to regulate matters between the Parties that the *lex mercatoria* (in relation to which the law applicable to the contract will be of major importance) comes into play.

Not every legal system is the same and to choose one system may mean that the Parties gain a number of possible remedies if they need them, whereas to choose another legal system might mean that no such remedies are available. For example, English law prides itself on its development of the law relating to Arbitration over a long number of years. Where English law is the law applicable to the Arbitration, where the Arbitration is taking place in England and where the law of the contract is English law then, even where the contract is completely silent on a point, the chances are that the law of England will have developed a remedy which can be used by the Parties in the circumstances to allow the Arbitration to keep moving and to reach a conclusion. The same considerations are likely to apply to adjudication. Parties should, therefore, pay particular advice to the choice of law for their contract (and by implication any adjudication flowing therefrom).

The same considerations apply to the enforcement, if necessary, of any award made.

In completing that section of the contract, the Guidance Notes in their worked example suggest that the Parties insert not only the law applicable to the contract but that the Parties also prorogate the jurisdiction of the Courts which they wish to have jurisdiction. Thus, although Parties are of course free to negotiate and agree their own provision, the Guidance Notes suggest that that part of the contract might read: 'The law of the contract is the law of England and Wales, subject to the jurisdiction of the courts of England and Wales'.

Selecting the nominee

It can happen in the course of a contract that the Adjudicator selected becomes no longer available. It may be that an Adjudicator who was available when named in a contract is for some reason no longer available when a dispute arises under the contract several years later. It may be that an Adjudicator later selected by the Parties for some reason requires to resign or becomes no longer available. It is only sensible, therefore, to make some provision for the appointment of a replacement Adjudicator and this is catered for in the NEC family of contracts.

The first course of action in such eventuality is, of course, for the Parties to seek to agree a replacement Adjudicator. That option is preserved in the NEC family of contracts which provides that its terms apply 'if the Parties cannot agree a choice'.

Where the Parties cannot agree a choice then the NEC family of contracts provides a procedure for the appointment of a replacement Adjudicator.

This is to be found in section 9 ('Disputes and termination') of the 1. General section of Part One – Data provided by the Employer in the Contract Data.

Again, there does not appear to be any indication as to whether this matter is intended to be the choice of the Employer only or whether it is intended to be a matter of negotiation and agreement between the Parties.

The provision reads: 'The person who will choose a new adjudicator if the Parties cannot agree a choice is [.....]'.

There might be inserted here, for example, 'The President of the time being of [.....]'.

It is suggested that it is important for the Parties to ensure that this section is completed because should the Adjudicator require to be replaced and the Other Party refuses to agree a replacement then, in the absence of an entry in this part of the contract, it might prove impossible to appoint a replacement Adjudicator and it might therefore prove impossible to proceed with the adjudication at all.

Selecting the tribunal

The drafters of the NEC family of contracts intend adjudication to be an interim form of dispute resolution and recognise the need to have an ultimate means of dispute resolution. The Guidance Notes state:

> Whilst the NEC system recognises the need to have an ultimate means for such resolution, an intermediate stage of independent dispute resolution has been introduced in the form of adjudication. It is the intention that all disputes should be resolved by the Adjudicator who is appointed jointly by the Employer and the Contractor and is able to act independently. However, any Party dissatisfied with the Adjudicator's decision may refer the dispute to the tribunal.

To have the right to refer the dispute to the tribunal, however, the Parties will require to make provision for a tribunal, since a tribunal is not automatically provided for in the NEC family of contracts but is information which requires to be inserted in the contract. Thus – with the possible exception of litigation, which it could be argued a Party cannot be denied – were the Parties to fail to insert any information as to the tribunal then it may well be the case that there would be no tribunal to which the dispute could be referred.

The section for the tribunal is contained in section 9 ('Disputes and termination') of the 1. General section of Part One – Data provided by the Employer in the Contract Data. It provides simply that 'the *tribunal* is [.....]'.

The suggestions for tribunals made in the Guidance Notes, by way of example, are Expert Determination, dispute resolution panels, Arbitration (strongly recommended in the Guidance Notes) and the Courts.

However, according to the Guidance Notes, while the Adjudicator is appointed jointly by the Employer and the Contractor, it is a feature of the NEC family of contracts that it is the Employer (alone) who is given a choice of tribunal and the Employer, if he wishes, inserts that choice in the Contract

Data. The Other Party presumably either agrees to contract upon that basis or refuses to do so.

It is intended to consider the suggested options next.

Choice of tribunal

Litigation

It is open to the Parties to decide to proceed directly to litigation if the decision of the Adjudicator is disputed and to thereby avoid all other forms of dispute resolution. This, it is suggested, can be achieved by simply inserting in the section 'The *tribunal* is …' the words 'litigation'. Such a provision should have the effect of excluding as the *tribunal* all other forms of dispute resolution except litigation.

Even where the word 'litigation' is not inserted, however, then on one view, access to the Courts cannot ultimately be denied to a Party. Therefore, providing that the Courts shall be the tribunal will often simply be confirming something which already exists. The choice of the Courts as the tribunal to review decisions of the Adjudicator raises some complex issues.

What is more complex, however, is the attitude which the Courts are likely to take were such a matter to come before them. As already noted, Clause 9 provides that 'The Adjudicator settles the dispute as independent Adjudicator and not as Arbitrator' which, on one interpretation makes the Adjudicator more akin to an Expert than to an Arbitrator. The Guidance Notes suggest that adjudication is not Arbitration but is a means by which an independent third party makes a quick decision where the Parties are unable to agree. The attitude which the Courts might take in seeking to review such an entity is unclear.

Much will, of course, depend upon the attitude adopted by the particular Courts before whom the matter is taken. Some Courts may be prepared to look at the whole dispute anew and arrive at their own decision (expressly not limited in that respect to the information, evidence or argument put to the Adjudicator). Other Courts may adopt a more limited approach of sitting in judgment upon the opinion of an Expert which they will not disturb on the basis of mere error of fact but only upon the basis of material error of law.

It is not clear precisely what the drafters of the NEC family of contracts envisaged, where the Courts are chosen by the Employer as the tribunal. In these circumstances, it may be sufficient merely to insert the words 'litigation' after the words 'the tribunal is ...' where they appear in the Contract Data section of the contract. However, a great deal of uncertainty as to what the Courts are likely to do could be removed were a proper clause clearly delineating the respective function of the Adjudicator and the Courts to be drawn up and incorporated into the contract (probably through the use of Option Z).

Arbitration

The drafters of the NEC family of contracts have made it clear in their Guidance Notes that in their view Arbitration is their preferred choice as tribunal. The Guidance Notes state that 'If arbitration is available under the *law of the contract* it is strongly recommended that arbitration is chosen as the *tribunal.*' The Guidance Notes go on to justify this choice on the grounds that 'The rationale for arbitration remains important particularly for disputes upon technical matters for which an arbitrator experienced in the technical context of the dispute is preferable to the courts'.

In order to achieve the selection of Arbitration as the tribunal, the Employer would simply, in the section 'The tribunal is …', insert the word 'arbitration' and the Other Party will apparently require to either contract or decline to contract on that basis.

However, because a number of countries have their own standard Arbitration procedures, in some of the contracts there has been inserted as an Optional Statement the following:

> If the tribunal is arbitration
>
> The arbitration procedure is [.....].

The rationale for this, according to the Guidance Notes, is that incorporating such procedures will automatically incorporate matters such as the appointment of Arbitrators, the replacement of Arbitrators and time limits, but that if the procedures selected do not include such provision then such provision should be included in the Contract Data.

So far as Arbitration procedures are concerned, the Guidance Notes make the following suggestions:

Arbitration worldwide

- Rules of Conciliation and Arbitration of the International Chamber of Commerce
- United Nations sponsored UNCITRAL rules
- The ACP/EEC Conciliation and Arbitration Rules

Arbitration within the United Kingdom

- The Institution of Civil Engineers' Arbitration Procedure (England and Wales) (1983)
- The Institution of Civil Engineers' Arbitration Procedure (Scotland) (1983)
- The JCT Arbitration Rules – 18 July 1988

These are understood to be in the process of being updated and as regards Scotland there should now be added the Model Code for Arbitration.

Arbitration generally

In relation to Arbitration generally, whether worldwide or within the United Kingdom, the Guidance Notes suggest that the Parties (or at least the Employer) give consideration to the following:

- On matters of procedure the power of decision should be given to the Arbitrator and not the Parties or their legal representatives once appointed.
- The Arbitrator should have certain qualifications which should include
  - appropriate training
  - the ability to manage an arbitration
  - qualification in the area of the dispute
  - qualification in the law of arbitration
  - available time for the arbitration
  - the ability to take an active role in the process.
- As far as possible, the exchange of written statements, including experts' reports, should apply.
- The Arbitrator must ensure that experts know that their primary duty is to the arbitration and not to the Parties.
- A limited timetable should be defined for oral hearings with equal sharing of time between the Parties.
- Case-management conferences at specified stages of the arbitration should be arranged in order to monitor time and expenditure.
- The arbitration needs to take into account any other specified requirements peculiar to the particular project or its expected disputes.

If necessary, therefore, in order to incorporate the above, where the Arbitration procedure specified in the optional statement is insufficient, it may be necessary to have a proper Arbitration Clause drawn up and incorporated into the contract (probably through the use of Option Z).

Expert Determination

At first sight, the choice of Expert Determination as the tribunal to review decisions of the Adjudicator seems a little odd.

Clause 9 already provides that 'The Adjudicator settles the dispute as independent Adjudicator and not as Arbitrator' which, on one interpretation makes the Adjudicator more akin to an Expert than to an Arbitrator. The Guidance Notes suggest that adjudication is not Arbitration but is a means by which an independent third party makes a quick decision where the Parties are unable to agree.

On that basis, providing for Expert Determination as the tribunal is akin to obtaining a second opinion (with the second opinion expressly not limited to the information, evidence or argument put to the Adjudicator), for Expert Determination is also a means by which the Parties to a contract jointly instruct a third party to decide an issue upon which they are unable to agree.

It will clearly be insufficient merely to insert the words 'Expert Determination' after the words 'the tribunal is ...' where they appear in the Contract Data section of the contract. A proper Expert Determination Clause will require to be drawn up and incorporated into the contract (probably through the use of Option Z).

Dispute Review Boards

The choice of Dispute Review Boards as the tribunal to review decisions of the Adjudicator is less surprising and more in line with modern construction practice.

As noted, Clause 9 already provides that 'The Adjudicator settles the dispute as independent Adjudicator and not as Arbitrator' which, on one interpretation, makes the Adjudicator more akin to an Expert than to an Arbitrator. The Guidance Notes suggest that adjudication is not Arbitration but is a means by which an independent third party makes a quick decision where the Parties are unable to agree.

On that basis, providing for a Dispute Review Board (DRB) as the tribunal is perhaps akin to obtaining a second opinion from a panel of experts (with the second opinion expressly not limited to the information, evidence or argument put to the Adjudicator), for DRBs can also be regarded as a means by which the Parties to a contract jointly instruct a panel of Experts to decide an issue upon which they are unable to agree.

As used to date, however, in a number of major construction projects such as the Hong Kong Airport and the Channel Tunnel (where it was called a Panel of Experts), members of the Board have been nominated by the Parties with some being independently appointed. For example, as well as Engineers the Hong Kong Airport DRB also had a Chinese Law Professor on the Board and the Channel Tunnel DRB also had a French Law Professor on the Board.

A feature of the DRBs used so far, however, has been that the Board is appointed at the commencement of the project. They keep pace with the project and make regular visits to the site (whether or not there is a dispute). They are often given the power to issue opinions only rather than issue decisions which are final and binding.

It is not clear whether the drafters of the NEC family of contracts envisaged, where a DRB is chosen by the Employer as the tribunal, that the DRB would be appointed at the commencement of the project and keep pace with it, or whether the DRB would be specifically constituted only when a dispute has arisen and review is properly sought of the Adjudicator's decision.

Either way, it will clearly be insufficient merely to insert the words 'Dispute Review Board' after the words 'the tribunal is ...' where they appear in the Contract Data section of the contract. A proper DRB Clause will require to be drawn up and incorporated into the contract (probably through the use of Option Z).

Other methods of alternative dispute resolution (ADR)

The suggestions made in the Guidance Notes are clearly only examples and are not intended to be exhaustive. Thus, it would be open to the Employer to select some other means of ADR (for example, mini-arb) as the tribunal.

Again, however, Clause 9 already provides that 'The Adjudicator settles the dispute as independent Adjudicator and not as Arbitrator' which, on one interpretation makes the Adjudicator more akin to an Expert than to an Arbitrator. The Guidance Notes suggest that adjudication is not Arbitration but is a means by which an independent third party makes a quick decision where the Parties are unable to agree. The form of tribunal chosen would therefore require to be compatible with that.

It is likely to be insufficient merely to insert the words 'mini-arb' or the like after the words 'the tribunal is …' where they appear in the Contract Data section of the contract. A proper ADR Clause will require to be drawn up and incorporated into the contract (probably through the use of Option Z).

Differences between Arbitration and other forms of dispute resolution (including adjudication)

There is a subtle but real distinction between Arbitration and other forms of dispute resolution. It can, in fact, sometimes be difficult to clearly establish exactly what procedure is being used and there has been extensive litigation in that respect.

Perhaps the easiest way in which to draw a practical distinction between these different methods of dispute resolution is to focus upon their intention and procedures as follows:

ADR such as Expert Determination/DRBs

These methods are aimed at having an Expert or Board (rightly or wrongly) determine the dispute between the Parties.

These methods do not have a developed body of law surrounding them and are largely dependent, so far as procedure is concerned, upon whatever is contained in the clause appointing them. There will not, for example, necessarily be a right to a hearing.

Arbitration as ADR

This method is a quasi-judicial process. Arbitration in many countries is surrounded by a body of law (which in some countries has been codified into statute). This might provide, for example, for the right to a hearing.

Adjudication under the NEC

Adjudication, a relatively new procedure, does not yet have a body of law developed around it (although it is now regulated by statute in some countries) and can be difficult to place in relation to the above methods since it carries characteristics of all of them.

To some extent, the NEC family of contracts seeks to clarify the matter because Clause 92.1 expressly provides that 'The Adjudicator settles the dispute as independent adjudicator and not as arbitrator' and that 'His decision is enforceable as a matter of contractual obligation between the Parties and not as an arbitral award'.

By that provision, it is clear that under the NEC family of contracts, adjudication is *not* Arbitration but at best occupies a middle ground on its own or at worst is akin to determination by an Expert or Board.

Summary

In looking at the selection of the tribunal by the Employer, therefore, the main differences to be appreciated in relation to the methods chosen might be in relation to the following:

The procedure to be followed

Arbitration

Arbitration is, wherever it is selected, likely to be surrounded by a body of law determining its procedure. These might include rules as to evidence, rules as to the entitlement to a hearing, and the applicable *lex mercatoria* may recognise a remedy where there has been any serious irregularity in these respects.

Other methods of ADR

Other methods of ADR, wherever they are selected, may not be surrounded by a body of law, so that unless the right to evidence, a hearing or the like can be found in the Clause setting up that ADR, then it may not be possible to derive that from any surrounding body of law.

The enforcement of any decision

Arbitration

In many countries, Arbitration has been developed to a quasi-judicial status such that the decision of the arbiter may be automatically enforced (without the need for resort to the Courts) in much the same way as a decision of the Courts.

Other methods of ADR

Not being so fully developed, other methods of ADR are likely to require a writ or summons to be taken out in the applicable jurisdiction before any decision of the tribunal could be enforced.

Other contractual matters

It is clearly possible for the Parties to adjust their NEC contract (using Option Z). So far as adjudication is concerned, in line with the principle of adjudication is a consensual process that the Parties should be allowed to adjust the position relating to adjudication as it applies to them. One Party, for example, may wish to amend the contract so as to provide for contractual summary provisions. Another Party, for example, may wish to amend the contract so as to avoid various aspects of enforcement. The extent to which adjustment is possible will, of course, depend in practice upon the relative bargaining positions of the respective Parties.

In addition, for specific matters the drafters of the NEC family of contracts have provided a number of options designated for the country to which they relate – viz. Option Y(UK) – and it is open to the Parties to incorporate these into their contract also.

Such amendment is usually territorial and by way of example the position in that respect can be illustrated as it applies in England and in Scotland.

England

In certain circumstances, section 41 of the Arbitration Act 1996 can, under the applicable Scheme, apply to adjudications in England.

It is not entirely clear whether the drafters of the UK legislation were intending to exclude the application of section 42(1) to the Scheme for Construction Contracts (England and Wales) Regulations, but if that was the intention then it was not achieved and at present s. 42(1) does apply.

That subsection provides that it is 'subject to the agreement of the parties' and therefore, if the Parties do not wish to give the Court the power to enforce a decision which an Adjudicator has made peremptory, then the Parties should (by Option Z) amend their NEC contract to expressly exclude that provision.

As noted earlier, however, much depends upon the relative bargaining position of the Parties before any such amendment can be incorporated into their contract.

Where the Parties envisage carrying out within the territory of England, Works which might fall within the definition of 'construction contracts' laid down in the Housing Grants, Construction and Regeneration Act 1996, then the Parties may wish to adopt and incorporate into their contract Option Y(UK) 2 which is specifically directed at that issue.

Scotland

In Scotland, there has existed for many years a record called the Books of Council and Session. This is an extremely important record which has proved useful in a number of respects. One of these is the facility it offers – in a number of areas – for a Party to agree to be bound by a stated decision and to consent to the registration of that agreement (and later the decision) in the Books of Council and Session for preservation and execution. Once that has been done a certified extract of the Books of Council and Session has the same force as an Order of the Court and it may be enforced in exactly the same way.

It is, however, a requirement that all of the Parties concerned have consented in writing. That consent can arise in a number of ways. For example, the Scheme for Construction Contracts in Scotland seeks to impose a duty upon a Party to sign, before a witness, the decision of the Adjudicator so as to give the decision that effect and make it registrable in the Books of Council and Session.

At an earlier stage, when submitting their dispute to adjudication the Parties could, for example, agree in writing in the Adjudicator's Contract to any decision made by the Adjudicator being recorded in the Books of Council and Session.

At an even earlier stage, the contract between the Parties could be adjusted so that it provides then for any decision issued by the Adjudicator to be recorded in the Books of Council and Session.

As noted earlier, however, much depends upon the relative bargaining position of the Parties before any such amendment can be incorporated into their contract.

Where the Parties envisage carrying out within the territory of Scotland, Works which might fall within the definition of 'construction contracts' laid down in the Housing Grants, Construction and Regeneration Act 1996, then the Parties may wish to adopt and incorporate into their contract Option Y(UK) 2 which is specifically directed at that issue.

Northern Ireland

Where the Parties envisage carrying out within the territory of Northern Ireland, Works which might fall within the definition of 'construction contracts' laid down in the Construction Contracts (Northern Ireland) Order 1997, then the Parties may wish to adopt and incorporate into their contract Option Y(UK) 2 which (while designated in relation to the legislation covering England and Wales and Scotland) is specifically directed at that issue.

Co-ordinating Main Contract and Sub-contract Adjudications

In general, the NEC family of contracts has set its face against adjudicating upon multiple disputes with the single exception of disputes affecting both Main Contracts and Sub-contracts. However, in order to co-ordinate such adjudications provision should be made in advance in the relevant contracts. Clause 91.2 provides:

> If a matter disputed under or in connection with a subcontract is also a matter disputed under or in connection with this contract, the Contractor may submit the subcontract dispute to the Adjudicator at the same time as the main contract submission. The Adjudicator then settles the two disputes together and references to the Parties for the purposes of the dispute are interpreted as including the Subcontractor.

The Guidance Notes comment on that Clause as follows:

> Where a dispute which affects work which has been subcontracted arises, and which may constitute a dispute between the Contractor and a Subcontractor as well as between the Contractor and the Employer, there is provision for the matter to be resolved between the three Parties by the Main Contract Adjudicator. This saves time and expense and prevents a dispute being dealt with by different Adjudicators who may make different decisions. This procedure is only possible if the terms of the subcontract permit the Contractor to submit the subcontract dispute to the main contract Adjudicator.

The essential provisions in this respect are, therefore, to be found in the NEC Engineering and Construction Subcontract. They are presumably subject to negotiation between the Contractor and the Sub-contractor.

In the Sub-contract Data Part One – Data provided by the Contractor, under Statements given in all sub-contracts, provision is made at 1. General, as follows:

> The Adjudicator in this subcontract is
>
> > Name [.....]
> >
> > Address [.....]
>
> The main contract Adjudicator is
>
> > Name [.....]
> >
> > Address [.....]

The same principles apply to the tribunal and provision is made in section 9. Disputes and Termination, as follows:

> The tribunal is [.....]
>
> The main contract tribunal is [.....]

Under Optional Statements it is also provided:

> If the *tribunal* or the *main contract tribunal* is arbitration
>
> • The arbitration procedure is [.....]

Clearly, these matters are something which, at the time of contracting, the Parties may wish to address if there are contracts involved.

Checklist for making provision for the resolution of disputes when entering into the NEC family of contracts

Where the Adjudicator is to be named in the contract

In these circumstances, so far as the resolution of disputes is concerned, the essential information which Parties should check has been inserted in the relevant NEC contract will be as follows:

Main contracts

CONTRACT DATA

Part One – Data provided by [the Party concerned]

Statements given in all contracts

1. General

The Adjudicator

- The *Adjudicator* is

Name [.....]   [This will identify the person who is to be
Address [.....]   the Adjudicator in relation to any
                          disputes arising under or in connection
Postcode [.....]   with that particular contract]
Tel. No [.....]
Fax. No [.....]

The law of the contract

- the *law of the contract* is the   [This will be very important in the adju-
  law of [.....]   dication generally and in establishing
                                       any *lex mercatoria* which may have to
                                       be applied]

9. Disputes and Termination

The nominee for replacement adjudicators

- The person or organisation   [This provides a mechanism for the
  who will choose a replace-   replacement of the Adjudicator]
  ment adjudicator if the Parties
  cannot agree a choice is [.....]

The Tribunal

- The *tribunal* is [.....]   [This specifies the body to whom a
                               Party dissatisfied with the decision of
                               the Adjudicator may take the matter]

Optional Statements

Where the tribunal selected is arbitration

- If the *tribunal* is arbitration   [This specifies that where the tribunal
* the arbitration procedure is   chosen is arbitration (the tribunal
  [.....]   recommended by the NEC) then the
                                       arbitration procedure to be used is
                                       stated and agreed]

Option Z

Here the Parties might insert any provisions which they specifically wish to
make regarding the resolution of disputes such as the application of the
Arbitration Act 1996 in England or the application of the Books of Council
and Session in Scotland.

Other contracts

The Adjudicator's Contract

Although this does not appear to be strictly necessary, the Guidance Notes suggest that once the person appointed as Adjudicator has been jointly agreed between the Parties and named in the contract by being inserted into Part One of the Contract Data as the contract is signed, then at the time of contracting both the name of the Adjudicator and the fact that the Adjudicator is also formally appointed at that time by the Parties is reflected by the Adjudicator and the Parties entering into and signing the NEC Adjudicator's Contract.

Sub-contracts

Co-ordinating main contract and sub-contract adjudications

1. General

* The *Adjudicator* in this subcontract is [.....]	[This allows for the co-ordination of adjudications in relation to main contracts and sub-contracts]
* The *main contract Adjudicator* is [.....]	

9. Disputes and termination

* The *tribunal* is [.....]	[This allows for the co-ordination of the tribunal in relation to main contracts and sub-contracts]
* The *main contract tribunal* is [.....]	

Optional Statements

If the *tribunal* or the *main contract tribunal* is arbitration	[This allows for the co-ordination of the arbitration procedure (if that is the tribunal selected) in relation to the main contracts and sub-contracts]
* the arbitration procedure is [.....]	

Checklist for making provision for the resolution of disputes when entering into the NEC family of contracts

Where the adjudicator is to be appointed at the time when any dispute arises

In these circumstances, so far as the resolution of disputes is concerned, the essential information which Parties should check has been inserted in the relevant NEC contract will be as follows:

Main contracts

CONTRACT DATA

Part One – Data provided by [the Party concerned]

Statements given in all contracts

1. General

The Adjudicator

* The *Adjudicator* is
  Name [.....]
  Address [.....]
  Postcode [.....]   [This section will be left blank]
  Tel. No [.....]
  Fax. No [.....]

The law of the contract

* the *law of the contract* is the law   [This will be very important in the
  of [.....]   adjudication generally and in estab-
                                            lishing any *lex mercatoria* which may
                                            have to be applied]

9. Disputes and Termination

The nominee for replacement Adjudicators

* The person or organisation who   [This section is also likely to be left
  will choose a replacement adju-   blank]
  dicator if the Parties cannot
  agree a choice is [.....]

The tribunal

* The *tribunal* is [.....]   [This specifies the body to whom a
                                     Party dissatisfied with the decision of
                                     the Adjudicator may take the matter]

Optional Statements

Where the tribunal selected is arbitration

* If the *tribunal* is arbitration   [This specifies that where the tribunal
* the arbitration procedure is [.....] chosen is arbitration (the tribunal
                                     recommended by the NEC) then the
                                     arbitration procedure to be used is
                                     stated and agreed]

Option Z

Here the Parties will insert a Clause which will make specific provision for the appointment (and, if necessary, replacement) of an Adjudicator when a dispute arises. It is important that the Clause makes sufficient provision for appointment (perhaps using an Adjudicator Nominating Body) such that non-co-operation by a Party cannot prevent an adjudication.

Here the Parties might also insert any provisions which they specifically wish to make regarding the resolution of disputes such as the application of the Arbitration Act 1996 in England or the application of the Books of Council and Session in Scotland.

Other contracts

The Adjudicator's Contract

Where the Adjudicator is being appointed at the time of the dispute rather than at the time of the contract there will be no requirement for the Parties and the Adjudicator to enter into an Adjudicator's Contract at that time. When a dispute has arisen and an Adjudicator has been appointed then that will be the time for an Adjudicator's Contract to be entered into. The Parties may wish to keep the NEC Adjudicator's Contract handy for that purpose. There is, however, no strict requirement to use the NEC Adjudicator's Contract (although it is clearly designed to integrate with the other NEC contracts) and the Adjudicator may have a contract of his or her own which the Parties may prefer to use.

Sub-contracts

Co-ordinating main contract and sub-contract adjudications

1. General

* The *Adjudicator* in this subcontract is [.....]

* The *main contract Adjudicator* is [.....]

[This allows for the co-ordination of adjudications in relation to main contracts and sub-contracts]

9. Disputes and termination

* The *tribunal* is [.....]

* The *main contract tribunal* is [.....]

[This allows for the co-ordination of the tribunal in relation to main contracts and sub-contracts]

Optional Statements

If the *tribunal* or the *main contract tribunal* is arbitration

* the arbitration procedure is [.....]

[This allows for the co-ordination of the arbitration procedure (if that is the tribunal selected) in relation to the main contracts and sub-contracts]

Book II

Procedures under the NEC family of contracts

Part I

Adjudication under the NEC (worldwide)

3. An overview of adjudication under the NEC (worldwide)

Introduction

Although now of worldwide application, the NEC family of contracts has its origins in England, a country with a long tradition in contracts and in particular in dispute resolution procedures

Within the United Kingdom, it appears to have been a prevalent feeling that all was not as well as it could be which, in 1985, led the newly-appointed Legal Affairs Committee of the ICE to recommend to its Council that a review be undertaken of alternative contract strategies for civil engineering design and construction with the objective of identifying the needs of good practice.

It was suggested that the review be fundamental and that is just what the review was. Those undertaking the review went right back to the basics of what was required, considered the use of the existing forms of standard contract but found them to be lacking in a number of respects and came up with what was truly an alternative form of contract with an alternative contract strategy.

After a period of consultation, the first edition of this new contract (called the New Engineering Contract) was in place by 1993. The initial response was positive, a fact not lost on Sir Michael Latham when he was jointly appointed by the industry and the Government of the day to carry out a review of the construction industry as a whole. Sir Michael Latham considered the requirements of a construction contract, contrasted the New Engineering Contract, and made a number of recommendations.

Those recommendations were taken on board by the ICE, who produced a second edition of their contract which was widened to become the NEC Engineering and Construction Contract and which, as the (November 1995) second edition, represents the present position.

Accordingly, in order to appreciate the underlying nature of this new contract and its accompanying new contract strategy – particularly as regards the resolution of disputes – it is proposed to consider the position under the following headings:

- The UK Latham and Egan Reports
- The worldwide philosophy of the NEC family of contracts
- The essential clause and approach to dispute resolution
- The *lex mercatoria*
- The conclusions

The UK Latham and Egan Reports

An adversarial culture and its associated disputes was identified by Sir Michael Latham as a problem in the UK construction industry (as, indeed, is reflected in the construction industries of other countries). The best approach to that problem, according to the Latham Final Report, was to avoid disputes altogether. To do so, however, would require a change of culture.

The Latham Final Report produced a series of interlocking recommendations which cannot be considered in isolation. For example, a spirit of co-operation, training, teamwork, the pre-pricing of variations and working in partnership might together (but not individually) produce a changed culture which might have the effect of avoiding disputes.

The Latham Final Report also recognised the importance of the Client and was strongly client-driven. The approach recommended – assessing the need, deciding upon risk acceptance, choosing the most suitable procurement route, preparing the project and design briefs – then led on to a consideration of the contract strategy.

As regards contract strategy, the Report incorporates a number of surveys on the use of traditional standard form contracts. The most significant features of those surveys were:

1. The main strengths of the traditional contracts were that they were well known (58%) and that they were fair (42%).
2. That the main weaknesses of traditional contracts were that they encouraged conflict (52%), were insufficiently clear (45%) and created a high level of mistrust (38%).
3. When asked to list their three most important changes to improve matters, the second most popular choice was for simpler contracts (40%).

To reflect these views, the most effective form of modern construction contract would, in the opinion of the Final Report, encompass the following considerations:

1. A specific duty for all Parties to deal fairly with each other, and with their subcontractors, specialists and suppliers, in an atmosphere of mutual co-operation.
2. Firm duties of teamwork, with shared financial motivation to pursue those objectives. These should involve a general presumption to achieve 'win-win' solutions to problems which may arise during the course of the project.
3. A wholly interrelated package of documents which clearly defines the roles and duties of all involved, and which is suitable for all types of project and any procurement route.
4. Easily comprehensible language and with Guidance Notes attached.
5. Separation of the roles of Contract Administrator, Project or Lead Manager and Adjudicator. The Project or Lead Manager should be clearly defined as the representative of the Client.

6. A choice of allocation of risks, to be decided as appropriate to each project but then allocated to the Party best able to manage, estimate and carry the risk.
7. Taking all reasonable steps to avoid changes to pre-planned Works information. But, where variations do occur, they should be priced in advance, with provision for independent adjudication if agreement cannot be reached.
8. Express provision for assessing interim payments by methods other than monthly valuations, i.e. mile-stones, activity schedules, or payment schedules. Such arrangements to also be reflected in the related sub-contract documentation. The eventual aim should be to phase out the traditional system of monthly measurement or remeasurement but meanwhile provision should still be made for it.
9. Clearly setting out the period within which interim payments must be made to all participants in the process, failing which they will have an automatic right to compensation, involving payment of interest at a sufficiently heavy rate to deter slow payment.
10. Providing for secure trust fund routes of payment.
11. While taking all possible steps to avoid conflict on site, providing for speedy dispute resolution if any conflict arises, by a pre-determined impartial Adjudicator/Referee/Expert.
12. Providing for incentives for exceptional performance.
13. Making provision where appropriate for advance mobilisation payments (if necessary, bonded) to Contractors and Sub-contractors, including (in respect of off-site prefabricated materials) for materials provided by part of the construction team.

Sir Michael Latham clearly believed that adherence to these contractual principles would lead to the *avoidance* of disputes altogether.

Following upon the Latham Report, the feeling remained that the UK construction industry (although at its best capable of delivering projects which matched those of any other construction industry in the world) was underachieving – both in terms of meeting its own needs and those of its clients – and the then Deputy Prime Minister (John Prescott MP) set up the Construction Task Force under the Chairmanship of Sir John Egan.

The much shorter Egan Report identified the key drivers for change and improvement as follows: committed leadership, a focus on the customer, integrated processes and teams, a quality-driven agenda and commitment to people. It set a number of targets in that respect which are presently being implemented as part of the project *Rethinking Construction*. It is not yet clear what progress is being made towards meeting these targets.

Recognising, however, that even with the best will in the world disputes will still arise in practice, the Latham Report suggested adjudication as an intermediate means of resolving disputes and after the change of Government the concept of adjudication was in fact incorporated into the UK legislation.

Accordingly, adjudication is available (and sometimes compulsory) within the United Kingdom as a speedy intermediate means of resolving disputes although the emphasis remains on the adoption of a contract and a contract strategy which will avoid disputes arising in the first place.

The worldwide philosophy of the NEC family of contracts

Introduction

Although its origins lie in the United Kingdom, the NEC family of contracts is intended for use worldwide.

What the drafters of the NEC family of contracts sought to do was to identify the current and future needs of good practice in the engineering and construction industry and as a result of that process what emerged in the NEC family of contracts is what they describe as a separate and distinct philosophy.

That philosophy, in terms of its interrelated objectives, was described as follows:

- There should be clarity and simplicity.
- There should be flexibility.
- There should be stimulus to good management.

We propose to consider each of these objectives in outline below.

Clarity and simplicity

Traditional Construction and Engineering contracts have a long history. They began as 'bespoke' contracts drafted by some of the larger contracting bodies. A similarity developed in relation to the individual contracts which then tended to become standardised, and that process was later carried out into the various institutions involved. Later, however, as problems arose, the response was another series of clauses extending the length of the standard form contracts. There was also a feeling that the standard form contracts were developing a bias in favour of one side or other of the industry.

From one point of view, as the clauses of the standard form contracts were interpreted in practice and by the Courts their meaning became clear and could be predicted with greater certainty. From another point of view, standard form contracts were seen to encourage rather than discourage disputes.

When the Legal Affairs Committee of the ICE came to consider the matter, they were not in favour of the continued use of standard form contracts in their existing form. The conclusion of the Committee was that a lot of material which could be effectively covered elsewhere (such as in the Specification) should be stripped out, legal jargon and attempts to para-phrase the existing law should be avoided, the sections should be drawn together in a logical manner and they should be expressed in clear and simple language.

Flexibility

Traditional Construction and Engineering contracts can be regarded as something of a straitjacket. For example, a contract might be predicated upon a Bill of Quantities and it would thereafter be anticipated that this would be referred to and reflected throughout the standard form contract.

Modern forms of contracting are considerably more varied. There is, for example, a concentration on procurement, a trend towards remeasurement and, more recently, partnering. Management contracts have proliferated to such an extent that the continued existence of the Main Contractor is now being called into question.

The combination of circumstances surrounding a particular project is now almost infinite, but the not inconsiderable objective of the Legal Affairs Committee of the ICE was to design a form of contract which would be sufficiently flexible to encompass all or any of these traditional or new concepts.

It has been sought to provide this flexible solution by means of a complex series of options amongst which the Parties can pick and choose (then or later) until they arrive at the situation where the Parties have achieved the contract which they want in relation to that particular project.

Stimulus to good management

Traditional standard form contracts were seen to impede rather than encourage good management practice.

Accordingly, the Legal Affairs Committee of the ICE aimed at the specific objective of providing a stimulus to good management by setting out the duties and responsibilities clearly and precisely.

Summary

Adjudication is made available (it is not compulsory) in the NEC family of contracts as a speedy intermediate means of resolving disputes.

Clearly, the intention – worldwide – is that if the philosophy behind the NEC family of contracts is fully embraced then that contract and its associated contract strategy should lead to the avoidance of disputes. So far as can be ascertained at present, that appears to be being borne out in practice in that while the NEC family of contracts has been used extensively, it has not so far resulted in an excessive amount of adjudication.

The essential clause and approach to dispute resolution

While the hope is that the philosophy behind the NEC family of contracts will lead to the avoidance of disputes, it is recognised there too that with the best will in the world, disputes will still sometimes arise.

Adjudication is therefore made available (it is not compulsory) in the NEC family of contracts. The hope is clearly also that the Parties will bring to their disputes and adjudication the same philosophy which they have brought to the NEC contract itself.

The essential clause

What might be considered the essential clause in this respect is to be found in Clause 10.1 of Core Clause 1. (It might have been expected that this essential clause might have been replicated in the Core Clause (9) which deals with the resolution of disputes, but it can presumably be inferred to apply there equally.)

The clause reads as follows:

> The Employer, the Contractor, the Project Manager and the Supervisor shall act as stated in this contract and in a spirit of mutual trust and co-operation. The Adjudicator shall act as stated in this contract and in a spirit of independence.

The approach to dispute resolution

The intention where the Parties use one or more of the NEC Engineering and Construction family of contracts is that the parties should adopt the philosophy which goes with it. Parties will not have entered into that contract with disputes in mind but where a dispute turns out to be unavoidable and resort is had to adjudication then the intention is clearly that the same philosophy (as reflected in Clause 10.1) will apply to that dispute and any adjudication. What is less clear is what is to happen where that philosophy does not prevail on the part of one or more of the Parties and that we consider in Book II, Section I.

The *lex mercatoria*

An NEC contract will never be entered into in a vacuum. That contract will always be affected by the law which applies to it and the law which surrounds it where it is being executed. It goes without saying that local legal advice should always be taken before an NEC contract is entered into and applied. The body of law which surrounds Works within the UK falling within the definition of 'construction contracts' and which we consider in the Part II is a good example of that, although every territory will have its own rules.

Where such a contract is entered into and a dispute arises which is taken to adjudication then, in an ideal world, it is theoretically possible for the Parties to resolve their dispute by adjudication using only the principles to be found in the NEC contract – which we refer to here as the NEC Principles.

Thus, where the Employer, the Contractor, the Project Manager and the Supervisor (as the case may be) act as stated in the NEC contract and in a spirit of mutual trust and co-operation and the Adjudicator acts as stated in the NEC contract and in a spirit of independence then it should theoretically be possible for the Parties to resolve their dispute by adjudication using only the NEC Principles.

It is, however, where something goes wrong or where one Party (perhaps under financial pressure) withdraws from the spirit of co-operation that difficulties may arise in the adjudication. These difficulties, it would appear, can only be resolved by having resort to the *lex mercatoria*.

Properly speaking, *lex mercatoria* refers to the law which was developed in Continental Europe for the administration of the commercial affairs of traders. The term *lex mercatoria* might, however, be used in much the same way to describe the law which has been developed internationally for the resolution of disputes and it is in that sense that we use it here.

It is obvious that Parties to a contract may decide to choose a law for the regulation of their affairs under the contract which is a different law from the law of the territory in which the Works or the adjudication is taking place. It is conceivable, therefore, that a number of different laws might, as the *lex mercatoria*, have a bearing on different aspects of an adjudication and these we consider below.

The proper law of the contract

This is the law which the Parties specify in the Contract Data as the 'law of the contract'. This will govern the substantive rights of the Parties arising from their contract.

The proper law of the adjudication

It was established in relation to arbitration that the agreement to arbitrate was a distinct agreement separate from the agreement embedded in the contract, and capable of surviving the termination of that embedded agreement. That separate arbitration agreement was in principle capable of being governed by a different proper law, although in most cases its proper law is likely to be the same as the proper law of the embedded agreement.

It is not yet clear whether the same analysis will be applied to adjudication (or even whether under the NEC adjudication can survive termination) but in any event, the proper law of the contract and the proper law of the adjudication agreement are likely to be the same.

The 'curial' law

This is the law which governs an individual reference to adjudication. Different jurisdictions will interpret the curial law in different ways but in many instances the curial law is likely to be the same as the proper law of the adjudication.

The *lex fori*

Where the embedded contract provides for the law of one country to apply but the adjudication itself takes place in another country where different laws apply, then the law of the country in which the adjudication is taking place (the *lex fori*) may allow principles of its law to be applied to the adjudication irrespective of the law which the Parties have chosen as the law of the contract.

Summary

Ascertaining the particular law to be applied to any particular point at any particular time (which, for convenience, we shall refer to here as the *lex mercatoria*) is a skilled legal task. In an ideal world, the NEC Principles should be enough to cover an adjudication arising under an NEC contract but in practice resort may have to be had to the *lex mercatoria* to successfully complete an adjudication. The body of law which surrounds works within the UK falling within the definition of 'construction contracts' and which we consider in Part II is a good example of a *lex mercatoria*, although what is the *lex mercatoria* will obviously vary in relation to every particular contract and territory.

The conclusions

From its origins in the UK, therefore, the NEC family of contracts has developed its own philosophy which is intended to be applied worldwide.

The philosophy of the NEC – reflected in the NEC Principles – depends upon a spirit of mutual trust and co-operation which should be applied not just to the contract but to any disputes and adjudications arising thereunder.

Where, for any reason, the NEC Principles prove insufficient to drive the adjudication to a satisfactory conclusion then resort may, in certain circumstances, be had to the *lex mercatoria*.

Section 1

What may precede the process of adjudication

Introduction

Adjudication is not necessarily automatic and, worldwide, certain pertinent considerations precede the process of adjudication which we consider in this section.

Consideration can first of all be given to what may or may not happen prior to the implementation of any procedure for the resolution of claims.

Consideration can then turn to the procedure to be used for the resolution of the claim in question, which in this case will be adjudication as provided for in the NEC contract being used.

The NEC family of contracts sets down certain requirements in relation to notification which must be followed in advance of an adjudication and we consider these next. Following upon such notification, consideration should turn to the settlement/crystallisation of disputes and a consideration of what disputes are properly referable to adjudication.

Where the dispute has not been settled but has crystallised into a 'proper' dispute which may or may not be referable to adjudication, consideration can then turn to the precise procedures for the resolution of that dispute by adjudication. The NEC family of contracts categorises disputes and sets down specific procedures which, in advance of any adjudication, must be followed in respect of each category of dispute and we consider these next. We also consider what, if anything, can be done to question these requirements.

Finally, if an adjudication is to proceed, we consider what is to be done in relation to the Works pending the resolution of the dispute by adjudication.

4. What must be done in advance of an adjudication

Introduction

What may happen prior to the resolution of any disputes

Although not expressly stated as such, it seems implicit that the NEC family of contracts does not envisage anything else – in the sense of any other contractually agreed dispute resolution procedure such as mediation or the like – happening in relation to the resolution of any disputes between the Parties other than the agreed procedure [adjudication] for resolving disputes contained in the contract between the Parties.

The Guidance Notes suggest that 'All disputes of whatever kind are *first* dealt with by adjudication'.

It could also be argued that it would be contrary to at least the spirit of the NEC family of contracts for either of the Parties to use the *lex mercatoria* to resort to any form of preliminary diligence in advance of an adjudication under the NEC contract.

What method is to be used to resolve any disputes

The NEC family of contracts envisages that, in terms of the contract, one method and one method only will be used to resolve any disputes arising under the contract and that method is adjudication. Adjudication is, under the NEC family of contracts, seen as being the originating, although intermediate, means of resolving all disputes between the Parties.

Core Clause 9 at Clause 90.1 states 'Any dispute arising under or in connection with this contract is submitted to and settled by the Adjudicator ...'.

The Guidance Notes state that 'It is the intention that *all* disputes should be resolved by the Adjudicator who is appointed jointly by the Employer and the Contractor and is able to act independently.'

Notification of the dispute

What notification is required in relation to disputes

The NEC family of contracts categorises disputes and then specifies a procedure for Notification of these disputes which requires to be followed.

In outline, the categorisation of disputes and the notification in relation to them is as follows:

Category of dispute	Notification required
An action	Not more than four weeks after becoming aware of the action
Not having taken an action	Not more than four weeks after becoming aware that the action was not taken
Any other matter	Notification is required but no time limit for notification is prescribed

In relation to the NEC Professional Services Contract

ADJUDICATION TABLE

Dispute about:	Notification of the dispute:
An action of the Employer	Notification of the dispute by the Consultant to the Employer being made not more than four weeks after the Consultant becomes aware of the action
The Employer not having taken an action	Notification of the dispute by the Consultant to the Employer being made not more than four weeks after the Consultant becomes aware of the action not having been taken

In relation to the NEC Engineering and Construction Contract

ADJUDICATION TABLE

Dispute about:	Notification of the dispute:
An action of the Project Manager or the Supervisor	Notification of the dispute by the Contractor to the Project Manager being made not more than four weeks after the Contractor becomes aware of the action
The Project Manager or the Supervisor not having taken an action	Notification of the dispute by the Contractor to the Project Manager being made not more than four weeks after the Contractor becomes aware of the action not having been taken
Any other matter	No time limit is provided for notification of the dispute to the Other Party

In relation to the NEC Engineering and Construction Subcontract

ADJUDICATION TABLE

Dispute about:	*Notification of the dispute:*
An action of the Contractor	Notification of the dispute by the Subcontractor to the Contractor being made not more than four weeks after the Subcontractor becomes aware of the action
The Contractor not having taken an action	Notification of the dispute by the Subcontractor to the Contractor being made not more than four weeks after the Subcontractor becomes aware of the action not having been taken
Any other matter	No time limit is provided for notification of the dispute to the Other Party

In relation to the NEC Engineering and Construction Short Contract

'... the dissatisfied Party notifies the other Party of the dissatisfaction within four weeks of becoming aware of it.'

Summary

With the exception of the NEC Engineering and Construction Short Contract, therefore, (which provides a notification period of four weeks in all cases) the NEC family of contracts imposes a time limit on the initial notification of the disputes as follows:

Dispute	*Time limit for notification*
An action on the part of the Employer/Project Manager or Supervisor/Contractor	Four weeks after first becoming aware of it
The Employer/ Project Manager or Supervisor/ Contractor not having taken an action	Four weeks after first becoming aware of it
Any other matter	No time limit imposed

The Guidance Notes suggest that these time limits are to be strictly observed and therefore should notification, where required, not be made within four weeks of becoming aware of the event then the right to submit that dispute to adjudication might well have been lost.

Form of notification

The NEC family of contracts does not specify the precise form which any notification has to take. Presumably, it will be sufficient if whatever form the notification takes is enough to convey the nature of the dissatisfaction.

Time limit for notification

Although the NEC family of contracts does not expressly specify what is to happen if notification is not made within the time limit set down, the Guidance Notes suggest: 'Time stipulations are clearly set out in the table and throughout the disputes procedure in order to avoid protracted exchanges and argument and to achieve prompt resolution of disputes.'

It might very well be the case, therefore (although the matter does not yet appear to have been tested and settled), that a failure to give notification in time will disentitle that Party from taking the dispute any further to adjudication. On another view, the notification procedure could be regarded as directory rather than mandatory, although in the circumstances that seems unlikely. The adjudicator has been given no express power to allow to adjudication disputes which have been notified late and it must be doubted whether such a power can be implied.

Clearly, it will be important for Parties under the NEC family of contracts to note carefully the date of all actions or failure to take actions and be prepared to prove, if challenged, that notification thereof was timeously made.

Settlement/crystallisation of the dispute

What is required for the settlement/crystallisation of disputes

As well as a procedure for the notification of disputes, the NEC family of contracts also provides a procedure for the settlement/crystallisation of disputes.

It is generally recognised in the construction industry worldwide that merely intimating a 'claim' does not amount to a proper 'dispute'. There might exist a 'difference' of views but something more must exist before that becomes a dispute. That something more is generally taken to be both the submission of a claim and the rejection of that claim (or sometimes silence in response to the claim which can be taken as rejection of the claim). That something more might result in a settlement of the claim. If not, that something more will 'crystallise' that claim into a proper 'dispute'. Only then will a dispute be considered to have arisen. Further, it is generally recognised, worldwide, that there should be some procedure under which any mistakes or oversights can be corrected without the need to resort to any formal dispute resolution procedure.

The Guidance Notes describe the intention as follows:

The initial period of two weeks after the [relevant Party's] notification gives the [Person affected] the opportunity to take or amend the action. This period of grace is intended to prevent the Adjudicator becoming involved with matters which may have been overlooked.

The NEC family of contracts provides such a procedure for the settlement/ crystallisation of disputes arising under its contracts as follows.

In relation to the NEC Professional Services Contract

ADJUDICATION TABLE

Dispute about:	Submission of the dispute:
An action of the Employer	Between two and four weeks after notification of the dispute by the Consultant to the Employer
The Employer not having taken an action	Between two and four weeks after notification of the dispute by the Consultant to the Employer
Any other matter	Between two and four weeks after notification of the dispute to the Other Party

Commentary This two-week period of grace after notification and before submission is regarded as a period of grace within which settlement or crystallisation of the dispute should take place.

In relation to the NEC Engineering and Construction Contract

ADJUDICATION TABLE

Dispute about:	Submission of the dispute:
An action of the Project Manager or the Supervisor	Between two and four weeks after notification of the dispute by the Contractor to the Project Manager
The Project Manager or the Supervisor not having taken an action	Between two and four weeks after notification of the dispute by the Contractor to the Project Manager
Any other matter	Between two and four weeks after notification of the dispute to the Other Party

Commentary This two-week period of grace after notification and before submission is regarded as a period of grace within which settlement or crystallisation of the dispute should take place.

In relation to the NEC Engineering and Construction Subcontract

ADJUDICATION TABLE

Dispute about:	*Submission of the dispute:*
An action of the Contractor	Between two and four weeks after notification of the dispute by the Subcontractor to the Contractor
The Contractor not having taken an action	Between two and four weeks after notification of the dispute by the Subcontractor to the Contractor
Any other matter	Between two and four weeks after notification of the dispute to the Other Party

Commentary This two-week period of grace after notification and before submission is regarded as a period of grace within which settlement or crystallisation of the dispute should take place.

In relation to the NEC Engineering and Construction Short Contract (Standard Format)

Any dispute	Between two and four weeks after notification of the dispute to the Other Party

Commentary This two-week period of grace after notification and before submission is regarded as a period of grace within which settlement or crystallisation of the dispute should take place.

Summary

For all its categories of dispute, therefore, the NEC Engineering and Construction family of contracts provides a period of grace after notification of the dispute and prior to submission of the dispute within which the dispute may not be submitted to adjudication.

This contractual procedure may also be regarded as a period of grace within which any claim will either be settled (in which case there will be no need for an adjudication) or upon rejection (in one form or another) will crystallise into a proper 'dispute' which may then properly go forward to adjudication.

It might be said to be within the spirit of the NEC family of contracts for the Parties to make a genuine effort to settle their differences and avoid the matter going forward to adjudication as a dispute.

It is not entirely clear what would happen were a Party to attempt to submit a dispute to the Adjudicator within the two-week period. Presumably, the Other Party could object and the Adjudicator could simply ask the Party to wait until the two-week period has expired and then resubmit the dispute.

Again, it will be important for Parties to carefully note when they first became aware of the problem, when they notified it, what efforts they have made during the period of grace and when the two-week period of grace has expired, so as to be able to establish all of these if challenged.

Disputes referable to adjudication

Disputes 'under or in connection with the contract'

The general approach of the NEC family of contracts is that 'any dispute arising *under or in connection with this contract* is submitted to and settled by the Adjudicator as follows' and it then proceeds to set out the procedure to be followed.

This is clearly a wide approach (especially as the third category of dispute used is 'any other matter') and it seems clear, therefore, that the overall intention of the NEC family of contracts is to allow virtually any dispute to go forward to adjudication.

In these circumstances, the major restriction in relation to what may be adjudicated upon is contained in the phrase 'under or in connection with this contract'. Different jurisdictions might have different interpretations as to what that means but the considerations relating thereto might include those following.

The validity of the contract

It is likely that questions may be raised as to whether or not the NEC contract in question which contains the adjudication clause has been properly entered into and is validly in existence, or whether the matter raised is a matter which as 'arising under or in connection with this contract'. It is not yet settled whether these are matters which may properly be submitted to adjudication, although it is likely that they are.

Other external considerations

Similarly, misrepresentation inducing contract, claims founded in tort or delict and collateral warranties may or may not be interpreted as arising 'under or in connection with this contract' and as a matter which may not be submitted for adjudication.

Certificates

Although it does not expressly say so, this clause by implication gives the Adjudicator the power to open up certificates and indeed, the Guidance Notes suggest that 'If the dispute concerned an amount due as certified by the Project Manager and the Adjudicator decides that the amount certified was incorrect, the Project Manager will be required to make a correction in the next certificate.'

Termination of the contract

Whether the power to adjudicate survives the termination of an NEC contract is, however, uncertain.

Summary

Litigation in some jurisdictions has arisen in the past in relation to words such as 'under a contract' or 'in connection with a contract' and differences of interpretation have been arrived at in relation to these different terms. But the 'belt-and-braces' approach adopted by the NEC in their definition of 'any dispute arising under or in connection with this contract' is likely to result in a wide interpretation in this respect.

Final time limits for disputes

The NEC family of contracts appears to provide a final time limit within which disputes must be submitted to adjudication.

The Guidance Notes describe the intention as follows: 'Time stipulations are clearly set out in the table and throughout the dispute procedure in order to avoid protracted exchanges and arguments and to achieve prompt resolution of disputes.'

The inference is, therefore, that these time limits – including the final time limit of four weeks for submission of the dispute to the Adjudicator – are intended to be strictly applied.

In relation to the NEC Professional Services Contract

ADJUDICATION TABLE

Dispute about:	Submission of the dispute:
An action of the Employer	Between two and four weeks after notification of the dispute by the Consultant to the Employer
The Employer not having taken an action	Between two and four weeks after notification of the dispute by the Consultant to the Employer
Any other matter	Between two and four weeks after notification of the dispute to the Other Party

Commentary The four-week limit of submitting a dispute to the Adjudicator is presumably intended to be strictly observed on pain of being disentitled from taking that dispute to adjudication.

In relation to the NEC Engineering and Construction Contract

ADJUDICATION TABLE

Dispute about:	*Submission of the dispute:*
An action of the Project Manager or the Supervisor	Between two and four weeks after notification of the dispute by the Contractor to the Project Manager
The Project Manager or the Supervisor not having taken an action	Between two and four weeks after notification of the dispute by the Contractor to the Project Manager
Any other matter	Between two and four weeks after notification of the dispute to the Other Party

Commentary The four-week limit of submitting a dispute to the Adjudicator is presumably intended to be strictly observed on pain of being disentitled from taking that dispute to adjudication.

In relation to the NEC Engineering and Construction Subcontract

ADJUDICATION TABLE

Dispute about:	*Submission of the dispute:*
An action of the Contractor	Between two and four weeks after notification of the dispute by the Subcontractor to the Contractor
The Contractor not having taken an action	Between two and four weeks after notification of the dispute by the Subcontractor to the Contractor
Any other matter	Between two and four weeks after notification of the dispute to the Other Party

Commentary The four-week limit of submitting a dispute to the Adjudicator is presumably intended to be strictly observed on pain of being disentitled from taking that dispute to adjudication.

In relation to the NEC Engineering and Construction Short Contract (Standard Format)

Any dispute   Between two and four weeks after notifica-
                               tion of the dispute to the Other Party

Commentary The four-week limit of submitting a dispute to the Adjudicator
is presumably intended to be strictly observed on pain of being disentitled
from taking that dispute to adjudication.

Summary

For all its categories of dispute, therefore, the NEC Engineering and Construction family of contracts appears to provide a final time limit [four weeks from
notification] within which the dispute must be submitted to adjudication.

It is not entirely clear what would happen were a Party to attempt to
submit a dispute to the Adjudicator outwith the four-week period. Presumably, the Other Party could object and the Adjudicator should object.

Again, it will be important for Parties to carefully note when they first
became aware of the problem, when they notified it, what efforts they have
made during the period of grace and when the four-week period expired, so
as to be able to establish all of these if challenged.

Categories of dispute

The categories of dispute referable

It is not clear why the drafters of the NEC family of contracts chose to cate-
gorise disputes, but the indications are that the intention is for these categories and their time limits to be strictly complied with failing which no
adjudication at all will be possible. The NEC family of contracts, through
Core Clause 9, categorises the disputes thereunder as follows:

In relation to the NEC Professional Services Contract

ADJUDICATION TABLE

Dispute about:	*Which Party may submit it to the Adjudicator?*	*When may it be submitted to the Adjudicator?*
An action of the Employer	The Consultant	Between two and four weeks after the Consultant's notification of the dispute to the Employer, the notification itself being made not more than four weeks after the Consultant becomes aware of the action

The Employer not having taken an action	The Consultant	Between two and four weeks after the Consultant's notification of the dispute to the Employer, the notification itself being made not more than four weeks after the Consultant becomes aware that the action was not taken
Any other matter	Either Party	Between two and four weeks after notification of the dispute to the Other Party.

In relation to the NEC Engineering and Construction Contract

ADJUDICATION TABLE

Dispute about:	Which Party may submit it to the Adjudicator?	When may it be submitted to the Adjudicator?
An action of the Project Manager or the Supervisor	The Contractor	Between two and four weeks after the Contractor's notification of the dispute to the Project Manager, the notification itself being made not more than four weeks after the Contractor becomes aware of the action
The Project Manager or the Supervisor not having taken an action	The Contractor	Between two and four weeks after the Contractor's notification of the dispute to the Project Manager, the notification itself being made not more than four weeks after the Contractor becomes aware that the action was not taken
Any other matter	Either Party	Between two and four weeks after notification of the dispute to the Other Party and the Project Manager.

In relation to the NEC Engineering and Construction Subcontract

ADJUDICATION TABLE

Dispute about:	Which Party may submit it to the Adjudicator?	When may it be submitted to the Adjudicator?
An action of the Contractor	The Subcontractor	Between two and four weeks after the Subcontractor's notification of the dispute to the Contractor, the notification itself being made not more than four weeks after the Subcontractor becomes aware of the action
The Contractor not having taken an action	The Subcontractor	Between two and four weeks after the Subcontractor's notification of the dispute to the Contractor, the notification itself being made not more than four weeks after the Subcontractor becomes aware that the action was not taken
Any other matter	Either Party	Between two and four weeks after notification of the dispute to the other Party.

In relation to the NEC Engineering and Construction Short Contract (Standard Format)

Any dispute

Summary

With the exception of the NEC Engineering and Construction Short Contract, therefore, the NEC family of contracts categorises the disputes which may be referred to adjudication as follows:

Dispute

An action of the part of the Employer/Project Manager or Supervisor/Contractor

The Employer/Project Manager or Supervisor/Contractor not having taken an action

Any other matter

The parties entitled to refer disputes

The NEC family of contracts, through Core Clause 9, defines which Parties may refer which disputes as follows:

In relation to the NEC Professional Services Contract

ADJUDICATION TABLE

Dispute about:	*Which Party may submit it to the Adjudicator?*
An action of the Employer	The Consultant
The Employer not having taken an action	The Consultant
Any other matter	Either Party

In relation to the NEC Engineering and Construction Contract

ADJUDICATION TABLE

Dispute about:	*Which Party may submit it to the Adjudicator?*
An action of the Project Manager or the Supervisor	The Contractor
The Project Manager or the Supervisor not having taken an action	The Contractor
Any other matter	Either Party

In relation to the NEC Engineering and Construction Subcontract

ADJUDICATION TABLE

Dispute about:	*Which Party may submit it to the Adjudicator?*
An action of the Contractor	The Subcontractor
The Contractor not having taken an action	The Subcontractor
Any other matter	Either Party

In relation to the NEC Engineering and Construction Short Contract (Standard Format)

Any dispute   Any Party

Summary

With the exception of the NEC Engineering and Construction Short Contract, therefore, the NEC family of contracts does place restrictions upon the Parties who may refer the disputes to adjudication as follows:

Dispute	*Party entitled to refer that dispute*
An action of the part of the Employer/Project Manager or Supervisor/Contractor	The Consultant The Contractor The Subcontractor
The Employer/Project Manager or Supervisor/ Contractor not having taken an action	The Consultant The Contractor The Subcontractor

Overall summary

It remains to be seen to what extent the adjudication provisions of the NEC family of contracts are interpreted as directory or advisory. However, if a strict view is taken then it would not, for example, be possible for an *employer* to refer an action of the Project Manager to the Adjudicator at all. If a strict view is taken, then the Parties will require to exercise care in relation to what disputes are referred to whom, and when.

5. What procedure is to govern the adjudication

Because the NEC family of contracts categorises disputes, the procedure set down for each category of dispute (action, failure to take action, any other matter) is the procedure which will be used to initiate an adjudication in relation to that category of dispute and those procedures, which are considered below, will require to be closely observed.

The categories of dispute

Actions

90.1 Any dispute arising under or in connection with this contract is submitted to and settled by the Adjudicator as follows:

ADJUDICATION TABLE

Dispute about:	Which Party may submit it to the Adjudicator?	When may it be submitted to the Adjudicator?
An action taken by the Project Manager or the Supervisor	The Contractor	Between two and four weeks after the Contractor's notification of the dispute to the Project Manager, the notification itself being made not more than four weeks after the Contractor becomes aware of the action.

According to the Guidance Notes, an 'action' [which can only be that taken by the Project Manager or the Supervisor] may, for example, be the following:

- an instruction
- an acceptance, non-acceptance, or rejection
- a certification
- an assessment
- a notification
- a decision

and the Guidance Notes go on to suggest that each instruction, acceptance, non-acceptance, rejection, certification, assessment, notice or decision is a separate action (and therefore, by implication, may be the subject of a separate dispute and therefore a separate adjudication).

The Guidance Notes continue that accordingly a dispute may, for example, be the following:

- an action which should not have been taken
- an action taken outside the specified time limits
- an action which is incomplete or ill-judged
- an action which is an assessment improperly made/calculated
- an action taken without authority.

Party entitled

In relation to a dispute about an action taken by the Project Manager or the Supervisor, the only Party who may submit that dispute to the Adjudicator is the Contractor. The Employer has no such entitlement and the basis for this is, apparently, that the Project Manager or Supervisor will always be acting on behalf of the Employer.

Notification time limit

From the point in time at which the Contractor becomes aware of the action taken by the Project Manager or the Supervisor, that Contractor has four weeks to make notification of the dispute about that action to the Project Manager.

The Guidance Notes suggest that the timetables are to be strictly observed and, if so, once those four weeks have passed without such notification then the right to submit that dispute to adjudication may have been lost and that dispute may no longer be referable to adjudication.

Submission time limit

Provided that notification of the dispute to the Project Manager has been made timeously by the Contractor so that the notification time limit has been observed, then it appears that – running from that notification – three new time periods come into play as follows:

Up to two weeks after notification

It appears that this two-week period is intended as a period of grace within which the Contractor may *not* submit to adjudication a dispute about an action taken by the Project Manager or the Supervisor.

The reason for this is, apparently, that it is intended to allow mistakes to be recognised and remedied so as to prevent the Adjudicator becoming involved with matters which have simply been overlooked by the Project Manager or the Supervisor.

Between two and four weeks after notification

This is the period within which the Contractor *may* submit to adjudication a dispute about an action taken by the Project Manager or the Supervisor.

More than four weeks after notification

It appears that four weeks after the Contractor's notification of the dispute to the Project Manager that Contractor may no longer submit the dispute to adjudication.

The Guidance Notes suggest that the timetables are to be strictly observed and, if so, once those four weeks have passed without such submission then the right to submit that dispute to adjudication may have been lost by the Contractor and that dispute may no longer be referable to adjudication.

Disputes not referable to adjudication ('action')

On the basis of the above analysis, under Core Clause 9 of the NEC family of contracts the following disputes may *not* be referable by the Contractor to adjudication:

• Disputes which have not been notified within four weeks of the Contractor becoming aware of the action taken by the Project Manager or the Supervisor.
• Disputes which are within a period of two weeks of the Contractor's notification to the Project Manager of the dispute relating to an action taken by the Project Manager or the Supervisor.
• Disputes which are outwith a period of four weeks after the Contractor's notification to the Project Manager of the dispute relating to an action taken by the Project Manager or the Supervisor.

Failure to take action

90.1   Any dispute arising under or in connection with this contract is submitted to and settled by the Adjudicator as follows:

ADJUDICATION TABLE

Dispute about:	*Which Party may submit to the Adjudicator?*	*When may it be submitted to the Adjudicator?*
The Project Manager or the Supervisor not having taken an action	The Contractor	Between two and four weeks after the Contractor's notification of the dispute to the Project Manager, the notification itself being made not more than four weeks after the Contractor becomes aware that the action was not taken

The nature of a dispute about inaction

According to the Guidance Notes, a 'failure to take an action' [which failure can only be made by the Project Manager or the Supervisor] may, for example, by inference include the following:

- failure to give an instruction
- a failure to accept, or a failure to reject
- a failure to certify
- a failure to assess
- a failure to give notification
- a failure to decide

and the Guidance Notes go on to suggest that each such failure is a separate action (and therefore, by implication, may be the subject of a separate dispute and therefore a separate adjudication).

The Guidance Notes go on to suggest that accordingly a dispute may, for example, be the following:

- the failure to take an action which should have been taken
- the failure to take an action within the specified time limits
- the failure to complete an action
- the failure to properly make/calculate an assessment
- the failure to have sufficient authority for an action.

Party entitled

In relation to a dispute about the Project Manager or the Supervisor not having taken an action, the only Party who may submit that dispute to the Adjudicator is the Contractor.

The Employer has no such entitlement and the basis for this is, apparently, that the Project Manager or Supervisor will always be acting on behalf of the Employer.

Notification time limit

From the point in time at which the Contractor becomes aware that the action has not been taken by the Project Manager or the Supervisor, that Contractor has four weeks to make notification of the dispute about that action to the Project Manager.

The Guidance Notes suggest that the timetables are to be strictly observed and, if so, once those four weeks have passed without such notification then the right to submit that dispute to adjudication may have been lost by the Contractor and that dispute may no longer be referable to adjudication.

Submission time limit

Provided that notification of the dispute to the Project Manager has been made timeously by the Contractor so that the notification time limit has been observed, then it appears that – running from that notification – three new time periods come into play as follows:

Up to two weeks after notification

It appears that this two-week period is intended as a period of grace within which the Contractor may *not* submit to adjudication a dispute about an action taken by the Project Manager or the Supervisor.

The reason for this is, apparently, that it is intended to allow failures to be recognised and remedied so as to prevent the Adjudicator becoming involved with matters which have simply been overlooked by the Project Manager or the Supervisor.

Between two and four weeks after notification

This is the period within which the Contractor *may* submit to adjudication a dispute about an action not having been taken by the Project Manager or the Supervisor.

More than four weeks after notification

It appears that four weeks after the Contractor's notification of the dispute to the Project Manager that Contractor may no longer submit the dispute to adjudication.

The Guidance Notes suggest that the timetables are to be strictly observed and, if so, once those four weeks have passed without such submission then the right to submit that dispute to adjudication may have been lost by the Contractor and that dispute may no longer be referable to adjudication.

Disputes referable to adjudication ('inaction')

On the basis of the above analysis, under Core Clause 9 of the NEC family of contracts the following disputes may *not* be referable by the Contractor to adjudication:

- Disputes which have not been notified within four weeks of the Contractor becoming aware of the action not having been taken by the Project Manager or the Supervisor.
- Disputes which are within a period of two weeks of the Contractor's notification to the Project Manager of the dispute relating to an action not having been taken by the Project Manager or the Supervisor.
- Disputes which are outwith a period of four weeks after the Contractor's notification to the Project Manager of the dispute relating to an action not having been taken by the Project Manager or the Supervisor.

Any other matter

90.1   Any dispute arising under or in connection with this contract is submitted to and settled by the Adjudicator as follows:

ADJUDICATION TABLE

Dispute about:	Which Party may submit it to the Adjudicator?	When may it be submitted to the Adjudicator?
Any other matter	Either Party	Between two and four weeks after notification of the dispute to the Other Party and the Project Manager

The nature of a dispute about any other matter

The Guidance Notes do not suggest what 'any other matter' might be and so the inference is that it means just that – any other matter (subject only to the restriction below).

It is not necessarily related to the Project Manager or the Supervisor.

By inference also, each other matter will be a separate action (and therefore, by implication, may be the subject of a separate dispute and therefore a separate adjudication).

Arising under or in connection with this contract

The only restriction which Clause 9 imposes in relation to such disputes is that the dispute arises under or in connection with the contract in question.

Exactly what that means is something which might require to be interpreted by the law of the contract or the *lex mercatoria*. It might exclude such matters as disputes about the validity of the contract itself or an allegation that the contract itself was induced by fraudulent misrepresentation.

However, since 'arising under the contract' and 'arising in connection with the contract' are both generally recognised terms, the fact that the NEC contract uses both terms is likely to point to a wide interpretation.

Certificates

The NEC contracts do not appear to specifically provide that any certificates shall be 'final' and therefore there would appear to be no restriction in Clause 9 effectively preventing the Adjudicator bringing certificates under review.

Party entitled

Both the Contractor and the Employer are entitled to submit such a dispute to the Adjudicator.

Notification time limit

The Party concerned must notify the dispute about any other matter to the Other Party and to the Project Manager but there is no specified time limit for doing so.

Submission time limit

Once notification of the dispute about any other matter has been made to the Other Party and to the Project Manager, then it appears that – running from that notification – three new time periods come into play as follows:

Up to two weeks after notification

It appears that this two-week period is intended as a period of grace within which Either Party may *not* submit to adjudication a dispute about any other matter.

The reason for this is, apparently, that it is intended to allow matters to be recognised and remedied so as to prevent the Adjudicator becoming involved with matters which have simply been overlooked by the Project Manager or the Supervisor.

Between two and four weeks after notification

This is the period within which Either Party *may* submit to adjudication a dispute about any other matter.

More than four weeks after notification

It appears that four weeks after the Party's notification of the dispute to the Other Party and to the Project Manager that Party may no longer submit that dispute to adjudication.

The Guidance Notes suggest that the timetables are to be strictly observed and, if so, once those four weeks have passed without such submission then the right to submit that dispute to adjudication may have been lost by the Party and that dispute may no longer be referable to adjudication.

'Other matter' disputes not referable to adjudication

On the basis of the above analysis, under Core Clause 9 of the NEC family of contracts the following disputes may *not* be referable by the Contractor to adjudication:

- Disputes which are within a period of two weeks of the Party's notification to the Other Party and to the Project Manager of the dispute relating to any other matter.
- Disputes which are outwith a period of four weeks after the Party's notification to the Other Party and to the Project Manager of the dispute relating to any other matter.

Other considerations

What can be done to question an application for adjudication

It does not appear to be envisaged that under the NEC family of contracts there will be much in the way of disagreement about the procedures to be adopted for the resolution of any disputes or any need to question these.

Where, however, a question does arise such as whether what has arisen is truly a 'dispute', whether any dispute has been properly crystallised and whether any time limits have been observed, then there does not appear to have been any procedure provided in the NEC family of contracts for resolving such questions. Where necessary, resort would have to be had to the law of the contract or the law of the territory.

It is, however, important for any Party with such a reservation to note that they must maintain any such objection throughout any adjudication or they may be treated as having waived the objection and to have consented to the adjudication.

What is to happen while the dispute is resolved by adjudication

The NEC family of contracts, unusually, makes express provision in this respect in each of its contracts along the following lines: 'Unless and until there is such a settlement, the [relevant Parties] proceed as if the action, inaction or other matter disputed were not disputed.'

The Guidance Notes suggest that submission of a dispute to adjudication does not entitle any Party to cease activities.

Clearly, therefore – and this is one of the aims and intentions of the very process of adjudication – a Party faced with an adjudication should (even if having reservations about the adjudication) proceed with both the Works and the adjudication (if necessary, under reservation) and then attempt to resolve the matter thereafter.

We consider what is involved in proceeding with an adjudication in the following Section II and what may follow an adjudication in the following Section III.

Section II

The process of adjudication

6. The appointment and referral of the dispute to the Adjudicator

Introduction

In this chapter, it is proposed to consider what is involved, under the NEC family of contracts, in the appointment of the Adjudicator and the referral of the dispute to the Adjudicator.

We have already examined in Section I what may precede an adjudication and, in particular, the notification of the dispute and the period of grace which is intended to settle the matter and avoid the need for any adjudication at all.

This section is concerned with the stage where settlement has not proved possible and the position has in effect moved from notification of a dispute to notification of intention to refer a dispute to adjudication. This involves the appointment of the Adjudicator and the referral of the dispute to the Adjudicator.

In relation to appointment, we shall consider first the various ways in which an Adjudicator may be appointed under the NEC contract and we shall also consider how the appointment of the Adjudicator is confirmed.

In relation to referral, we shall consider the manner in which the dispute is referred to the Adjudicator and the time limits for doing so.

Finally, we shall seek to summarise what is involved under the NEC family of contracts in the appointment and referral of a dispute to the Adjudicator.

In this chapter we shall deal with the subject under the following headings:

- Overview
- Notification of the dispute
- The appointment of the Adjudicator
- The reference of the dispute to the Adjudicator
- Summary

Overview

Introduction

As earlier noted, it is at present open to Parties to either accept the NEC contracts as they stand (which involves the Adjudicator being named in the contract) or amend the NEC contracts (to allow for appointment of the Adjudicator at the time when a dispute arises) and here we consider in outline both situations.

Unamended NEC contract (Adjudicator named in the contract)

'Notification'

For each of its categories of dispute, the NEC family of contracts provides for the Party involved to give 'notification' of the existence of that dispute to the appropriate person(s). No requirements have been specified in the NEC family of contracts as to the form which this 'notification' is to take. For a dispute which falls into the category of 'any other matter' notification may be given at any time. For other categories of dispute, notification must be given within four weeks of the Party becoming aware of the existence of that category of dispute.

The position is not entirely clear, but the indications are that these time limits are intended to be strict and that a failure to observe them will disentitle the Party from taking the dispute any further or on to adjudication.

'Appointment'

After notification, a two-week period of grace then applies. The dispute may then be submitted to the Adjudicator within two and four weeks of notification of the dispute. Again, the position is not entirely clear, but the indications are that these time limits are intended to be strict and that a failure to observe them – especially the four-week limit – will disentitle the Party from taking the dispute any further or on to adjudication.

So far as the 'appointment' of the Adjudicator is concerned, where the NEC contract is unamended then nothing further will require to be done as regards the appointment because the Adjudicator will already have been appointed by the Parties at the time of contracting. This, having been agreed by the Parties, will appear in the Contract Data as follows:

> The Adjudicator is
>
> Name [.....]
>
> Address [.....]

Assuming that no difficulties have intruded (which, if so, may require the use of the nomination procedures) then the Party concerned will be aware of the identity and situation of the Adjudicator.

'Submission' (or 'Referral')

In this situation, 'submission' (or 'referral') of the dispute to the Adjudicator will simply involve the Party concerned submitting the dispute to the Adjudicator. No requirements have been specified in the NEC family of contracts as to the form which this submission is to take.

Amended NEC contract (Adjudicator appointed at the time of the dispute)

'Notification'

Assuming that no adjustments have been made in this respect, it will remain the position that for each of its categories of dispute, the NEC family of contracts provides for the Party involved to give 'notification' of the existence of that dispute to the appropriate person(s). No requirements have been specified in the NEC family of contracts as to the form which this 'notification' is to take. For a dispute which falls into the category of 'any other matter', notification may be given at any time. For other categories of dispute, notification must be given within four weeks of the Party becoming aware of the existence of that category of dispute.

The position is not entirely clear, but the indications are that these time limits are intended to be strict and that a failure to observe them will disentitle the Party from taking the dispute any further or on to adjudication.

'Appointment'

Assuming that no adjustments have been made in this respect, it will remain the position that after notification, a two-week period of grace will then apply. The dispute may then be submitted to the Adjudicator within two and four weeks of notification of the dispute.

Again, the position is not entirely clear, but the indications are that these time limits are intended to be strict and that a failure to observe them – especially the four-week limit – will disentitle the Party from taking the dispute any further or on to adjudication.

The amendment is likely to relate to the manner in which the Adjudicator is appointed. This is clearly a matter for the Parties, but sensibly such amendment will provide a procedure for the appointment of the Adjudicator when a dispute arises within, say, seven days and will fit in with the other requirements of the NEC contract noted above.

Under this 'bespoke' procedure, the Party concerned will implement the agreed procedure for the appointment of the Adjudicator at the time of the dispute.

'Submission' (or 'Referral')

In this situation, 'submission' (or 'referral') of the dispute to the Adjudicator will simply involve the Party concerned submitting the dispute to the Adjudicator appointed. No requirements have been specified in the NEC family of contracts as to the form which this submission is to take.

Summary

Assuming that any amendment relates only to the method and time of appointment of the Adjudicator and that the main thrust of the NEC contracts remains unaffected, then under this procedure, which does not impose any requirements as to the precise form which any intimation must take, the overall timetable from 'notification' to 'submission or referral' will involve a period of at least two weeks and one day after notification before a dispute can be submitted to adjudication and may also involve a final time limit within which a dispute can be submitted to adjudication of four weeks after notification.

Notification of the dispute

The NEC family of contracts provides, in relation to all categories of dispute, that the Party concerned give notification of the dispute to the relevant person(s) (which may be the Other Party and/or the Project Manager).

No provision whatsoever is made, however, in relation to the format which that notification must take.

NEC PRINCIPLES

It is to be expected that, in accordance with NEC principles, the Party concerned will make full and proper notification of the nature of the dispute.

There is, however, no provision within the NEC adjudication procedures for this aspect to be addressed.

LEX MERCATORIA

In adjudication generally, considerable attention is paid to the extent to which the dispute upon which an attempt is being made to finally adjudicate is the same dispute of which the Parties were originally given notification.

In the event, therefore, that a Party attempt to have adjudicated a dispute of which no previous notification has been made, then any remedy would require to come from the *lex mercatoria*.

The appointment of the Adjudicator

Introduction

As a general principle, the will of the Parties should always prevail and it is not thought that the NEC family of contracts is any different in that respect. We therefore consider that aspect first in relation to the appointment of the Adjudicator.

As noted, the preferred approach of the drafters of the NEC family of contracts is for the Adjudicator to be named in the contract at the time of contracting. Even then, however, some provision – in this instance a nominating body – requires to be made to cover the eventuality of the named Adjudicator no longer being available. We consider this arrangement next.

It is also possible, if so desired, to amend the NEC contract so as to allow for the appointment of a suitable Adjudicator at the point in time at which the dispute arises and we consider what is involved in that respect.

Finally, once that appointment has been made, it will normally be sought to have that appointment confirmed and we consider also the means by which that might be done.

Notwithstanding the fact that an NEC contract exists which names an Adjudicator, it would be open to the Parties to the contract – provided that *all* of the Parties were in agreement (and subject to suitable compensation being made, if necessary, to the named Adjudicator) – to agree that some other suitable person should act as the Adjudicator in relation to a particular dispute. Such a step would have the advantage of allowing the Adjudicator chosen to closely match the dispute which had arisen. It does, however, require the agreement of *all* of the Parties involved.

If adopting this course of action it would clearly be advisable for the Parties to alter the written contract into which they have entered by means of a written amendment of their contract.

The formal appointment of the Adjudicator will be considered under the following headings:

- Appointment of the Adjudicator under an unamended NEC contract
- Appointment of the Adjudicator under an amended NEC contract
- Confirming the appointment of the Adjudicator.

Appointment of the Adjudicator under an unamended NEC contract

By naming in the contract

NEC PRINCIPLES

This is the preferred option of the drafters of the NEC family of contracts. The intention is that at the time when the NEC contract in question is being entered into, the Parties will agree upon and name the Adjudicator in their NEC contract.

This is achieved by completing the necessary sections of the NEC contract and in particular that relating to Contract Data as follows:

CONTRACT DATA

1. General

The Adjudicator is

Name [.....]

Address [.....]

It is to be expected that, in accordance with NEC principles, having named an Adjudicator in their contract the Parties will (unless *all* of the Parties agree to the contrary) respect the appointment of the Adjudicator named in the contract.

Properly drafted, the NEC contract concerned should be able to cope with any impediment which arises in relation to the use of the Adjudicator named in the contract, failing which resort may have to be had to the *lex mercatoria*.

LEX MERCATORIA

Even though the Parties have named an Adjudicator in their contract it is possible that something might arise to prevent that Adjudicator acting. The NEC contract may make provision for that eventuality, failing which resort may have to be had to the law of the contract or the law of the territories in which the Works are being carried out if the right to adjudicate is not to be lost altogether.

As noted above, the procedure under the NEC family of contracts for naming the Adjudicator in the contract is for the Parties to agree upon the name of an Adjudicator which is then inserted in the Contract Data section of the contract which the Parties sign.

In the event of that named Adjudicator not, for some reason, being available when a dispute actually arises, then it seems open to the Parties to together agree upon the choice of a replacement Adjudicator.

In the event that the Parties cannot agree upon the choice of a new Adjudicator then, if the Parties have completed that section of the contract, the contract may have nominated a person or body who will choose a new Adjudicator and we consider that provision next.

Should that section of the Contract Data not have been completed, however, and the Parties are unable to agree upon an Adjudicator, then it may not be possible to proceed any further with the adjudication unless the *lex mercatoria* can fill that lacuna.

By nominating

NEC PRINCIPLES

Where the NEC contract is unamended and the Adjudicator is named in the contract at the outset then clearly in the period between entering into the contract and the dispute arising circumstances may arise in which the named Adjudicator is no longer available and a replacement Adjudicator has to be found. The NEC family of contracts allows provision to be made for this eventuality.

In the first place, the NEC family of contracts envisages that it will be open to the Parties to agree upon the identity of a replacement Adjudicator. It might be said to be in accordance with the NEC principles for the Parties to reach such an agreement.

In case the Parties feel they may not be able to, however, the Parties are allowed to make provision in their contract for a procedure allowing a replacement Adjudicator to be nominated. This is achieved by completing the necessary sections of the NEC contract and in particular that relating to Contract Data as follows:

CONTRACT DATA

9. Disputes and termination

The person who will choose a new adjudicator if the Parties cannot agree a choice is [.....]

Properly drafted, therefore, the NEC family of contracts should be able to cope with any impediment which arises in relation to the use of the Adjudicator named in the contract, but should this section not be completed and the Parties are unable to reach agreement then resort may have to be had to the *lex mercatoria.*

LEX MERCATORIA

Even though the Parties have named an Adjudicator in their contract it is possible that something might arise to prevent that Adjudicator acting. The NEC contract allows provision for that eventuality, but if no such provision is made and the Parties cannot agree then resort may have to be had to the law of the contract or the law of the territories in which the Works are being carried out if the right to adjudicate is not to be lost altogether.

As noted above, the procedure under the NEC family of contracts for a replacement Adjudicator is first of all for the Parties to seek to agree upon the name of a replacement Adjudicator.

In the event that the Parties cannot agree upon the choice of a new Adjudicator then, if the Parties have completed that section of the contract, the contract may have nominated a person or body who will choose a new Adjudicator.

No specific time limits or procedures have been laid down in this respect and therefore it is presumably intended that within a reasonable time one of the Parties will approach the Person or Body named who will, again within a reasonable time, nominate a replacement Adjudicator. That Adjudicator should confirm willingness to act within a reasonable time and (so far as not inferred) an Adjudicator's contract is likely to be entered into at that time.

Should that nomination section of the Contract Data not have been completed, however, and the Parties are unable to agree upon an Adjudicator, then it may not be possible to proceed any further with the adjudication unless the *lex mercatoria* can fill that lacuna.

Appointment of the Adjudicator under an amended NEC contract

By 'bespoke' provision in the contract

NEC PRINCIPLES

The difficulty with naming the Adjudicator in the contract (the preferred option of the drafters of the NEC family of contracts) is that in a large project the named Adjudicator may have to cover a large number of potential disputes not all of which may fall within his or her particular expertise. Some Parties therefore prefer to defer the appointment of the Adjudicator until the dispute has arisen and then to select an Adjudicator whose skills closely match the dispute in question. It is not, as presently advised, considered to be in any way contrary to NEC principles for this to be done by the Parties.

To do so, however, would require amending the NEC contracts. This will normally be done by leaving the section for naming the Adjudicator blank or striking it out and using Option Z to provide for additional conditions of contract covering the appointment of the Adjudicator.

The extent of any amendment will clearly be a matter for the Parties.

The important consideration in respect of 'bespoke' procedure is to adopt conditions which will ensure that an Adjudicator is appointed and which cannot be thwarted by a recalcitrant Party unwilling to submit to adjudication. A frequently encountered provision is to delegate to a (named) Nominating Body not just the selection but the actual nomination of an Adjudicator suitable for the dispute in hand. Where the Parties have agreed to such a provision then the nomination by the Nominating Body will be binding upon the Parties and the adjudication can proceed. This might also involve provision for the use (either as a matter of course or as a last resort) of an (unnamed) Adjudicator Nominating Body.

LEX MERCATORIA

Amending contracts can be fraught with difficulty and the effect achieved by the amendment can often be a question of interpretation. Here, resort may have to be had to the *lex mercatoria.*

It is possible that the law of the contract or the law of the territories in which the Works are being carried out may have rules which affect this position.

Confirming the appointment of the Adjudicator

Introduction

NEC PRINCIPLES

By whatever means the Adjudicator is appointed (and whether or not the NEC contract is amended) the appointment of the Adjudicator will normally be confirmed by the Adjudicator and the Parties entering into an Adjudicator's Contract.

There is in fact no requirement to have an Adjudicator's Contract at all but the Adjudicator will normally insist upon one and it is generally advisable to have one.

Where the Adjudicator is named in the NEC contract into which the Parties are entering then it is envisaged that at that time the Parties and the Adjudicator will also enter into the Adjudicator's Contract. Alternatively, if the Adjudicator is being appointed at the time when the dispute arises then the Adjudicator and the Parties can enter into an Adjudicator's Contract at that time.

Although there is no specific requirement to use it, the NEC Adjudicator's Contract is available for this purpose. It has, of course, been drafted with the other NEC contracts in mind. It might be considered in accordance with the NEC principles to use the NEC Adjudicator's Contract and adhere to its principles.

We consider below the provisions of the NEC Adjudicator's Contract.

LEX MERCATORIA

There is, of course, nothing to prevent the Adjudicator and the Parties entering into a 'bespoke' Adjudicator's Contract but in the event of a dispute relating thereto it may be necessary to involve the *lex mercatoria* to resolve any such dispute.

The NEC Adjudicator's Contract

The Adjudicator's Contract is intended for use with any of the family of NEC Engineering and Construction Contracts (which themselves contain the detailed adjudication procedures). The First Edition was published in 1994 and taking into account experience in use and harmonisation with revised editions, this – the Second Edition – was published in 1998. By these means, no conflict should arise between the NEC Engineering and Construction Contract being used and the Adjudicator's Contract. The Form of Agreement used to constitute the Adjudicator's Contract in these circumstances will be that provided for use where a United Kingdom Scheme for Construction Contracts does not apply.

It is also possible to use the NEC Adjudicator's Contract to resolve a dispute in which the form of contract being used is something other than one of the family of NEC Engineering and Construction Contracts. In that eventuality, a conflict could arise between the Contract being used and the Adjudicator's Contract. Clause 1.7 gives priority to the terms of the Adjudicator's Contract in such circumstances but the Guidance Notes suggest that it may be necessary and safer to amend either contract to resolve any such conflict. The Form of Agreement used to constitute the Adjudicator's Contract in these circumstances will be that provided for use where a United Kingdom Scheme for Construction Contracts does not apply.

It is also possible to use the NEC Adjudicator's Contract to resolve disputes in relation to which the Housing Grants, Construction and Regeneration Act 1996 (together with any of the Schemes brought in under Regulations relating thereto) applies. The Form of Agreement used to constitute the Adjudicator's Contract in these circumstances will be that provided for use only when the 'United Kingdom Housing Grants, Construction and Regeneration Act 1996 Scheme for Construction Contracts Regulations 1998 applies'.

Whichever Form of Agreement is used, it is drafted as a simple contract and is provided as a convenient means for the two Parties and the Adjudicator to record their agreement to the appointment of the Adjudicator.

Conditions of contract

Commentary In interpreting these conditions of contract, the Guidance Notes are not to be used for legal interpretation of meaning. The duties and procedures to be followed are, as in other NEC documents, stated in the present tense for simplicity of use. Where actions are permitted but not obligatory, the term 'may' is used. In this contract, except where the context shows otherwise, words in the singular also mean in the plural and the other way round and words in the masculine mean in the feminine and neuter.

1. General

Actions

1.1   The Parties and the Adjudicator shall act as stated in this contract and in the *contract between the Parties*. The Adjudicator shall act impartially.

Commentary The Guidance Notes (which should not be used for legal interpretation) indicate that this clause states the general obligations of the Parties and the Adjudicator in terms of two contracts, viz. the Adjudicator's Contract and the Contract between the Parties.

The Contract between the Parties – for example, the Contract, Subcontract, Professional Services Contract or any other contract in the family of NEC Engineering and Construction Contracts – may include requirements and procedures to be followed by the Parties and the Adjudicator in the adjudication process. Those requirements and procedures are, by this clause, incorporated by reference into the Adjudicator's Contract.

Where the Works are within UK territory covered by the Housing Grants, Construction and Regeneration Act 1996 and any Schemes for Construction Contracts then there will be requirements and procedures to be followed by the Parties and the Adjudicator in the adjudication process. For the avoidance of doubt, those requirements and procedures are, by this clause, incorporated by reference into the Adjudicator's Contract.

Where a conflict arises then the Adjudicator's Contract will take priority (Clause 1.7) over the Contract between the Parties. [It could perhaps be added that the Statute or Regulations will take priority over the Contract between the Parties].

The Guidance Notes add 'the requirement for the Adjudicator to act impartially is fundamental to the whole scheme of adjudication. Any failure by the Adjudicator to so act would be a serious breach of his obligations'.

1.2   The Adjudicator notifies the Parties as soon as he becomes aware
  • of any matter which may present him with a conflict of interest, or
  • that he is unable to act.

Commentary The Guidance Notes indicate that the purpose of this clause is to identify any matter which may affect the Adjudicator in carrying out his duties. The consequences of the notification are not stated on the grounds that they will vary according to the circumstances.

The example is given of a contractor entering into a sub-contract with a sub-contractor with whom the Adjudicator may have some connection. It is suggested that on being so informed, the Parties may on the one hand decide that the conflict of interest is so small that they are content for the Adjudicator to continue to act and will rely on his duty to act impartially or may on the other hand decide to terminate the Adjudicator's appointment under the termination clause.

Identified and defined terms

1.3 In these conditions of contract, the Adjudicator and the Parties are those identified in the Form of Agreement. The terms in italics are those identified in the Contract Data and defined terms have capital initials.

Commentary The Guidance Notes explain that the conventions used in these conditions of contract (the terms in italics are those identified in the Contract Data and defined terms have capital initials) are those which apply generally in NEC contracts. The Adjudicator and the Parties are those named in the Form of Agreement.

1.4 Expenses are the cost of
- printing, reproduction and purchase of documents, drawings, maps, records and photographs
- telegrams, telexes, faxes and telephone calls
- postage and delivery charges
- travelling, hotel and similar expenses
- room charges
- charges by others for help in adjudication

incurred by the Adjudicator for an adjudication.

Commentary The Guidance Notes explain that this clause lists the Expenses to which the Adjudicator may be entitled in addition to his fee.

Interpretation

1.5 In this contract, except where the context shows otherwise, words in the singular also mean in the plural and the other way round and words in the masculine mean in the feminine and neuter.

Commentary This clause is self-explanatory.

1.6 This contract is governed by the law of the contract.

Commentary This clause is self-explanatory.

1.7 If a conflict arises between this contract and the *contract between the Parties* then this contract prevails.

Commentary The Guidance Notes observe:

> The contract between the Parties may conflict with provisions in the Adjudicator's Contract. This clause establishes priorities where there is such conflict. Priority has been given to the Adjudicator's Contract in order to ensure that the protection of the Adjudicator provided by clauses 4.1 and 4.2 (against risks) is preserved. Where an adjudication takes place under the Scheme, because of the statutory nature of the Scheme's provisions, the latter must automatically have priority over the Adjudicator's Contract and the Contract between the Parties.

1.8   If as a result of the *contract between the Parties*, another party has become a party to the dispute, references to Parties in this contract are interpreted as including the other party.

Commentary The Guidance Notes observe that if the Contract between the Parties has a 'joinder' clause, it may be that a dispute in a sub-contract may also comprise a dispute in the main contract. The 'joinder' provisions would then permit the sub-contractor to be joined as a party involved in the dispute in the main contract adjudication and in those circumstances the term 'Parties' is to be interpreted in such a way that the term includes the sub-contractor.

Communications

1.9   Each communication which this contract requires is in a form which can be read, copied and recorded. Writing is in the *language of this contract*. A communication has effect when it is received at the last address notified by the recipient for receiving communications or, if none is notified, at the address of the recipient stated in the Form of Agreement.

Commentary The Guidance Notes suggest that the phrase 'in a form which can be read, copied and recorded' in the above clause includes a letter sent by post, telex, cable, electronic mail, facsimile transmission, and on disc, magnetic tape or other electronic means.

It is also noted, however, that communications are effective only when they have been received.

2. Adjudication

2.1   The Adjudicator reaches a decision on a dispute referred to him under and in accordance with the *contract between the Parties*.

Commentary The Guidance Notes suggest it is important that the Adjudicator clearly identifies the issue which is in dispute and then gives a decision only on that dispute. In everything he does he must follow any procedures laid down in the contract between the Parties and the Scheme where applicable. It follows that the Adjudicator should be aware of all relevant provisions in the contract between the Parties and in any relevant Scheme. Any departure from these may give a Party grounds for challenging his decision. No timing is stated in this clause. If the Contract between the Parties does not include timing for an adjudication, and if there are no relevant statutory requirements, the Parties and the Adjudicator should seek to agree appropriate times, in order to avoid delay.

2.2   The Adjudicator may obtain from others help that he considers necessary in reaching his decision.

Commentary The Guidance Notes suggest that this clause gives the Adjudicator a power in addition to those he may have in the Contract between the Parties. The purpose in giving the Adjudicator this power is to enable him to arrive at a fair settlement of the dispute within the time available. However, any decision he makes must be his own and any payments he makes to specialists under this clause are part of the expenses defined in Clause 1.4 which the Adjudicator is entitled to recover. This clause does not impose a requirement upon the Adjudicator to obtain the consent of the Parties before taking such a step, but the Guidance Notes note that the Scheme includes a similar power to 'appoint experts, assessors or legal advisers' provided that the Adjudicator notifies the Parties of his intention and go on to suggest that the Adjudicator would be well advised to inform the Parties that he is seeking help from others.

2.3   The Parties and the Adjudicator keep the Adjudicator's decision and information provided for an adjudication as confidential to those who have a proper interest in them.

Commentary The Guidance Notes observe that it is possible that the Adjudicator's decision can be used to resolve other disputes between the Parties which have not been notified but that this clause limits the further use which the Parties may make of the Adjudicator's decision. However, the Guidance Notes observe that there are many who (quite legitimately and permissibly) may need to be advised of the Adjudicator's decision, such as the Banks, Insurers, Auditors or Parent Company of the Parties.

2.4   The Adjudicator keeps documents provided to him by the Parties until termination.

Commentary This clause is self-explanatory.

3.   Payment

3.1   Unless otherwise agreed, the Parties pay the Adjudicator his Fee and Expenses in equal shares. The Adjudicator's Fee is for the time he spends on an adjudication and the time spent travelling.

Commentary The Guidance Notes observe that the Adjudicator's fee is stated in the Contract Data and that this will normally be in the form of an hourly rate with time spent on travelling and preparation work also payable at the hourly rate. Because the intention under the NEC system is that the Adjudicator be paid for resolving specific disputes only, no specific provision has been made for an appointment fee and any appointment fee required and agreed should therefore be stated in the Contract Data.

The Guidance Notes also observe that under some forms of contract [other than the NEC which do not cater for these additional duties as they see the Adjudicator's function as being confined only to dealing with specific disputes as they arise] the Parties may require the Adjudicator, before a dispute arises, to perform certain tasks such as visiting the site periodically, reading the contract documents to familiarise himself with the contract details and the progress being made etc. Where this is the case then the Guidance Notes suggest that details of the agreed arrangements be incorporated into the Adjudicator's Contract and any fee relating thereto clearly stated.

The normal NEC rule under this clause (3.1) is that the Parties pay the fee and expenses of the Adjudicator in equal shares. However, the Guidance

Notes note that under the Scheme Adjudicators decide the apportionment of fees and expenses and suggest that the Parties are free to agree with the Adjudicator that he should decide the apportionment of his fee and expenses in a particular dispute and again details of the agreed arrangements be incorporated into the Adjudicator's Contract.

3.2   After each decision on a dispute has been communicated to the Parties and after termination the Adjudicator invoices each Party for that Party's share of his *fee* and Expenses.

Commentary This clause is self-explanatory.

3.3   Any value added tax or sales tax which the law requires the Parties to pay to the Adjudicator is included in the invoice.

Commentary This clause is self-explanatory.

3.4   The Parties pay the Adjudicator within three weeks of the date of the invoice or, if a different period is stated in the Contract Data, within the period stated. If a payment is late, interest is paid on the late payment.

Commentary This clause is self-explanatory.

3.5   If one of the Parties fails to pay, the other Party pays the Adjudicator the amount due with interest and recovers the payment from the defaulting Party.

Commentary The Guidance Notes observe that this clause describes the joint and several liability of the Parties for payment of the Adjudicator's fee and expenses. Although the Parties are required to pay the amount due to the Adjudicator in equal shares, he can recover the full amount from the other Party if one defaults. This avoids the need for the Adjudicator to take legal action against the defaulting party, possibly disqualifying himself from further adjudication under the contract. As between the Parties, the one in default is required to reimburse the other any payments made to the Adjudicator on his behalf. If under Clause 1.8 there are more than two parties to a dispute, Clause 1.5 applies as to 'Party' in the singular or plural.

3.6   Interest is calculated at the *interest rate* and is compounded annually and is assessed from the date by which the payment should have been made until the date when it is made.

Commentary The Guidance Notes observe that the interest rate stated in the Contract Data should be based on an appropriate reliable annual base rate. The additional percentage [above base rate] is intended to reflect current commercial rates.

3.7   Payments are in the *currency of this contract* unless otherwise stated in this contract.

Commentary This clause is self-explanatory.

4. Risks

4.1   The Adjudicator, his employees and agents, are not liable to the Parties for an action or failure to take action in an adjudication unless the action or failure to take action is in bad faith.

Commentary The Guidance Notes observe that this clause protects the Adjudicator from legal actions by one of the Parties, such as for breach of contract or negligence. It is important for achieving a successful adjudication that the Adjudicator should not be concerned that a disappointed Party may pursue him personally over the decision. Rather than taking action against the Adjudicator, a disappointed Party should refer the dispute to Arbitration or other tribunal or dispute resolution procedure stated in the Contract between the Parties.

The Guidance Notes also observe, however, that if a Party believes that the Adjudicator has acted in bad faith, that is, dishonestly or with the intention of deceiving, then that Party is free to take legal action against the Adjudicator.

4.2   The Parties indemnify the Adjudicator, his employees and agents, against claims, compensation and costs arising out of the Adjudicator's decision unless his decision was made in bad faith.

Commentary The Guidance Notes consider that this clause protects the Adjudicator against legal action against him by a Third Party which may arise as a consequence of the Adjudicator's decision and observes that since Third Parties are not parties in the Adjudicator's Contract, such actions would be based on grounds other than breach of contract.

5. Termination

5.1   The Parties may, by agreement, terminate the appointment of the Adjudicator for any reason. They notify him of the termination.

Commentary The Guidance Notes observe that the Parties are able to terminate the Adjudicator's appointment, on condition that they both agree to do so. Termination is effected by both Parties notifying the Adjudicator of their agreement to terminate. In the absence of any express provision regarding payment, the payment clauses in Section 3 of the Adjudicator's Contract apply, i.e. that the Parties pay the Adjudicator (equally in the absence of provision to the contrary) his fee and Expenses calculated in accordance with Clause 3.1.

5.2   The Adjudicator may, by notifying the Parties, terminate his appointment if
   • he considers that he cannot act because of a conflict of interest
   • he is unable to act as Adjudicator, or
   • he has not been paid an amount due within five weeks of the date by which payment should have been made.

Commentary This clause states the circumstances which entitle the Adjudicator to terminate his appointment.

5.3   Unless previously terminated, the Adjudicator's appointment terminates on the date stated in the Contract Data.

Commentary The Guidance Notes note that in some circumstances,
adjudicable disputes may arise over a considerable period of time. In order
to avoid lengthy appointments provision is made in this clause for a termination date to be stated in the Contract Data. In normal circumstances, a date of
one year after completion of the work or services is recommended. If an
Adjudicator is required after this termination date, the Adjudicator's
Contract may be extended by agreement, or a new contract negotiated. If a
different person is appointed as Adjudicator, a new Adjudicator's Contract
will be required. Alternatively, the Parties may elect not to make an appointment at that stage on the basis that disputes are then unlikely to occur.
Appointments of Adjudicators under the Scheme are for particular disputes
as they arise. Thus the duration of appointment is not relevant.

The referral of the dispute to the Adjudicator

The NEC family of contracts provides, in relation to all categories of
dispute, that the Submitting Party may submit the dispute to the Adjudicator
between two and four weeks after notification of the dispute.

Running from notification of the dispute, therefore (a point in time which
the Parties should carefully record and note), there is an excluded period
before and after and a small 'window of submission' within which disputes
may be submitted to the Adjudicator. According to the Guidance Notes
these time limits are to be strictly adhered to.

TIME LIMITS FOR 'SUBMISSION' OR 'REFERRAL'

Day 1   Notification of the dispute.
'Period of Grace' within which the dispute may not be
submitted or referred to the Adjudicator.

Week 2   'Window of submission' within which the dispute may be
submitted or referred to the Adjudicator.

Week 4   Time limit for submission or referral of the dispute to the Adjudicator.

No provision whatsoever is made, however, in relation to the format which
that submission must take.

NEC PRINCIPLES

It is to be expected in accordance with NEC principles (and it is clearly in
their interest to do so) that the Party concerned will make a full and proper
submission in relation to the dispute.

The Guidance Notes suggest that:
It is important that the Adjudicator has all the relevant information to
enable him to put himself in the position of the Project Manager or
Supervisor when the action was taken or not taken as the case may be.

Information has therefore to be as full as is appropriate to the dispute. The Party submitting the dispute to the Adjudicator is obliged to include full information about the dispute.

LEX MERCATORIA

In adjudication generally, the referral appears to assume less importance being merely the mechanism for formally handing the preconceived dispute to the Adjudicator and setting the clock running for production of the decision by the Adjudicator. It is relatively unlikely, therefore, that the *lex mercatoria* will require to be called upon at this stage.

Time limits in launching an adjudication

The NEC family of contracts lays down a number of time limits for the notification and submission of disputes.

The significance of these time limits has not yet been tested but the Guidance Notes suggest they are to be adhered to, and no provision is made for the relaxation of these time limits even where good reason exists for the delay. It is presumably envisaged that that particular dispute will be regarded as beyond adjudication and that the Works will simply proceed towards a conclusion.

It would appear prudent therefore, as is always the case in adjudication, that a careful record be kept of any notification and submission of disputes and that these time limits be strictly observed.

Summary

Unamended NEC contract

Where the NEC contract involved is unamended, the position as regards the appointment and referral of the dispute to the Adjudicator can be summarised as follows:

Notification

For each category of dispute, notification of the dispute requires to be made to the relevant person (with time limits for doing so imposed for some categories of dispute).

Notification does not require to be in any particular form but it is to be expected that the Party will provide sufficient information about the dispute.

Appointment

The Adjudicator will already have been appointed by the Parties in their contract. This will appear in the Contract Data as follows:

The Adjudicator is

Name [.....]

Address [.....]

and an NEC Adjudicator's Contract confirming the appointment is likely to have been entered into at the same time.

The Submitting Party will check the availability of that Adjudicator and in the event of non-availability will activate the nomination provisions (if completed) in the contract (which while incorporating the terms of the Adjudicator's Contract might necessitate a new Adjudicator's Contract).

Submission or Referral

Having confirmed the appointment of the Adjudicator, referral simply involves the Submitting Party submitting the dispute to the Adjudicator for which there are no formal requirements but for which a certain amount of formality should be adopted, as well as ensuring that the Adjudicator has sufficient information to come to a decision.

A failure to submit the dispute to the Adjudicator within four weeks of the original notification may result in the adjudication being time-barred.

Amended NEC contract

Where the NEC contract involved has been amended, this will usually be for the purpose of providing for the Adjudicator to be appointed at the time of the dispute and the position as regards the appointment and referral of the dispute to the Adjudicator can be summarised as follows:

Notification

For each category of dispute, notification of the dispute requires to be made to the relevant person (with time limits for doing so imposed for some categories of dispute).

Notification does not require to be in any particular form but it is to be expected that the Party will provide sufficient information about the dispute.

Appointment

The procedures incorporated into the contract for the appointment of the Adjudicator at the time of the dispute will require to be closely followed but so too will the other requirements (especially notification and the time limits following thereon).

Once the Adjudicator is appointed as provided for in the contract, it is likely to be necessary to confirm the appointment of the Adjudicator and enter into an Adjudicator's Contract. The NEC Adjudicator's Contract can be used for this purpose.

Submission or Referral

Having confirmed the appointment of the Adjudicator, referral again simply involves the Submitting Party submitting the dispute to the Adjudicator for which there are no formal requirements but for which a certain amount of formality should be adopted, as well as ensuring that the Adjudicator has sufficient information to come to a decision.

A failure to submit the dispute to the Adjudicator within four weeks of the original notification may result in the adjudication being time-barred.

7. Initiating the adjudication

Introduction

Once the procedure for the appointment and submission of the dispute to the Adjudicator has been gone through, the Adjudicator will then seize jurisdiction over the dispute. Here again there will be an opportunity for a Party concerned to maintain an objection to that jurisdiction or to reserve their position in that respect.

If that stage is passed through, then the Adjudicator will then have regard to his or her duties and will determine the ambit of the dispute to be determined.

In this chapter it is therefore proposed to consider these matters under the following headings:

- Seizing the jurisdiction
- Objections to jurisdiction
- The duties of the Adjudicator
- The ambit of the dispute

Seizing the jurisdiction

Some procedures for resolving disputes make specific provision allowing the person appointed to determine the dispute to hear and determine objections to the jurisdiction of that person to hear the dispute in question. Other procedures do not make any such provision. The NEC family of contracts does not make any provision in that respect.

NEC principles

It might be said to be presumably in accordance with the NEC principles that the Adjudicator will simply seize jurisdiction and the Parties will co-operate in the adjudication and that any valid objections will be ironed out in the course of the adjudication.

Lex mercatoria

Where a Party has a serious objection to jurisdiction in relation to a proposed adjudication under an NEC contract, therefore, then resort will have to be had to the *lex mercatoria*.

Where the NEC family of contracts is being used outwith the United Kingdom, then so far as concerns that *lex mercatoria* and the jurisdiction of the Adjudicator and the seizing of that jurisdiction, much will depend upon the law adopted as the law of the contract. Essentially, a difference of approach appears to have opened up between the laws of those countries which follow a civil law system and the laws of those countries which follow a common law system.

The civil law approach

The civil law approach is characterised by what is known as *competenz competenz* (a principle originally developed in Germany) and this allows an Arbitrator and, by analogy, an Adjudicator to rule upon their own jurisdiction.

Under this approach an Adjudicator could rule upon his or her jurisdiction by deciding issues such as whether the difference or dispute in question did or did not arise out of and in connection with the contract involved.

The common law approach

The common law approach holds that unless given the express power to do so, an Arbitrator and, by analogy, an Adjudicator do not have the power to determine their own jurisdiction and that, if disputed, the question of jurisdiction can be decided by a Court either before the proceedings commence or afterwards on a question of the enforceability of any decision.

Under this approach an Adjudicator would be regarded as having no right to bind the Parties in ruling upon his or her jurisdiction and where issues were raised (such as whether the difference or dispute in question did or did not arise out of and in connection with the contract involved) the Adjudicator would simply proceed but subject to review by the courts.

Objecting to jurisdiction

As earlier noted, the NEC family of contracts does not make any provision for the Adjudicator to rule upon his or her jurisdiction.

NEC PRINCIPLES

While it might be said to be presumably in accordance with the NEC principles that the Adjudicator will simply seize jurisdiction and the Parties will co-operate in the adjudication, it might also be said to be wise for any Party with an objection to jurisdiction to take care to maintain that objection throughout any adjudication.

LEX MERCATORIA

Where a Party has a serious objection to jurisdiction, there would appear to be nothing to prevent that Party from running an objection to jurisdiction under the *lex mercatoria* at the same time as running the adjudication. Alternatively, the objection to jurisdiction could be raised under the *lex mercatoria* after the adjudication has been completed (either originally or perhaps in defence to enforcement). In either event, however, in order to preserve that objection to jurisdiction it is, as noted above, important that the objection is maintained throughout the adjudication.

The duties of the Adjudicator

The primary duties

NEC PRINCIPLES

Clause 92.1 of the NEC contracts provides that 'The Adjudicator settles the dispute as independent adjudicator and not as arbitrator.'

The Guidance Notes suggest that 'an intermediate stage of independent dispute resolution has been introduced in the form of adjudication' and adds 'It is the intention that all disputes should be resolved by the Adjudicator who is appointed jointly by the Employer and the Contractor and is able to act independently.' It also states that 'As a person independent of both Employer and Contractor, he [the Adjudicator] is required to give a decision on the dispute within stated time limits.'

Clearly, therefore, the concept of 'independence' on the part of the Adjudicator is central to the drafters of the NEC family of contracts. In fact, this is potentially a very significant provision in that it does not simply require an Adjudicator under the NEC family of contracts to *act* independently but to *be* independent. That means, in effect, that the Adjudicator must have no connection with either Party.

Independence and impartiality have been described as distinct but related concepts. It is arguable that the latter, the lesser, is included in the former, the greater. Thus, in practice, while an Adjudicator must obviously act impartially (something most professional people are capable of doing even if connected with the Parties in some way), here the Adjudicator must go beyond that and be independent (something which is taken to mean having no connection with the Parties or the dispute).

Furthermore, as well as independence, the framers of the NEC contracts have added another requirement which is that the Adjudicator settle the dispute not as an Arbitrator but as an independent Adjudicator. The precise significance of this clause has yet to be determined but in one respect it could have significant consequences as to the way in which the Adjudicator's duties are performed and the status of the Adjudicator's decision.

Were the Adjudicator to be regarded as akin to an Arbitrator (which is expressly excluded) then (apart from the possible application of parts of the Arbitration Act 1996) he or she would essentially be sitting in judgment upon a consensual adversarial contest. In those circumstances, where the Arbitrator makes a patent mistake, in law at least, then that can be remedied in further proceedings.

Were, however, the Adjudicator to be regarded as an Expert (which it does not expressly say he is to be) then on interpretation, if Parties give an Expert the power to decide their dispute then the Parties are bound by the decision produced even where there is a patent error in it.

In fact, the NEC contract describes the function as that of an 'independent adjudicator'. This is a relatively new animal, the precise significance of which has yet to be determined. However, if the whole Clause is given a purposeful interpretation then the new animal of 'independent adjudicator' may be interpreted as being closer to an Expert and further away from an

Arbitrator, in which case the decisions of such an Adjudicator may be even more difficult to challenge in enforcement proceedings or in any final determination.

LEX MERCATORIA

No matter what the contract specifies as the primary duty of the Adjudicator, wherever the NEC contract is used worldwide the laws of the territory in which it is being used may impose additional requirements as regards the duties of the Adjudicator. An example of this can be seen in Europe in relation to those countries which have adopted the European Convention on Human Rights or Rules of Natural Justice.

The secondary duties

NEC PRINCIPLES

There are no secondary duties expressly imposed upon the Adjudicator by the NEC family of contracts.

Presumably, it is intended and inferred that the Adjudicator, as a professional, will discharge any secondary duties implicit in the office of Adjudicator and will do no more and no less than what is required thereunder.

Obviously, the Adjudicator will require to have regard to the terms of the Parties' NEC contract (including any amendments they have made thereto) and to the law applicable to the contract as specified in the Contract Data section of the NEC contract.

The Adjudicator's duty to act in accordance with any relevant terms of the contract

This point, although not covered by Clause 9, is covered by the Adjudicator's Contract as follows:

1. General

Actions

1.1   The Parties and the Adjudicator shall act as stated in this contract and in the *contract between the Parties*.

Interpretation

1.6   This contract [i.e. the Adjudicator's Contract] is governed by the *law of the contract*.

1.7   If a conflict arises between this contract and the *contract between the Parties* then this contract prevails.

Adjudication

2.1   The Adjudicator reaches a decision on a dispute referred to him under and in accordance with the *contract between the Parties*.

LEX MERCATORIA

While the *lex mercatoria* might imply primary duties on the part of an Adjudicator into an NEC contract, it is unlikely to do so in relation to any secondary duties.

The ambit of the dispute

NEC PRINCIPLES

The NEC family of contracts, in common with many contracts providing for adjudication, clearly intends that the process will be used for the speedy resolution of individual disputes.

The NEC contracts do not expressly say so, but the Guidance Notes (although they may not be used as an aid to interpretation) provide 'The Parties are not permitted to widen a dispute referred to the Adjudicator beyond that notified under Clause 90.1.'

It often happens in construction matters that when faced with a demand for payment or performance the other Party will seek to raise a cross-claim. There is, therefore, a temptation to seek to bring such cross-claims into an adjudication in order to reduce or offset any likely award. On the basis of the above, however, such offsetting will not be permitted or will at least be discouraged, leaving the Parties, if so advised, to bring separate adjudications.

To that principle, however, the NEC family does recognise one exception – that relating to Main Contracts and Sub-contracts – and that we consider below.

LEX MERCATORIA

The *lex mercatoria* will almost always regard the ambit of any dispute to be regulated under a contract as a matter solely to be regulated by the provision of the contract itself.

Main Contracts and Sub-contracts

NEC PRINCIPLES

As the Guidance Notes point out, where a dispute arises which affects work which has also been sub-contracted, then the dispute might affect not only the Employer and the Contractor but also the Contractor and the Sub-contractor.

In these circumstances, the NEC family of contracts makes provision – but only if the necessary provisions have in fact been incorporated into the relevant contracts – for a single Adjudicator (usually the Main Contract Adjudicator) to adjudicate upon the dispute for the three Parties involved. As the Guidance Notes observe, this saves time and expense and prevents a dispute being dealt with by different Adjudicators who may make different decisions.

This is, however, possible only where the relevant provisions are in the respective contracts.

The Main Contract

The provision here is Clause 91.2 which is activated by agreeing upon the joint appointment of an Adjudicator under the Main (ECC) Contract and provides:

> If a matter disputed under or in connection with a subcontract is also a matter disputed under or in connection with this contract, the *Contractor* may submit the subcontract dispute to the *Adjudicator* at the same time as the main contract submission. The *Adjudicator* then settles the two disputes together and references to the Parties for the purposes of the dispute are interpreted as including the Subcontractor.

In relation to this point the Guidance Notes suggest:

> Where a dispute which affects work which has been subcontracted arises, and which may constitute a dispute between the Contractor and a Subcontractor as well as between the Contractor and the Employer, there is provision for the matter to be resolved between the three parties by the main contract Adjudicator. This saves time and expense and prevents a dispute being dealt with by different adjudicators who make different decisions. This procedure is only possible if the terms of the subcontract permit the Contractor to submit the subcontract dispute to the main contractor Adjudicator.

The Sub-contract

In order to make this procedure work, the essential provision has to be in the Sub-contract.

In the Sub-contract Data, at Part One – Data provided by the Contractor, in relation to Statements given in all sub-contracts, there is, under the heading 1. General, provision for information to be inserted in relation to the following:

> The Adjudicator in this subcontract is
>
> Name [.....]
>
> Address [.....]
>
> The main contract Adjudicator is
>
> Name [.....]
>
> Address [.....]

Where these provisions (which should be negotiated and agreed amongst the Parties involved) match then it may be possible for the same Adjudicator to consider disputes under the Main Contract and Sub-contract in the same adjudication.

LEX MERCATORIA

The *lex mercatoria* is likely to regard any interrelationship between the Main Contract and Sub-contract as a matter solely for the interpretation of those contracts.

8. The conduct of the adjudication

Introduction

The NEC family of contracts says very little, if anything, about the manner in which an adjudication under an NEC contract is to be conducted.

In much the same way as adjudication generally, the essentials of an adjudication under the NEC family of contracts is likely to encompass the following:

- Putting the case for the Submitting Party
- Putting the case for the Party Responding
- Adjustment of the cases
- The function of the Adjudicator
- The approach of the Adjudicator
- Specific powers available to the Adjudicator
- Fairness in the Adjudication
- Co-operation by the Parties
- Terminating the Adjudication
- Other matters relating to the Adjudication

Putting the case for the Submitting Party

NEC PRINCIPLES

Although not expressly provided for, it might be said that NEC principles call for the Submitting Party to produce full and fair details of the dispute to be adjudicated.

Clause 91.1 simply provides that 'The Party submitting the dispute to the Adjudicator includes with his submission information to be considered by the Adjudicator.'

The Guidance Notes suggest in relation to this:

It is important that the Adjudicator has all the relevant information to enable him to put himself in the position of the Project Manager or Supervisor when the action was taken or not taken as the case may be. Information has therefore to be as full as is appropriate to the dispute. The Party submitting the dispute to the Adjudicator is obliged to include full information about the dispute.

It has already been suggested (see the 'submission' or 'referral' of the dispute) that the Parties attach considerable importance to the formality of their submission and the definition and contents of the submission.

Note that the time limit for submitting the case to adjudication is four weeks from the date of the original notification of the dispute to the Other Party and/or the Project Manager (as the case may be).

LEX MERCATORIA

The information to be provided by one Party in a contractually provided dispute resolution procedure will generally be regarded as a matter to be determined from the contract alone. Only where any failure in that respect reaches the standard of a lack of fairness or a breach of natural justice or a breach of human rights, is the *lex mercatoria* likely to intervene.

Putting the case for the Party Responding

NEC PRINCIPLES

Clause 91.1 simply provides that 'Any further information from a Party [presumably including the case from the Party Responding] to be considered by the Adjudicator is provided within four weeks from the submission.'

Clause 91.1 further provides that 'The four week periods in this clause may be extended if requested by the Adjudicator in view of the nature of the dispute and agreed by the Parties.' Note, however, that under these terms it is not open to the Party Responding to ask for an extension of time for putting their case. It appears that the request for an extension can come only from the Adjudicator, can be made by the Adjudicator only on the ground that the application for an extension is made in view of the dispute, and that an extension requested by the Adjudicator on that basis can only be granted if agreed by *all* the Parties.

The Guidance Notes suggest in relation to this that 'The Other Party should, as quickly as practicable and no later than four weeks after the submission of the dispute, submit to the Adjudicator any information upon which he relies by way of a response.'

It has already been suggested (see The 'submission' or 'referral' of the dispute) that the Parties attach considerable importance to the formality of their submissions and the definition and contents of the submissions.

It might equally be described as in accordance with NEC principles for the Party Responding to make a full response.

LEX MERCATORIA

Any required response in relation to a contractually provided dispute resolution procedure is likely to be regarded as a matter for the contract alone and the *lex mercatoria* is likely to become involved only where it can be shown that the Party Responding has been denied a fair opportunity to make an adequate response at all.

Adjustment of the cases

NEC PRINCIPLES

Clause 91.1 simply provides that 'Any further information from a Party [presumably including adjustments to their cases by either Party] to be considered by the Adjudicator is provided within four weeks from the submission.'

Clause 91.1 further provides that 'The four week periods in this clause may be extended if requested by the Adjudicator in view of the nature of the dispute and agreed by the Parties.' Note, however, that under these terms it is not open to the Party Responding to ask for an extension of time for putting their case. It appears that the request for an extension can come only from the Adjudicator, can be made by the Adjudicator only on the ground that the application for an extension is made in view of the dispute, and that an extension requested by the Adjudicator on that basis can only be granted if agreed by *all* the Parties.

The Guidance Notes suggest in relation to this that:

> Whilst either Party may amend his submission or issue further information and responses within the four weeks after submission (or longer period as requested by the Adjudicator and agreed by the Parties), it is intended that this four week (or other) period is used by the Parties to assist the Adjudicator in reaching as rapid a decision as is reasonably possible.

It has already been suggested (see The 'submission' or 'referral' of the dispute) that the Parties attach considerable importance to the formality of their submissions and the definition and contents of the submissions.

The general approach under the NEC appears to be that – within overall time limits which are to be strictly observed (but which can in certain circumstances be extended) – the Parties should be given freedom to adjust and accordingly it might be said to be in accordance with NEC principles to allow, and not to object to, relatively full adjustment of the Parties' respective cases.

LEX MERCATORIA

In general, being allowed to state a case and respond to a case is regarded as the acceptable legal minimum and the *lex mercatoria* is unlikely to concern itself with the adjustment of cases.

The function of the Adjudicator

NEC PRINCIPLES

There are no specific case management powers conferred upon the Adjudicator by the NEC family of contracts.

Presumably, it is intended and inferred that the Adjudicator as a professional will, with the co-operation of the Parties, case manage the adjudication in a suitable manner.

The control over such a situation, should that be necessary, will presumably require to come from the law which applies to the contract or the law relating to the territory within which the adjudication is being conducted.

It appears to be inferred by the drafters of the NEC family of contracts that the Adjudicator will conduct the adjudication in a reasonable manner and that the Parties will co-operate therewith. It is not entirely clear what is to happen if these are not forthcoming.

LEX MERCATORIA

It is by no means clear that the *lex mercatoria* will infer into a contractually provided dispute resolution procedure a power of case management on the part of the Adjudicator where that is not provided for in the contract.

The approach of the Adjudicator

NEC PRINCIPLES

The only specific reference in this respect is in Clause 92.1 which provides: 'The Adjudicator settles the dispute as independent adjudicator and not as arbitrator.'

An Arbitrator (which the NEC Adjudicator is expressly stated not to be) generally speaking receives the evidence of the Parties and then issues his decision upon that evidence.

An Expert (which again the NEC Adjudicator is not expressly stated to be) is in a more complex situation which is largely governed by the terms of his appointment. In general, however, it may be considered that an Expert has a greater capacity than an Arbitrator to bring his or her own expertise and inquisition to the decision.

It is not yet clear and it has not yet been determined just what the new animal called the 'independent adjudicator' is entitled to do in the course of an adjudication, but it could be argued that an independent Adjudicator is more akin to an Expert than an Arbitrator and, if so, that the Parties to an NEC adjudication can expect the independent Adjudicator to be considerably proactive.

LEX MERCATORIA

It is extremely unlikely that any *lex mercatoria* would infer powers on the part of an Adjudicator in relation to a contractually provided dispute resolution procedure. Where, however, a power is expressly given (e.g. to act as an 'independent adjudicator') or excluded (e.g. not to act as an Arbitrator) then the *lex mercatoria* may be available to provide the parameters of these functions where those functions are generally recognised by law.

Specific powers available to the Adjudicator

NEC PRINCIPLES

Very little, if anything, in the way of specific powers are given to the Adjudicator in Clause 9. The Guidance Notes suggest that 'the Adjudicator may call for information which has to be provided within the four week or other period.'

It might be inferred – although it would require to be an inference implied into the contract – that an Adjudicator under the NEC family of contracts could:

- give directions as to the conduct of the adjudication
- make site visits and inspections (although any necessary third party consents would have to be obtained first)
- carry out tests (although any necessary third party consents would have to be obtained first)
- if a legal Adjudicator, appoint Experts and assessors as required
- if an Expert Adjudicator, appoint legal advisers as required
- call for documentary submissions
- call for oral representations.

The drafters of the NEC family of contracts appear to have inferred that the Adjudicator will act in a reasonable manner and that the Parties will co-operate in that respect. It is not entirely clear what is to happen should these not materialise.

LEX MERCATORIA

It is possible, if asked, that the *lex mercatoria* (provided that it recognises an 'independent adjudicator' as a being in law) might be prepared to rule on whether or not any of the above powers fall to be inferred into the capacity of a person acting as an 'independent adjudicator'.

Fairness in the adjudication

NEC PRINCIPLES

It is clearly vital (even if nowhere expressly stated) that an adjudication arising under an NEC contract is conducted fairly.

As a professional, the Adjudicator can normally be relied upon to conduct his or her adjudication fairly.

So far as fairness is concerned, Clause 9 does make specific reference to one important aspect and that is by providing that 'Any communication between a Party and the Adjudicator is communicated also to the other Party.'

The Guidance Notes also emphasise this by suggesting: 'This clause requires communications between a Party and the Adjudicator also to be communicated to the other Party. The Party making the communication should also issue it to the other side.'

LEX MERCATORIA

Should it be necessary to do so, such situations will presumably be controlled under the *lex mercatoria* as the law applicable to the contract or the law of the territory in which the adjudication is being conducted. Of particular relevance will be whether or not that territory has incorporated the United Nations or the European Conventions on Human Rights.

Co-operation by the Parties

NEC PRINCIPLES

Those familiar with the NEC family of contracts will be aware of the importance which this family of contracts attaches to the co-operation of the Parties. Presumably, notwithstanding that a dispute has arisen between the Parties, similar co-operation is expected in an adjudication under the NEC.

It is, in fact, described as perhaps the most important characteristic of the NEC family of contracts that they should be a stimulus to good management. As the Guidance Notes put it: 'This aspect …is founded upon the proposition that foresighted, co-operative management of the interactions between the parties can shrink the risks inherent in construction work'.

The Guidance Notes also suggest: 'A secondary but important theme is that people will be motivated to play their part in collaborative management if it is in their commercial and professional interest to do so'.

Finally, the Guidance Notes note:

> This approach has pervaded the drafting ...and is the basis for most of the procedures... In designing, ...the motivation of each party in each action he is to take has been considered against good management criteria. Because this is motivation-driven, it does not appear in the words ...but it is intended to result directly from the way in which the procedures are operated.

The framers of the NEC family of contracts clearly hope that this spirit of co-operation and motivation will prevent disputes arising in the first place and it is, presumably, hoped that the same approach is followed through in resolving any disputes which *do* arise.

No express provision is made in Clause 9 in relation to what is to happen should a dispute arise which evaporates goodwill, motivation and co-operation on the part of one or more of the Parties.

LEX MERCATORIA

It is by no means certain that in relation to a contractually provided dispute resolution procedure the *lex mercatoria* would infer a power on the part of an Adjudicator, when reaching the decision, to draw inferences in relation to non-co-operation by a Party unless the contract clearly gave that power.

However, it could be argued that a person such as an 'independent adjudicator', exercising what is clearly a quasi-judicial function, does have certain powers open to him or her in these circumstances.

For example, it could be argued that such an Adjudicator has an implied power to draw inferences from non-co-operation and attach such weight to that as, in his or her opinion, is justified.

Such a power would require, however, to be implied from the law applicable to the contract or the law relating to the territory in which the adjudication is being conducted. These will clearly vary, but since the NEC contract and its adjudication can be used worldwide, space precludes an examination of the various possibilities. This is clearly something upon which an Adjudicator should take local expert advice.

Terminating the adjudication

Revoking the adjudication

NEC PRINCIPLES

It follows from the principle of adjudication being contractual that the Parties should be able, by their agreement, to withdraw from an adjudication and bring the process to a premature end without the need for a decision by the Adjudicator.

Even at a basic level, an adjudication involves participants in a substantial amount of (perhaps irrecoverable) time, effort and cost. It is also capable of resulting in the loss of a certain amount of goodwill. For these and other reasons, the adjudication of a dispute is something which most Parties attempt to avoid if possible.

One of the benefits of the two-week period of grace between notification of the dispute and submission of the dispute which is provided for in Clause 9 is that it allows a Party who had failed to appreciate the seriousness of the situation and who had not realised that what was in their mind a 'difference' had, in the minds of the Other Party, grown into a 'dispute', to take corrective action to resolve the dispute and avoid an adjudication. By the same token, when considered submissions have been made by one Party and a considered response made by the Other Party (and sometimes with a few 'signals' picked up from the approach to the dispute of the Adjudicator), the dispute can sometimes then (retaining the goodwill) be amicably resolved without the need for a full adjudication.

While getting an adjudication started is a relatively simple exercise, bringing an adjudication which has started to an early conclusion may not, however, be so simple, unless the Parties are in agreement in that respect.

It is only sensible, therefore, to allow the Parties to withdraw from an adjudication by revoking the appointment of the Adjudicator and bringing an adjudication to a premature end. Unusually, however, neither Clause 9 nor the Guidance Notes make any reference to this aspect at all.

There is, however, almost certainly an implied power on the part of the Parties which would allow this to happen. Accordingly, for Clause 9 standing alone, revocation of the appointment of an Adjudicator is, therefore, a matter which would appear to have been left to the law of the contract or the law of the territory in which the adjudication is taking place. There is, however, provision for revocation in the NEC Adjudicator's Contract where the Parties have entered into such a contract.

Clause 9 standing alone

Getting an adjudication started where Clause 9 stands alone is relatively simple.

Once having launched an adjudication, however, bringing that adjudication to an early conclusion may not, however, be so simple. A Submitting Party who has had a change of mind may not be able to halt an adjudication alone. Similarly, a Party Responding who has lost heart in the proceedings may not be able to halt an adjudication alone. Together, however, the Parties might be able to bring an adjudication to an early conclusion. Although no express provision for such an eventuality has been made in Clause 9, adjudication is, in principle, contractual and, therefore, where *both* Parties agree to bring an adjudication to a conclusion then it ought to be possible for them to achieve that.

Procedure for revocation by the Parties

Where the Parties to an NEC Engineering and Construction Contract containing Core Clause 9 together decide (whether on the grounds of default, misconduct or any other non-offensive ground) to bring an adjudication to an early conclusion by revoking the appointment of the Adjudicator, then the Parties presumably simply signal their intention to do so. There is no specific requirement for this to be in writing (or for the consent of the Adjudicator) although it would clearly be desirable for the Parties so to do.

Fees

Clause 9 does not, of itself, contain any specific provision providing for the payment of fees and expenses to the Adjudicator by the Parties (presumably on the basis that it is expected that the Parties will have agreed an Adjudicator's Contract with the Adjudicator) and neither does Clause 9 give the Adjudicator the power to allocate any fees or expenses or the right to recover any outstanding fees and expenses jointly and severally from the Parties (which would allow the Adjudicator to recover all sums due from one Party leaving it to that Party to recover any balance due from the Other Party).

Where an Adjudicator has been formally appointed in an adjudication but then finds that appointment revoked (without payment) by the Parties then it would be open (in the absence of default or misconduct) to an Adjudicator to argue (in Court or otherwise) for an entitlement to payment of reasonable fees and expenses down to the point of revocation either on the basis of *quantum meruit* or on the basis of a simple implied term.

Certainly, without an express power in the contract given to the Adjudicator to allocate fees and expenses between the Parties an Adjudicator is unlikely to be regarded as having the power to do so. Without an express power to an Adjudicator in the contract to recover fees and expenses jointly and severally as between the Parties an Adjudicator is unlikely to be regarded as having the power to do so.

Clause 9 standing with an Adjudicator's Contract

Getting an adjudication started under Clause 9 is relatively simple. Bringing the adjudication to an early conclusion thereafter may be assisted by the NEC Adjudicator's Contract.

Once having launched an adjudication, therefore, the Adjudicator's Contract does make provision for bringing the adjudication to an end by Clause 5.1: 'The Parties may, by agreement, terminate the appointment of the Adjudicator for any reason. They notify him of the termination.'

A Submitting Party who has had a change of mind may not be able to halt an adjudication alone. Similarly, a Party Responding who has lost heart in the proceedings may not be able to halt an adjudication alone. By agreement together, however, the Parties to an Adjudication Contract have the power (Clause 5.1) to bring an adjudication to an early conclusion.

Procedure for revocation by the Parties

Clause 5.1 entitles the Parties to an Adjudication Contract, by agreement, to terminate the appointment of the Adjudicator for any reason. The Parties require to notify the Adjudicator of the termination. There is no specific requirement for this to be in writing (or for the consent of the Adjudicator to be obtained) although it would clearly be desirable for the Parties so to do.

Fees

The Adjudicator's Contract does not, of itself, contain any specific provision providing for the payment of fees and expenses to the Adjudicator on termination. However, Clause 3.1 provides that the Adjudicator's fee [defined as the time the Adjudicator spends on an adjudication and the time spent travelling] and expenses [defined as including the cost of printing, reproduction and purchase of documents, drawings, maps, records and photographs; telegrams, telex, faxes and telephone calls; postage and delivery charges; travelling, hotel and similar expenses; room charges and charges by others for help in an adjudication] should be paid by the Parties in equal shares. The Adjudicator's Contract *expressly* gives the Parties the power to agree otherwise.

Where an Adjudicator's Contract exists and an Adjudicator has been formally appointed in an adjudication but then finds that appointment revoked (without payment) by the Parties then it would be open (in the absence of default or misconduct) to an Adjudicator to argue (in Court or otherwise) for an entitlement to payment of reasonable fees and expenses down to the point of revocation, either on the basis of *quantum meruit* or on the basis of a simple implied term.

Certainly, without the agreement of the Parties otherwise, the express provision of the Adjudicator's Contract (Clause 3.1) that the Parties pay the fees and expenses of the Adjudicator in equal shares is likely to be applied. The Adjudicator, therefore, is likely to be seen as having no power to allocate fees and expenses between the Parties. Without an express power to an Adjudicator in the contract to recover fees and expenses jointly and severally as between the Parties, an Adjudicator is unlikely to be regarded as having the power to do so and (if so allowed) will need to recover an equal share from each Party.

LEX MERCATORIA

Even though not expressly provided for, it is likely that the *lex mercatoria* would, where necessary, infer a power on the part of the Parties to agree to withdraw their adjudication from the Adjudicator. So, too, might the *lex mercatoria* provide for the removal of an Adjudicator who has misbehaved.

Resignation of the Adjudicator

NEC PRINCIPLES

The resignation circumstances

Clause 9 standing alone

Clause 9 makes provision for the resignation of an Adjudicator. The precise circumstances in which an Adjudicator is entitled to resign are not stated, although the Explanatory Notes suggest that one possible reason for an Adjudicator not being able to act is if there is a conflict of interest and go on to further suggest that the Employer should check for conflicts of interest before naming a proposed Adjudicator in the Contract Data. Clause 92.2 provides:

> If the Adjudicator resigns or is unable to act, the Parties choose a new adjudicator jointly. If the Parties have not chosen a new adjudicator jointly within four weeks of the Adjudicator resigning or becoming unable to act, a Party may ask the person stated in the Contract Data to choose a new adjudicator and the Parties accept his choice. The new adjudicator is appointed as Adjudicator under the NEC Adjudicator's Contract. He has power to settle disputes that were currently submitted to his predecessor but had not been settled at the time when his predecessor resigned or became unable to act. The date of his appointment is the date of submission of these disputes to him as Adjudicator.

Voluntary resignation

Clause 9 makes no express provision as to the *circumstances* in which an Adjudicator appointed under the NEC family of contracts can resign, although clearly the ability of an Adjudicator to resign can be implied from the provision 'If an Adjudicator resigns ...'(Clause 92.2).

Presumably, resignation may take place *at any time*. No provision is made for the involvement or consent of the Parties. There is no requirement for the notice of resignation to be in writing, although it would clearly be more prudent to do so.

The question of any liability on the part of an Adjudicator in respect of resignation may, however, be more complex in the absence of specific provision covering the circumstances of resignation.

Clause 9 standing with an Adjudicator's Contract

Clause 5.2 of the Adjudicator's Contract provides:

> The Adjudicator may, by notifying the Parties, terminate his appointment if
>
> - he considers that he cannot act because of a conflict of interest
> - he is unable to act as Adjudicator, or
> - he has not been paid an amount due within five weeks of the date by which payment should have been made.

Voluntary resignation

Where an Adjudicator's Contract is completed by the Parties then the Adjudicator's Contract does make specific provision as to the *circumstances* in which an Adjudicator appointed under that Contract may voluntarily resign. These are:

- where the Adjudicator considers that he cannot act because of a conflict of interest
- where the Adjudicator is unable to act
- where the Adjudicator has not been paid an amount due within five weeks of the date by which payment should have been made.

Presumably, resignation may take place *at any time*. No provision is made for the involvement or consent of the Parties. There is a requirement for the Adjudicator to notify the Parties but no requirement for this to be in writing, although it would clearly be more prudent to do so.

The question of any liability on the part of an Adjudicator in respect of resignation will, however, be less complex since the Adjudicator's Contract makes specific provision as to risks (on which see below).

The consequences of a resignation

Faced with a resignation, a number of issues will then require to be resolved by the Parties.

Fees

Amongst the first of these issues will be the payment of the fees of the Adjudicator who has resigned. Clause 9 in fact makes no express provision in respect of the fees and expenses of a resigning Adjudicator and on the face of it there is no such entitlement.

It might be open to an Adjudicator to argue for an entitlement to fees and expenses by implication from the Scheme in the two circumstances provided for in the Scheme (para 9(4)), namely where (i) the Adjudicator has resigned because the dispute is the same or substantially the same as one which has previously been referred to adjudication, and a decision has been taken in that adjudication, and (ii) the Adjudicator has resigned because a dispute varies significantly from the dispute referred to him or her in the referral notice and for that reason he or she is not competent to decide it.

The success of such an argument would depend upon the extent to which the Court is prepared (as yet an undecided question) to imply the terms of a Scheme into the contract between the Parties where there is already a contract in existence. Were a Court to do so, however, it would presumably then fall to the Adjudicator to determine by way of fees and expenses such reasonable amount as has been reasonably incurred by him or her as Adjudicator and to make a determination of how such fees and expenses shall be apportioned between the Parties. The Parties will then be jointly and severally liable for such sums – which means that an Adjudicator can recover all sums due to him or her from one Party, leaving it to that Party to recover the share due from the Other Party. There is no express provision for dealing with the situation where the level of fees and expenses proposed by the Adjudicator is disputed by the Parties. Presumably, the Adjudicator would require to sue (under paragraph 9(4)) for his or her fees. The Parties could seek to defend the action and argue that the fees and expenses were unreasonable, although any Court is likely to have regard to the discretion given to the Adjudicator. Should the matter become an issue, however, then the Court would have available to it the various taxation procedures in existence.

Voluntary resignation by an Adjudicator in all other circumstances is likely to mean that (in the absence of any agreement to the contrary by the Parties or express agreement in any Adjudicator's Contract) the Adjudicator has forfeited his or her fees.

There will often be such provision when the Parties and the Adjudicator agree an Adjudicator's Contract covering the actions of an Adjudicator acting under the Schemes, although in the NEC Adjudicator's Contract there is in fact no provision made as to the payment of the Adjudicator's fees and expenses or cancellation fees on resignation.

Appointing a replacement Adjudicator

Another of the first of the issues to be decided where an Adjudicator resigns is how to get to a decision in the adjudication. Clause 92.2 provides that if the Parties do not agree a replacement jointly then the nomination section applies.

If that part of the Contract Data which provides for a person to choose a new Adjudicator has been completed and that person does in fact choose a new Adjudicator then the Parties have contractually agreed to accept that choice and that person is the new Adjudicator.

What is less clear is what is to happen where, the Parties not being able to agree upon a new Adjudicator, that part of the Contract Data has not been completed or the person selected is, for some reason, unwilling to act.

Clause 92.2 provides that the new Adjudicator is appointed as Adjudicator under the NEC Adjudicator's Contract. This could, presumably, be interpreted as meaning that the whole terms of the NEC Adjudicator's Contract (without the need for signature) is implied into the contract between the new Parties and covers the new Adjudicator.

The Explanatory Notes suggest that it is only any existing disputes on which the original Adjudicator has *not* made a decision that may be referred to the replacement Adjudicator after his appointment and this is, of course, in keeping with the very concept of adjudication.

So far as the aspect of time is concerned, Clause 92.2 makes it clear that the date of the new Adjudicator's appointment is the date of submission of these disputes to him as Adjudicator and the Explanatory Notes suggest that the time periods in the contract will then run from submission of the disputes to the replacement Adjudicator.

The time for the decision of the Adjudicator set down in Clause 91.1 is within four weeks (or as extended) of the end of the period for providing information.

No provision is made for the resigning Adjudicator to pass to the replacement Adjudicator any formal pleadings or documentation submitted and nor is there any express obligation upon the Parties so to do, but that is perhaps implied by the part of Clause 92.2 which provides 'The date of [the appointment of the Replacement Adjudicator] is the date of submission of the disputes to him.'

Liability

Clearly, Parties can be considerably inconvenienced where, a Notice of Adjudication and Referral Notice having been issued and considerable time, effort and expense invested in pursuing or defending the adjudication, the Adjudicator suddenly issues a notice of resignation at the eleventh hour. Fees may have to be paid and further expenditure incurred in appointing a new Adjudicator and re-referring the dispute to the new Adjudicator.

Some Parties may feel inclined to seek to recover all or some of some of the expenditure incurred from the Adjudicator who has resigned, but much will depend upon the terms of the contract involved. Clause 9 does not, however, on its own contain an immunity clause. although regard should be had to the terms of the Adjudicator's Contract in this respect.

Clause 9 standing with an Adjudicator's Contract

Paragraph 4 of the Adjudicator's Contract does in fact provide for risks as follows:

4.1   The Adjudicator, his employees and agents are not liable to the Parties for an action or failure to take action in an adjudication unless the action or failure to take action is in bad faith.

4.2   The Parties indemnify the Adjudicator, his employees and agents against claims, compensation and costs arising out of the Adjudicator's decision unless his decision was made in bad faith.

In combination, these clauses are likely to preclude any such claims unless bad faith – a tricky concept into which the Courts are often loathe to delve – can be specifically averred and proved.

LEX MERCATORIA

Where the parties have entered into the NEC Adjudicator's Contract, revocation and resignation will be adequately catered for (together with any liability arising therefrom).

Where Clause 9 is standing alone, however, disputes over revocation and resignation together with any liability flowing therefrom are possible. No assistance will be gained from the contract itself (although something may be inferred from the law applicable to the contract) but the extent to which the *lex mercatoria* would become involved in any such disputes is uncertain.

Other matters relating to the adjudication

Immunity on the part of the Adjudicator and his agents and employees

Clause 9 makes no provision in relation to immunity but there is provision made in the Adjudicator's Contract as follows:

4.   Risks

4.1   The Adjudicator, his employees and agents, are not liable to the Parties for an action or failure to take action in an adjudication unless the action or failure to take action is in bad faith.

4.2   The Parties indemnify the Adjudicator, his employees and agents, against claims, compensation and costs arising out of the Adjudicator's decision unless his decision was made in bad faith.

Confidentiality on the part of the Adjudicator and the Parties

Clause 9 makes no provision in relation to confidentiality but there is provision made in the Adjudicator's Contract as follows:

2. Adjudication

2.3   The Parties and the Adjudicator keep the Adjudicator's decision and information provided for an adjudication as confidential to those who have a proper interest in them.

Retention of the papers by the Adjudicator

Clause 9 makes no provision in relation to confidentiality but there is provision made in the Adjudicator's Contract as follows:

2.   Adjudication

2.4   The Adjudicator keeps documents provided to him by the Parties until termination.

9. The decision of the Adjudicator

Introduction

The decision of the Adjudicator is, of course, the aim of the exercise. It is proposed to consider that here in relation to the following:

- The (basic) time for the decision
- Late decisions
- Extending the time for the decision
- The adjudicator's decision
  - The award
  - Interest
  - Costs
  - Adjudicator's fees and expenses
  - Other matters
  - Reasons
  - Correcting the decision

The (basic) time for the decision

NEC PRINCIPLES

Clause 90.9 provides: 'The Adjudicator notifies his decision within four weeks of the end of the period for providing information.'

Clearly, it is the intention of the drafters of the NEC family of contracts that adjudication decisions are arrived at without delay and in order to provide a procedure which would *speedily* arrive at a temporarily binding decision there required to be a time limit set upon the process. The time limit selected – a four-week period – was made a basic essential requirement in the contract.

In this respect, the provision is clearly, to some extent, an open-ended provision of four weeks, and we consider next the extent to which and the circumstances under which that basic period may be extended.

LEX MERCATORIA

Where a contractually provided dispute resolution procedure provides both a time within which the decision has to be made and (as we shall see later) also provides for the consequences of failing to do so, then the *lex mercatoria* is unlikely to become involved. Only where the provision of the decision within a specified time is an essential of the contract is the *lex mercatoria* likely to intervene in any way.

Late decisions

NEC PRINCIPLES

Clause 91.1 provides a time limit for the decision of the Adjudicator as follows: 'The Adjudicator notifies his decision within four weeks of the end of the period for providing information.'

The period for providing information is four weeks from the date of the submission of the dispute to the Adjudicator. Note, however, that that both the four-week period for providing information and the four-week period for the decision of the Adjudicator may be extended in certain restricted circumstances, namely where requested by the Adjudicator on the ground only that it is in view of the nature of the dispute and that any extension requires to be agreed by all the Parties.

Accordingly, where an extension of time has been requested by the Adjudicator (on a valid ground) and agreed by the Parties then that will set the time limit for the decision. Otherwise, the time limit for the decision shall be within four weeks of the end of the period for providing information.

Once that time limit (whatever it might be in the individual case) is reached then – unlike some other adjudication procedures – the NEC family of contracts makes no provisions which would allow the decision of an Adjudicator to be received late (unless *all* the Parties together agreed to waive that defect and to treat the late decision as valid).

LEX MERCATORIA

It is highly unlikely that the *lex mercatoria* would intervene to turn a decision which is late and invalid into one which is valid.

Extending the time for the decision

NEC PRINCIPLES

There will be occasions where the basic time limit set down for a decision will require to be extended but, in order to prevent abuse of the extension procedure and provide a procedure which would *speedily* arrive at a temporarily binding decision, a sensible procedure will seek to control the circumstances in which extensions are allowed. In that respect, Clause 91.1 provides:

> The Adjudicator notifies his decision within four weeks of the end of the period for providing information [the period for providing information is 'within four weeks from the submission']. The four week periods in this clause may be extended if requested by the Adjudicator in view of the nature of the dispute and agreed by the Parties.

The Guidance Notes suggest:

> In complex disputes and for other valid reasons, the Adjudicator may require a period greater than the four weeks stated. For example, the

Adjudicator may require time to visit the Working Areas and may need to consult with other people to help him in arriving at a decision.

The Guidance Notes suggest that these time limits are to strictly adhered to.

It is noteworthy that the basic four-week periods cannot be extended merely because the Adjudicator or the Parties happen to be very busy at the time. On a strict reading of the Clause, there is only one ground for extension – viz., 'in view of the nature of the dispute'. Also on a strict reading of the Clause an application for an extension must come from the Adjudicator (only) and can be granted only if (all) the Parties agree. Clearly, strictly read, the scope is narrow under Clause 9 for extending the basic period of four weeks for the decision of the Adjudicator.

LEX MERCATORIA

It is highly unlikely that the *lex mercatoria* would intervene to adjust (one way or the other) a contractually provided time limit.

The Adjudicator's decision

NEC PRINCIPLES

Clause 90.2 simply provides: 'The Adjudicator settles the dispute by notifying the Parties and the Project Manager of his decision together with his reasons within the time allowed by this contract.'

As the Guidance Notes make clear, no further details are given in the clause as to how the decision and its associated reasons are to be drafted. In general, however, an adjudication decision will resemble the following:

- The award
- Interest
  - Costs
  - Adjudiactor's fees and expenses
- Other matters
- Reasons
- Correcting the decision

It is proposed to consider each of these items individually below.

LEX MERCATORIA

It is unlikely that the *lex mercatoria* will become involved in this matter.

The award

NEC PRINCIPLES

Neither Clause 9 (except in one specific instance – 'If the Adjudicator's decision includes assessment of additional cost or delay caused to the Contractor, he makes his assessment in the same way as a compensation event is assessed') nor the Guidance Notes go into any detail in relation to the manner in which an award should be drafted by the Adjudicator.

The award itself should, it is suggested, be short and clear and capable of enforcement by the Parties if necessary.

It is suggested in the Guidance Notes that where contradictory facts are submitted by the Parties, the Adjudicator should state his findings. He should summarise the arguments submitted to him, and then state his decision clearly.

The Guidance Notes warn Adjudicators that the decision may be subject to careful scrutiny, particularly by a Party who may be dissatisfied with the decision and that it is also possible that the Adjudicator's award will be produced and made subject to close scrutiny in some future Arbitration or litigation.

The Guidance Notes suggest that, for completeness, matters which should be included in the overall decision of the Adjudicator are:

*   The precise nature of the dispute referred to the Adjudicator.
*   Details of the contract.
*   Details of the appointment of the Adjudicator.
*   Circumstances leading to the reference.
*   The procedures followed by the Adjudicator.
*   Information upon which the decision is based.

How much detail the Adjudicator includes in the reasons and how much detail the Adjudicator includes in the award will be a matter of professional judgement.

The Guidance Notes suggest that the award of the Adjudicator may simply be that the Project Manager or Supervisor should have acted or should not have acted, but in certain circumstances he may also decide what action should have been taken. In the cases in which he decides that the Project Manager or Supervisor acted or did not act in accordance with the contract or in any other matter which he decides in the Contractor's favour, he assesses both financial and time effects. Thus, as the Guidance Notes point out, the award might comprise the Adjudicator's opinion on what, say, the Project Manager's decision should have been in accordance with the contract. It might include assessment of a compensation event, what money is payable by one Party to the Other or what changes to the programme are required.

The Guidance Notes also go on to state that the Adjudicator's task is as stated and suggest that he will in his review of the action or inaction decide and state the duties and obligations of the Project Manager, Supervisor or the Parties which are to be followed and complied with as a contractual obligation.

The Guidance Notes make further suggestions about the decision of the Adjudicator and any eventual award as follows:

*   It is suggested that if the Adjudicator decides in the Contractor's favour but it is too late for the action or inaction to be implemented then he will deal with the matter by deciding the effect on the Prices and Completion Data using the same assessment procedure that is used for compensation events.

- It is suggested that in other circumstances, it may be appropriate for the Adjudicator to change the disputed action or inaction and give by way of example the instance where the Contractor disputes the existence of a Defect which has been notified by the Supervisor. The Guidance Notes point out that the Adjudicator may decide in the Contractor's favour and, if so, if corrective work had not started the Contractor would be relieved of any obligation to correct, and if the corrective work had been completed then the Adjudicator would decide on the financial and time effects.
- In other instances, it is suggested, should the Project Manager still require additional or remedial work then he may instruct such work as a change to the Works Information and that this would be a normal compensation event.
- It is suggested that if the Adjudicator disagrees with the Project Manager's assessment of delay to the Completion Date, he will overrule the Project Manager's decision and the Completion Date will be set in accordance with what the Adjudicator decides. If, however, it is too late to allow the Contractor to revise his programme, the Adjudicator's decision will be in respect of the effect on the Prices only.
- It is suggested that if the dispute concerns an amount due as certified by the Project Manager and the Adjudicator decides that the amount certified was incorrect, the Project Manager will be required to make a correction in the next certificate.

As noted above, the Adjudicator is also required to state the reasons for his decision which should show how they led to the decision reached. How much detail the Adjudicator includes in the reasons and how much detail the Adjudicator includes in the award will be a matter of professional judgement.

LEX MERCATORIA

The *lex mercatoria i*s unlikely to become involved in relation to the form which an award must take.

Interest

NEC PRINCIPLES

Interest naturally features in the NEC family of contracts and Clause 51.3 provides:

> If an amount due is corrected in a later certificate ... following a decision of the Adjudicator interest on the correcting amount is paid. Interest is assessed from the date when the incorrect amount was certified until the date when the correcting amount is certified and is included in the assessment which includes the correcting amount.

So far as adjudication is concerned, the power on the part of an Adjudicator to award interest must come from the contract and without such a provision in the contract there is probably no power on the part of the Adjudicator to add an award of interest to any award made.

Core Clause 9 does give a power to award interest but this appears to be *only* in the restricted circumstances where there are Certificates.

LEX MERCATORIA

As a matter of principle, there is no right to interest and therefore it is unlikely that the *lex mercatoria* would become involved in this issue, except perhaps in the negative sense of striking out an award of interest where the contract makes no provision for an award of interest. Some countries, however, have legislation providing for interest generally and where this exists in the *lex mercatoria* it may be enforced.

Costs

NEC PRINCIPLES

Core Clause 9 makes no specific provision in respect of costs and nor does the Adjudicator's Contract. In theory, therefore, there is no power anywhere – not in the Contracts or the Adjudicator's Contract – to award costs.

The drafters of the NEC family of contracts clearly envisage that there will be no award and allocation of costs in adjudications under their contracts.

LEX MERCATORIA

Some jurisdictions have, by precedent, recognised in some circumstances the actions of the Parties as conferring an implied power on the part of an Adjudicator to award costs. If, therefore, the Parties wish to avoid costs being put at issue then Parties will need to exercise some care in their conduct and take care to say nothing in their correspondence which could be interpreted as by implication putting costs at issue.

Adjudicator's fees and expenses

NEC PRINCIPLES

Core Clause 9 makes no specific provision in this respect but provision is made in the Adjudicator's Contract as follows:

Clause 3.1

> Unless otherwise agreed, the Parties pay the Adjudicator his fee and Expenses in equal shares.

Clause 3.2

> After each decision on a dispute has been communicated to the Parties and after termination the Adjudicator invoices each Party for that Party's share of his fee and Expenses.

This is a matter which one would expect to see regulated by the Adjudicator's Contract. The drafters of the NEC family of contracts clearly do not envisage the Adjudicator ordering his or her fees and Expenses to be paid by only one Party. Instead, it is envisaged that (unless the Parties agree otherwise) the fees and Expenses of the Adjudicator will be shared equally and paid after the decision has been issued.

Accordingly, the NEC Adjudicator's Contract, however, envisages (in the absence of any other agreement) the equal sharing of Adjudicator's fees and Expenses. There will never, therefore (in the absence of any other agreement by the Parties), be any question of the Adjudicator allocating his fees and Expenses. It appears to be envisaged under the NEC Adjudicator's Contract that there will be no requirement for fees and Expenses 'up-front' in that it is only after each decision on a dispute has been communicated to the Parties that the Adjudicator invoices each Party for his share. The power of resignation for non-payment of the Adjudicator's Account for more than five weeks would therefore appear to relate not to the current dispute but to any future disputes.

LEX MERCATORIA

Clause 9 does not make any specific provision about an entitlement to, or the allocation of, Adjudicator's fees and Expenses. In the absence of an Adjudicator's Contract an Adjudicator may be hard pressed to recover any fees save by resorting to the *lex mercatoria* on some *quantum meruit* basis.

Other matters

NEC PRINCIPLES

In theory, an Adjudicator should be able to include in the decision any other matter which the Parties have referred to him. Neither Clause 9 nor the Adjudicator's Contract make any specific provision (either of an inclusionary or exclusionary nature) regarding any other matters which an Adjudicator may or may not include in the overall decision.

LEX MERCATORIA

It is unlikely that the *lex mercatoria* will be involved in this issue.

Reasons

NEC PRINCIPLES

The NEC family of contracts, under Clause 9, clearly envisages that reasons will be provided automatically by the Adjudicator in every adjudication. No specific provision is made in the Adjudicator's Contract in this respect. However, Core Clause 90.2 provides: 'The Adjudicator settles the decision by notifying the Parties and the Project Manager of his decision *together with his reasons* ...'.

It is suggested in the Guidance Notes that where contradictory facts are submitted by the Parties, the Adjudicator should state his findings. He or she should summarise the arguments submitted, and then state his or her decision clearly. That could be done in the reasons.

The Guidance Notes warn Adjudicators that the decision may be subject to careful scrutiny, particularly by a Party who may be dissatisfied with the decision, and that it is also possible that the reasons for the Adjudicator's award will be made subject to close scrutiny in some future arbitration or litigation.

The Guidance Notes suggest that, for completeness, matters which should be included in the overall decision (perhaps in the section for reasons) of the Adjudicator are:

- The precise nature of the dispute referred to the Adjudicator.
- Details of the contract.
- Details of the appointment of the Adjudicator.
- Circumstances leading to the reference.
- The procedures followed by the Adjudicator.
- Information upon which the decision is based.

How much detail the Adjudicator includes in the reasons and how much detail the Adjudicator includes in the award will be a matter of professional judgement.

LEX MERCATORIA

It is possible that the *lex mercatoria* will recognise the provision of reasons in decisions as being such a fundamental right that the law should intervene to ensure that they are provided.

Correcting the decision

NEC PRINCIPLES

Neither Clause 9 nor the Adjudicator's Contract make any provision for the correction of mistakes by the Adjudicator.

LEX MERCATORIA

It is possible, however, that a 'slip rule' may be implied from either the law applicable to the contract or the law of the territory in which the adjudication is taking place.

Section III

What may follow the process of adjudication

Introduction

Following upon the process of adjudication, one of two things are likely to happen within the time limit set down for the adjudication – either the Adjudicator will fail to issue a decision or the Adjudicator will issue a decision. It is open to a Party to an NEC contract to express dissatisfaction with either of these events and thereafter (where suitable provision has been made) to seek to have the dispute finally determined by the tribunal.

However, pending that final determination by the tribunal (which can only take place after completion or termination, although notification of dissatisfaction must be made earlier) the Parties to an NEC contract must in the intervening period treat the decision of the Adjudicator as binding.

Of course, simply providing that a decision is to be treated as binding in the interim may not automatically have that effect in practice and resort must sometimes be had to enforcement proceedings. Sometimes it may also be necessary for any objections to jurisdiction carried forward to be raised in defence to enforcement proceedings.

Lastly, it remains to consider the means available for final determination of the dispute by review in the tribunal.

- The nature and effect of the Adjudicator's decision
- Dissatisfaction with the Adjudicator failing to reach a decision.
- Dissatisfaction with the decision of the Adjudicator.
- The status of the Adjudicator's decision.
- Interim enforcement of the decision of the Adjudicator.
- Objections to jurisdiction in defence to enforcement proceedings.
- Final determination.
  - The procedure of the tribunal.
  - The agreement of the Parties.
  - Expert determination.
  - Dispute review boards.
  - Some other procedure.
  - Arbitration.
  - Litigation.

10. The nature and effect of the Adjudicator's decision

Dissatisfaction with the Adjudicator failing to reach a decision

As the Guidance Notes make clear, time stipulations are clearly set out in the table and throughout the dispute procedure in order to avoid protracted exchanges and argument and to achieve prompt resolution of disputes. The indications are that these time limits are intended to be strictly complied with. These time limits do not set an exact time limit for the completion of an adjudication because there is (limited) provision for the time limit to be extended. The time limit for any extension of time is, however, also strictly controlled and therefore Parties will be well aware of the point in time at which the process of adjudication will be completed.

The time limit for the completion of the process of adjudication

Clause 91.1 provides a time limit for the decision of the Adjudicator as follows: 'The Adjudicator notifies his decision within four weeks of the end of the period for providing information', but that period can be extended.

The end of the period for providing information is four weeks from the date of the submission of the dispute to the Adjudicator but that period can be extended.

The normal time limit for the completion of the process of adjudication and the notification by the Adjudicator of his or her decision is therefore within four weeks of the end of the period for providing information.

However, both the above four-week period for providing information and the four-week period for the decision of the Adjudicator may be extended in certain restricted circumstances, namely where requested by the Adjudicator on the ground only that it is in view of the nature of the dispute and that any extension requires to be agreed by all the Parties.

The Guidance Notes suggest:

> In complex disputes and for other valid reasons, the Adjudicator may require a period greater than the four weeks stated. For example the Adjudicator may require time to visit the Working Areas and may need to consult with other people to help him in arriving at a decision.

Accordingly, where an extension of time has been requested by the Adjudicator (on a valid ground – the only one of which appears to be 'the nature of the dispute') and agreed by the Parties, then that will set the time limit for the decision. The Parties will normally agree an extension for a stipulated period of time. The Guidance Notes suggest that those time limits are to be strictly complied with. There is no express provision in the NEC family of contracts allowing the Parties to validly receive the decision of the Adjudicator late. Accordingly, at that point in time (the time provided for by the contract of which the Parties ought to be aware and which signifies the end of the process of adjudication) one of two things should happen. The Adjudicator will either fail to notify the Parties of his or her decision by that point of time (which we consider here) or the Adjudicator notifies the Parties of his or her decision (which we consider next).

Failure to reach a decision

Core Clause 9 deals together with a Party being dissatisfied with either the decision of the Adjudicator or the failure of the Adjudicator to notify the Parties of the decision and the Clause (93) is a little difficult to interpret in that respect.

Clause 93.1 provides: 'If after the Adjudicator fails [to notify his decision] within the time provided by this contract, a Party is dissatisfied, that Party notifies the other Party of his intention to refer the matter which he disputes to the tribunal.'

Clause 93.1 goes on, in this respect, to provide: 'It [the dispute] is not referable to the tribunal unless the dissatisfied Party notifies his intention within four weeks of the time provided by this contract for this notification if the Adjudicator fails to notify his decision within that time'.

Clause 93.1 further provides that 'The tribunal proceedings are not started before Completion of the whole of the works or earlier termination.'

The first point to note about this provision is that if the Adjudicator in question fails to reach a decision and notify the Parties of that decision within the time limit provided by the contract, then the NEC family of contracts does not make provision for the Parties to go through the process of adjudication again with a new Adjudicator who may be capable of reaching a decision. Instead, on such failure by the Adjudicator, under the NEC family of contracts matters appear to proceed directly to the tribunal stage.

Clearly, however, unless the Parties have inserted into their contract (or perhaps reached an agreement upon later) information providing for a form of tribunal, then there will be no tribunal to undertake the procedure and the process of adjudication might well come to an end right there.

Assuming, however, that the Parties have inserted information into the Contract Data section of their NEC contract which provides for some form of tribunal, then the procedure for involving that tribunal where the Adjudicator has failed to notify a decision within the time provided for in the contract appears to envisage a two-stage process.

The first stage – notification of intention to refer the dispute to the tribunal – appears to be required at an earlier stage, namely within four weeks of the time provided by the NEC contract for notification by the Adjudicator of his or her decision.

The second stage – the tribunal considering the matter – appears to be postponed under this Clause in that the Clause appears to suggest that, except in the case of earlier termination of the contract, the tribunal proceedings may not be started before Completion of the whole of the Works.

This provision is likely to be significant in that, although the tribunal hearing itself is delayed until completion or termination, the notification of intention to proceed with that requires to be given at a much earlier stage and, since the Guidance Notes suggest that these time limits are to be strictly construed, it follows that upon the failure of an Adjudicator to timeously notify the Parties of his or her decision, the right to refer the dispute to the tribunal may be lost if there is a failure to timeously notify intention to refer the dispute to the tribunal.

Where, however, notification has been given in time of the intention to refer to the tribunal the failure of the Adjudicator to notify the Parties of the decision, then the dispute will be considered anew by the tribunal and we consider that in the following section.

LEX MERCATORIA

In general, where a contractually provided dispute resolution procedure provides for the consequences of failure of its procedures, then matters will be left to the contract and the *lex mercatoria* will not interfere.

However, it is possible that where, *per incuriam*, the Parties omitted to insert sufficient details into the contract to provide them with a remedy, the *lex mercatoria* will intervene.

Dissatisfaction with the decision of the Adjudicator

NEC PRINCIPLES

Under the NEC family of contracts, adjudication is intended to be only an intermediate process. Provision can, therefore, be made in the NEC contracts for the dispute – following upon the process of adjudication – to be considered further by what is called the *tribunal*.

Dissatisfaction with a decision

Core Clause 9 deals together with a Party being dissatisfied with either the decision of the Adjudicator or the failure of the Adjudicator to notify the Parties of the decision and the Clause (93) is a little difficult to interpret in that respect.

Clause 93.1 provides: 'If after the Adjudicator [notifies his decision] a Party is dissatisfied, that Party notifies the other Party of his intention to refer the matter which he disputes to the tribunal.'

Clause 93.1 goes on, in this respect, to provide: 'It [the dispute] is not referable to the tribunal unless the dissatisfied Party notifies his intention within four weeks of the time provided by this contract for this notification if the Adjudicator fails to notify his decision within that time'.

Clause 93.1 further provides that 'The tribunal proceedings are not started before Completion of the whole of the works or earlier termination.'

Clearly, however, unless the Parties have inserted into their contract (or perhaps reached an agreement upon later) information providing for a form of tribunal, then there will be no tribunal to undertake the procedure and the process of adjudication might well come to an end right there.

Assuming, however, that the Parties have inserted information into the Contract Data section of their NEC contract which provides for some form of tribunal, then the procedure for involving that tribunal where a Party is dissatisfied with the decision of the Adjudicator appears to envisage a two-stage process.

The first stage – notification of intention to refer the dispute to the tribunal – appears to be required at an earlier stage, namely within four weeks of notification by the Adjudicator of his or her decision.

The second stage – the tribunal considering the matter – appears to be postponed under this Clause in that the Clause appears to suggest that, except in the case of earlier termination of the contract, the tribunal proceedings may not be started before Completion of the whole of the Works.

This provision is likely to be significant in that, although the tribunal hearing itself is delayed until completion or termination, the notification of intention to proceed with that requires to be given at a much earlier stage and, since the Guidance Notes suggest that these time limits are to be strictly construed, it follows that upon the failure of an Adjudicator to timeously notify the Parties of his or her decision, the right to refer the dispute to the tribunal may be lost if there is a failure to timeously notify intention to refer the dispute to the tribunal.

Where, however, notification has been given in time of the intention to refer to the tribunal the decision of the Adjudicator, then the dispute will be considered anew by the tribunal and we consider that in the following section.

LEX MERCATORIA

In general, where a contractually provided intermediate dispute resolution procedure provides for the consequences of dissatisfaction with any decision arrived at, then matters will be left to the contract and the *lex mercatoria* will not interfere.

However, it is possible that where, *per incuriam*, the Parties omitted to insert sufficient details into the contract to provide them with a remedy, the *lex mercatoria* will intervene.

The status of the Adjudicator's decision

NEC PRINCIPLES

In a contractually provided dispute resolution procedure, the contract can attach such significance to various stages in the procedure as appears to the drafters of the contract to be appropriate.

The provisions of the NEC family of contracts in relation to the status of the Adjudicator's decision may be significant in this respect. While the drafters of the NEC family of contracts are frank in recognising that adjudication may be an intermediate dispute resolution process pending final determination, they also recognise that the Parties could, if they wished, accept the decision of the Adjudicator as being the final determination of the dispute.

In unique and potentially significant wording, Clause 90.2 provides that 'The decision [of the Adjudicator] is *final* and binding unless and until revised by the tribunal.'

The Guidance Notes suggest that 'The Adjudicator's decision is binding and must be implemented. It can only be changed by a subsequent decision of the tribunal.'

What is potentially significant about this wording is that it does not simply provide that the decision of the Adjudicator shall be binding, but provides that the decision of the Adjudicator shall be *final* and binding. Potentially, what that (as interpreted by any Court) is capable of meaning is that if for some reason (for example, failure to provide for a tribunal at all in the contract or failure to timeously refer the matter to any tribunal named) the matter cannot be referred to a tribunal, then the decision of the Adjudicator is not only binding but is also final (in the sense of being conclusive or determinative in relation to the dispute).

Accordingly, it is suggested that under the NEC family of contracts the decision of the Adjudicator can be looked at in two stages.

Temporarily binding

Clause 9 makes it clear that the decision of the Adjudicator is binding unless and until revised by the tribunal.

Where, therefore, the Parties *do* make provision in their contract for a tribunal (by inserting the necessary information into that section of the Contract Data), then that, as the Guidance Notes suggest, means that adjudication will be regarded as an intermediate procedure and that the Parties have contractually agreed that the decision of the Adjudicator is binding upon them and should be observed by the Parties as such in the interim period pending any review and final determination of the dispute by the tribunal.

Finally binding

The Parties are not, however, obliged to make use of the tribunal procedure set out in the NEC family of contracts. It is, therefore, open to the Parties to expressly agree that the decision of the Adjudicator shall be the final determination of the dispute between the Parties or to impliedly so agree by not inserting details of a tribunal into the Contract Data section of the contract.

Either way, the wording adopted in the NEC family of contracts – 'The decision [of the Adjudicator] is *final* and binding unless and until revised by the tribunal' – is likely to have the effect of making any such decision of the Adjudicator final and determinative of the dispute between the Parties.

LEX MERCATORIA

It is possible that the *lex mercatoria*, as an avenue of last resort, will allow Parties who have not left themselves with a contractually provided avenue of appeal to resolve any manifest injustices by litigation. There has also, however, been a considerable amount of litigation in some jurisdictions as to whether or not the right of the Courts to intervene is excluded where the Parties have contractually agreed that any such decision shall be 'final'.

Interim enforcement of the decision of the Adjudicator

NEC PRINCIPLES

In view of the fact that the Parties have specifically agreed in their contract to the process of adjudication and have contractually agreed to treat any decision of the Adjudicator as final and binding unless and until revised by any tribunal, it might be said to be in accordance with NEC principles that the Parties will observe and abide by that requirement.

It sometimes happens in practice, however, that although contractually bound to do so, a Party does not in fact observe as temporarily binding the decision of the Adjudicator. No specific provision is made in the NEC family of contracts for this eventuality and therefore the enforcement of any decision of the Adjudicator will be a matter of the law applicable to the contract or the law of the territory in which the adjudication is being conducted.

LEX MERCATORIA

Where the law applicable to the contract and the law of the territory in which the adjudication is being conducted is the same, then any necessary enforcement of the decision of the Adjudicator will be relatively straightforward. Where these laws differ, however, then the position may be more problematic. Either way, however, the *lex mercatoria* will generally seek to allow the enforcement of decisions which the Parties have contractually agreed are to be treated as binding.

Objections to jurisdiction in defence to enforcement proceedings

NEC PRINCIPLES

As earlier noted, the NEC family of contracts does not provide any machinery under which objection to an adjudication (or its 'jurisdiction') may be raised and decided by the Adjudicator before any adjudication commences.

In practice, therefore, a Party with such an objection may have to allow the adjudication to proceed (taking care to preserve that objection) and then seek to raise their objection later. There is no specific procedure for this to be done under the NEC family of contracts. The objection may be raised on review in any tribunal proceedings. It might be said to be in accordance with NEC principles for the Party to pay any money due in observance of the decision of the Adjudicator and then seek to recover that money later if successful on review before the tribunal. It may be, however, that in some circumstances such as threatened insolvency, any such objection may also have to be raised in defence to enforcement proceedings brought under the *lex mercatoria.*

LEX MERCATORIA

Where the law applicable to the contract and the law of the territory in which the adjudication is being conducted is the same, then both any necessary enforcement of the decision of the Adjudicator and any relevant defences thereto will be relatively straightforward. Where these laws differ, however, then the position may be more problematic. Either way, however, the *lex mercatoria* will generally define which objections to jurisdiction may validly be raised in defence to enforcement proceedings thereunder.

11. Final determination

NEC principles

As earlier noted, under the NEC family of contracts it is open to the Parties to accept the decision of the Adjudicator as finally determinative of the dispute between them and there is no obligation upon the Parties to provide for and use the tribunal procedure which is not provided automatically under the NEC family of contracts. Accordingly, where a Party is dissatisfied with the decision of the Adjudicator and wishes to have the matter reviewed by a tribunal then there are a number of stages to be gone through.

The tribunal

Clearly, in the first place there requires to be a tribunal to which the decision of the Adjudicator can be referred. The NEC family of contracts makes provision for a 'tribunal' but leaves it to the Parties to insert the details of just what that 'tribunal' is to be.

Accordingly, should – for example – an NEC contract be completed in a hurry and no details are inserted into the contract about the nature of any tribunal, then it would appear to follow that (unless subsequently agreed by all the Parties) there will be no tribunal and (save perhaps for litigation in some circumstances) no avenue of appeal against the decision of an Adjudicator.

The procedure for a referral to the tribunal

Under the NEC family of contracts – as they are entitled to do – review of the dispute by the tribunal is postponed to completion of the Works or earlier termination. However, there are procedures which, it appears, must be complied with prior to that stage.

Essentially, notice of dissatisfaction with the decision of the Adjudicator or the failure of the Adjudicator to notify the Parties of the decision must be made within stipulated time limits (time limits which the Guidance Notes suggest will be strictly adhered to and which may result in the loss of the right to review by the tribunal if they are not observed).

This procedure requires ascertaining firstly the time limit for the decision in that particular case and then applying the time limits thereto.

The time limit for the decision

Clause 91.1 provides a time limit for the decision of the Adjudicator as follows: 'The Adjudicator notifies his decision within four weeks of the end of the period for providing information'.

The period for providing information is four weeks from the date of the submission of the dispute to the Adjudicator.

Note, however, that that both the four-week period for providing information and the four-week period for the decision of the Adjudicator may be extended in certain restricted circumstances, namely where requested by the Adjudicator on the ground only that it is in view of the nature of the dispute and that any extension requires to be agreed by all the Parties.

The Guidance Notes suggest:

> In complex disputes and for other valid reasons, the Adjudicator may require a period greater than the four weeks stated. For example the Adjudicator may require time to visit the Working Areas and may need to consult with other people to help him in arriving at a decision.

Accordingly, where an extension of time has been requested by the Adjudicator (on a valid ground) and agreed by the Parties, then that will set the time limit for the decision. Otherwise, the time limit for the decision shall be within four weeks of the end of the period for providing information. The Guidance Notes suggest that these time limits are to be strictly adhered to.

Time limit for referral to the tribunal

Clause 93.1 provides: 'If after the Adjudicator notifies his decision ..., a Party is dissatisfied, that Party notifies the other Party of his intention to refer the matter which he disputes to the tribunal.'

Clause 93.1 goes on, in this respect, to provide: 'It [the dispute] is not referable to the tribunal unless the dissatisfied Party notifies his intention within four weeks of notification of the decision'.

Clause 93.1 further provides that 'The tribunal proceedings are not started before Completion of the whole of the works or earlier termination.'

This provision appears to envisage a two-stage process. There must first be a notification of intention to refer the dispute to the tribunal and then secondly the tribunal considers the matter.

The second stage – the tribunal considering the matter – appears to be postponed under this Clause in that the Clause appears to suggest that, except in the case of earlier termination of the contract, the tribunal proceedings may not be started before Completion of the whole of the Works.

Despite that, notification of intention to refer the dispute appears to be required at an earlier stage, namely within four weeks of notification of the Adjudicator's decision.

The Guidance Notes suggest that these time limits are to be strictly construed. If so, the right to refer the dispute to the tribunal may be lost where there is a failure to timeously notify intention to refer the dispute to the tribunal. Only where these requirements are complied with will the Parties obtain (on completion of the Works or termination) a review of the dispute by whatever form of tribunal is provided for. We consider the procedure for review and the tribunals next.

Lex mercatoria

In some territories, it is considered that as a matter of public policy no one should ever be denied access to the Courts. Where Parties have left themselves without an avenue of appeal, therefore, then in these territories the *lex mercatoria* may provide the Parties with some form of remedy. Other territories, however, do allow the jurisdiction of the Courts to be excluded by the Parties and in these territories the *lex mercatoria* may decline to become involved and the Parties may be left without an avenue of appeal.

The procedure of the tribunal

NEC PRINCIPLES

The NEC family of contracts in fact specifies the procedure of the tribunal and that provision is, in fact, likely to be a very important provision. Core Clause 93.2 provides:

> The *tribunal* settles the dispute referred to it. Its powers include the power to review and revise any decision of the Adjudicator and any action or inaction of the Project Manager or the Supervisor related to the dispute. A Party is not limited in the tribunal proceedings to the information, evidence or arguments put to the Adjudicator.

The most important aspect of the above Clause is that it makes it expressly clear that the review by the tribunal is not an appeal but is in effect a rehearing at which fresh and new evidence may be led.

LEX MERCATORIA

The extent to which, if it is looking at the matter, the *lex mercatoria* will follow its own procedures or have regard to the above provision is problematic.

The agreement of the Parties

NEC PRINCIPLES

It would appear that under the NEC family of contracts agreement between the Parties that the decision of the Adjudicator shall be final could be arrived at expressly in advance in their contract, impliedly in their contract by making no provision for a tribunal or expressly afterwards upon receipt of the decision of the Adjudicator.

LEX MERCATORIA

The *lex mercatoria* is unlikely to interfere with such an agreement unless any consent was not freely given.

Expert Determination

NEC PRINCIPLES

Procedural requirements

As previously noted, Clause 93 (which applies whether or not Option Y(UK) 2 has been adopted) specifies a timetable for submitting the decision or failure to make a decision to the tribunal. The Guidance Notes suggest that these timetables are to be strictly adhered to, and it may well be that if the requirements have not been observed then the right to review by Expert Determination may have been lost. It is possible that the Parties may agree to vary this in their contract.

The time for review

Clause 93 (which applies whether or not Option Y(UK) 2 has been adopted) provides that the Expert Determination is not to be started before Completion of the whole of the Works or earlier termination. It is possible that the Parties may agree to vary this in their contract,

The procedure on review

The procedure for the tribunal is provided for by Clause 93.2 (which applies whether or not Option Y(UK) 2 has been adopted) and which provides:

> The [expert determinator] settles the dispute referred to [him/her].
> [His/her] powers include the power to review and revise any decision
> of the Adjudicator and any action or inaction of the Project Manager or
> the Supervisor related to the dispute. A Party is not limited in the
> [expert determination] proceedings to the information, evidence or
> arguments put to the Adjudicator.

It is clear from that provision that in Expert Determination the Expert sits not as akin to a Court of Appeal but as akin to a body which is rehearing the dispute *de novo* (and is not limited to either the ambit of the dispute previously put to the Adjudicator or to the information, evidence or argument previously put to the Adjudicator).

Review by Expert Determination

All of the above will apply to review where the Employer has selected Expert Determination as the tribunal. However, as earlier noted, that is unlikely to be all and, properly drafted, the selection of Expert Determination as the tribunal will have involved the incorporation into the NEC contract of an 'expert clause' from which further procedural requirements may have arisen.

Expert Determination does not have a formal and regulated procedure such as that which can apply in the case of adjudication, Arbitration or litigation. The only procedural guidance for review by Expert Determination will come from the Expert Clause, perhaps aided by the *lex mercatoria*. On that basis, it may or may not be competent for the Expert as the tribunal to:

- give procedural directions
- carry out site visits and tests
- take legal or other Expert advice
- act inquisitorially
- hold a hearing
- allow representation.

Nor does Expert Determination have a set procedure for the form of the decision. The only guidance for the form of the Expert's decision will come from the Expert Clause, perhaps aided by the *lex mercatoria*. On that basis, the determination of the Expert as the tribunal (signed, dated and witnessed) may or may not include:

- Details of the contract and the Parties
- Details of the Expert
- Details of the Dispute
- The Proceedings before the Adjudicator
- The Proceedings before the Expert
- The issue to be reviewed
- Procedural Directions
- The Submissions of the Parties
- The decision
- Interest
- Costs
- Fees and expenses
- Reasons

LEX MERCATORIA

The extent to which the *lex mercatoria* would be prepared to be involved in such a matter and, if so, what it would make of a procedure which unlike say, Arbitration, does not have an accompanying body of law is problematic.

Dispute Review Boards

NEC PRINCIPLES

Procedural requirements

As previously noted, Clause 93 (which applies whether or not Option Y(UK) 2 has been adopted) specifies a timetable for submitting the decision or failure to make a decision to the tribunal. The Guidance Notes suggest that these timetables are to be strictly adhered to, and it may well be that if the requirements have not been observed then the right to review by the DRB as the tribunal may have been lost. This may be varied by agreement of the Parties.

The time for review

Clause 93 (which applies whether or not Option Y(UK) 2 has been adopted) provides that the tribunal proceedings before the DRB are not to be started before Completion of the whole of the Works or earlier termination. This may be varied by agreement of the Parties.

The procedure on review

The procedure for the tribunal is provided for by Clause 93.2 (which applies whether or not Option Y(UK) 2 has been adopted) and which provides:

> The [DRB] settles the dispute referred to it. Its powers include the power to review and revise any decision of the Adjudicator and any action or inaction of the Project Manager or the Supervisor related to the dispute. A Party is not limited in the [DRB] proceedings to the information, evidence or arguments put to the Adjudicator.

It is clear from that provision that the DRB sitting as a Tribunal sits not as akin to a Court of Appeal but as akin to a body which is rehearing the dispute *de novo* (and is not limited to either the ambit of the dispute previously put to the Adjudicator or to the information, evidence or argument previously put to the Adjudicator).

Review by DRB

All of the above will apply to review where the Employer has selected a DRB as the tribunal. However, as earlier noted, that is unlikely to be all and, properly drafted, the selection of a DRB as the tribunal will have involved the incorporation into the NEC contract of a 'dispute review board clause'.

DRBs do not have a formal and regulated procedure such as that which can apply in the case of adjudication, Arbitration or litigation as such, although various styles for DRB Clauses exist. The only procedural guidance for review by DRB will come from the DRB Clause, perhaps aided by the *lex mercatoria*.

It does not appear to be envisaged by the drafters of the NEC family of contracts that where a DRB is selected as the tribunal it will, as they normally do, keep pace with the Works. Rather, it appears to be envisaged that the DRB will be akin to a Panel of Experts and will be constituted only where there has been a dispute which has been submitted to an Adjudicator, the Adjudicator has either issued a decision or failed to timeously issue a decision, and the dissatisfied Party has complied with the procedural timetable for review. On that basis, it may or may not be competent for the DRB as the tribunal to:

- give procedural directions
- carry out site visits and tests
- take legal or other expert advice
- act inquisitorially
- hold a hearing
- allow representation.

Nor do DRBs have a set procedure for the form of the decision (which are often given in the form of opinions). Here, however, the decision of the DRB as the tribunal will be final (subject only to such review by the Courts as the *lex mercatoria* might allow). The only guidance for the form of the decision by the DRB will come from the DRB Clause, perhaps aided by the *lex mercatoria*. On that basis, the determination of the DRB as the tribunal (signed, dated and witnessed) may or may not include:

- Details of the contract and the Parties
- Details of the DRB
- Details of the Dispute
- The Proceedings before the Adjudicator
- The Proceedings before the Board
- The issue to be reviewed
- Procedural Directions
- The Submissions of the Parties
- The decision
- Interest
- Costs
- Fees and expenses
- Reasons

LEX MERCATORIA

The extent to which the *lex mercatoria* would be prepared to be involved in such a matter and, if so, what it would make of a procedure like a DRB which unlike say, Arbitration, does not have an accompanying body of law, is problematic.

Some Other Procedure

NEC PRINCIPLES

The NEC family of contracts provides merely examples and does not provide an exclusionary list of bodies or persons who may act as the tribunal. Thus, the Parties could agree that the tribunal could be any other reasonable entity such as mini-arb or mediation or the like.

Procedural requirements

As previously noted, Clause 93 (which applies whether or not Option Y(UK) 2 has been adopted) specifies a timetable for submitting the decision or failure to make a decision to the tribunal. The Guidance Notes suggest that these timetables are to be strictly adhered to, and it may well be that if the requirements have not been observed then the right to review by whatever else is provided for as the tribunal may have been lost. This could be varied by agreement of the Parties.

The time for review

Clause 93 (which applies whether or not Option Y(UK) 2 has been adopted) provides that the tribunal proceedings by whatever means are not to be started before Completion of the whole of the Works or earlier termination. This could be varied by agreement of the Parties.

The procedure on review

The procedure for the tribunal is provided for by Clause 93.2 (which applies whether or not Option Y(UK) 2 has been adopted) and which provides:

> The [Means adopted] settles the dispute referred to it. Its powers include the power to review and revise any decision of the Adjudicator and any action or inaction of the Project Manager or the Supervisor related to the dispute. A Party is not limited in the [Means adopted] proceedings to the information, evidence or arguments put to the Adjudicator).

It is clear from that provision that whatever means are adopted as the tribunal, when sitting as a tribunal it sits not as akin to a Court of Appeal but as akin to a body which is rehearing the dispute *de novo* (and is not limited to either the ambit of the dispute previously put to the Adjudicator or to the information, evidence or argument previously put to the Adjudicator.

Review by some Other Procedure

All of the above will apply to review by whatever means the Employer has selected as the tribunal. However, as earlier noted, in order to make those means work effectively, a clause regulating the proceedings of those means should be incorporated into the NEC contract.

Adopting 'ad hoc' means of dispute resolution as the tribunal carries the consequence that no formal and regulated procedure such as that which can apply in the case of adjudication, Arbitration or litigation will exist. The only procedural guidance for review by whatever means are adopted will come from any clause incorporated, perhaps aided by the *lex mercatoria*.

On that basis, it may or may not be competent for the Other Procedures adopted as the tribunal to:

- give procedural directions
- carry out site visits and tests
- take legal or other Expert advice
- act inquisitorially
- hold a hearing
- allow representation.

Nor will the Other Procedures adopted have a set procedure for the form of the decision. The only guidance for the form of the decision by the Means adopted will come from any clause regulating those means, perhaps aided by the *lex mercatoria*. On that basis, the determination of the tribunal (signed, dated and witnessed) by whatever Means are provided for may or may not include:

- Details of the contract and the Parties
- Details of the Other Procedures adopted
- Details of the Dispute
- The Proceedings before the Adjudicator
- The Proceedings before the Tribunal
- The issue to be reviewed
- Procedural Directions
- The Submissions of the Parties
- The decision
- Interest
- Costs
- Fees and expenses
- Reasons

LEX MERCATORIA

The extent to which the *lex mercatoria* would be prepared to be involved in such a matter and, if so, what it would make of some Other Procedure which unlike say, Arbitration, does not have an accompanying body of law, is even more problematic.

Arbitration

NEC PRINCIPLES

Arbitration is the preferred option of the drafters of the NEC family of contracts. Indeed, so keen are the drafters that Arbitration be selected as the tribunal that they have included in the section dealing with Optional Statements a provision which reads:

> If the tribunal is arbitration
>
> The arbitration procedure is [.....]

What is less clear is what is to happen where the Arbitration procedure specified clashes with the procedures for final determination (Arbitration) specified in the NEC contract.

Procedural requirements

As previously noted, Clause 93 (which applies whether or not Option Y(UK) 2 has been adopted) specifies a timetable for submitting the decision or failure to make a decision to the Arbitration tribunal. The Guidance Notes suggest that these timetables are to be strictly adhered to, and it may well be that if the requirements have not been observed then the right to review by whatever else is provided for as the tribunal may have been lost. This could conflict with the provisions of the Arbitration procedure specified. This could be varied by agreement of the Parties.

The time for review

Clause 93 (which applies whether or not Option Y(UK) 2 has been adopted) provides that the tribunal proceedings by whatever means are not to be started before Completion of the whole of the Works or earlier termination. This could conflict with the provisions of the Arbitration procedure specified. This could be varied by agreement of the Parties.

The procedure on review

The procedure for the tribunal is provided for by Clause 93.2 (which applies whether or not Option Y(UK) 2 has been adopted) and which provides:

> The [Arbitral tribunal] settles the dispute referred to it. Its powers include the power to review and revise any decision of the Adjudicator and any action or inaction of the Project Manager or the Supervisor related to the dispute. A Party is not limited in the [Arbitration] proceedings to the information, evidence or arguments put to the Adjudicator.

It is clear from that provision that where Arbitration is adopted as the tribunal, when sitting as an Arbitral tribunal it sits not as akin to a Court of Appeal but as akin to a body which is rehearing the dispute *de novo* (and is not limited to either the ambit of the dispute previously put to the Adjudicator or to the information, evidence or argument previously put to the Adjudicator). This could conflict with the provisions of the Arbitration procedure specified.

Review by Arbitral tribunal

As earlier noted, Arbitration as a means of review is significantly different from other methods of dispute resolution.

Unlike the other possible procedures which may be adopted as the tribunal, Arbitration is in most territories accompanied by a body of law. Simply specifying the Arbitration procedures will usually be enough, although a check will clearly require to be made as to the extent to which those procedures might conflict with the above provisions and, if necessary, vary the contract to resolve such conflicts.

LEX MERCATORIA

The *lex mercatoria* is much more likely to intervene in relation to Arbitration which is usually accompanied by a significant body of law setting out the requirements to be observed in relation thereto.

Litigation

NEC PRINCIPLES

Litigation is an option which the drafters of the NEC family of contracts mention. The Parties could, apparently, accept litigation as the tribunal, although in some territories it could be argued that that right applies whether or not express provision is made.

What is less clear is what is to happen where the rules of court clash with the procedures for final determination (litigation) specified in the NEC contract.

Procedural requirements

As previously noted, Clause 93 (which applies whether or not Option Y(UK) 2 has been adopted) specifies a timetable for submitting the decision or failure to make a decision to the Arbitration tribunal. The Guidance Notes suggest that these timetables are to be strictly adhered to, and it may well be that if the requirements have not been observed then the right to review by whatever else is provided for as the tribunal may have been lost. This could conflict with the rules of the Court involved.

The time for review

Clause 93 (which applies whether or not Option Y(UK) 2 has been adopted) provides that the tribunal proceedings by whatever means are not to be started before Completion of the whole of the Works or earlier termination. This could conflict with the rules of the Court involved. This could be varied by agreement of the Parties.

The procedure on review

The procedure for the tribunal is provided for by Clause 93.2 (which applies whether or not Option Y(UK) 2 has been adopted) and which provides:

> The [Court] settles the dispute referred to it. Its powers include the power to review and revise any decision of the Adjudicator and any action or inaction of the Project Manager or the Supervisor related to the dispute. A Party is not limited in the [Court] proceedings to the information, evidence or arguments put to the Adjudicator.

However, as earlier noted, Courts prefer to follow their own rules and, while content to sit as a Court of Appeal on a point of law, are often reluctant to sit as a Court of first instance on highly technical matters.

However, even while applying its own rules, it is clear from that provision that where litigation is adopted as the tribunal, it may – if it chooses – approach the matter not as akin to a Court of Appeal but as akin to a body which is rehearing the dispute *de novo* (and is not limited to either the ambit of the dispute previously put to the Adjudicator or to the information, evidence or argument previously put to the Adjudicator).

LEX MERCATORIA

The *lex mercatoria* effectively intervenes to provide the legal procedure where litigation is selected as the tribunal.

Part II

Adjudication under the NEC (in relation to 'Construction Contracts' within the UK)

An overview of adjudication under the NEC in the UK

As earlier noted, no NEC contract is entered into in a vacuum. Instead, such a contract will be influenced by the law applicable to that contract and possibly by the law of the territory in which the contract is being executed.

The United Kingdom is a particularly good example of that effect. By coming onto the territory of the United Kingdom, an entity exposes itself to the possible application of a raft of legislation. Some of that legislation might apply to the UK as a whole. Other pieces of legislation may affect only England and Wales, Scotland or Northern Ireland in their own particular way having regard to their own legal systems. For example, the United Kingdom has at last incorporated the European Convention on Human Rights into its domestic law and an entity operating within the United Kingdom might well find itself subject to that law. As another example, in certain circumstances an entity might find itself affected by the UK insolvency laws. As an even more relevant example, that entity might find itself subject to the UK legislation relating to construction (see also Appendix A, judgment extract 1).

The construction legislation with which we are here concerned applies territorially in the United Kingdom. The Housing Grants, Construction and Regeneration Act 1996 c. 53 applies – with differences – to England and Wales and to Scotland, while the Construction Contracts (Northern Ireland) Order 1997 SI No 274 (N.I.) applies to Northern Ireland. It might have been thought convenient to have only one standard set of rules applying to such construction in the UK but in fact, while there are certain similarities there are also certain differences, and each territory has its own unique legislation.

Furthermore, certain differences of interpretation are emerging from the Courts in the different territories.

The application of the particular piece of UK legislation is closely defined. The application of the Act is first territorially defined, then temporarily defined, and finally defined by reference to the definition (whether or not a 'construction contract') of the Works involved. It is entirely possible, therefore, that for the same set of Works being carried out in the same place, some disputes arising therefrom will be covered by the applicable UK legislation, while some other disputes arising therefrom will not be covered by the applicable UK legislation.

Where the Works in question, being within the definition of 'construction contracts' and all other conditions being satisfied, are *prima facie* covered by the applicable UK legislation (whether that be from England and Wales, Scotland or Northern Ireland), then the next stage is to compare the provisions of the contract concerned (so far as they relate to payment and adjudication) with the essential requirements of the UK legislation (so far as they relate to payment and adjudication). Where the provisions in the contract are 'compliant', in the sense that they match the essential requirements of the legislation, then the terms of that contract may, under UK law, regulate matters of payment and adjudication arising thereunder. Where the provisions in the contract are not 'compliant', in the sense that they do not match the essential requirements of the legislation, then the terms of that legislation may (it is only an entitlement), under UK law, regulate matters of payment and adjudication arising thereunder to a greater or lesser (as yet not finally determined) extent.

This situation is likely to give rise to practical problems in practice. We have already noted that from the same set of Works some disputes may have to be resolved under one procedure while other disputes may have to be resolved under other procedures. Another difficulty is that the Parties may, under the NEC family of contracts, come upon this situation in a number of ways. The Parties may be operating under an NEC contract which contains only Clause 9 standing alone or the Parties may have foreseen the situation and incorporated Option Y(UK) 2 into their contract. To a greater or lesser extent (again, not yet finally determined) these contracts may be interpreted as compliant or non-compliant with the essential requirements of the applicable UK legislation.

It is important to bear in mind that what the applicable UK legislation gives the Parties where the contract is found to be non-compliant is an 'entitlement' not an 'obligation'. Accordingly, it is open to a Party so entitled not to take up their entitlements. The consequences are that adjudication remains essentially consensual so that, for example, a Party entitled to have the applicable UK legislation applied may nevertheless agree with the other Party to run their adjudication under the contract adjudication procedures. Similarly, where the compliance point at issue is a moot one, the Parties could nevertheless agree that the secondary UK legislation in the form of the applicable Scheme will apply in its entirety so that their adjudication is to be run under the statutory adjudication procedures.

It could be said to be only in accordance with NEC principles that the Parties (and it is suggested that it is primarily a matter for the Parties rather than the Adjudicator) should seek to reach an agreement as to the procedures which are to apply to their adjudication. It is, however, where one of the Parties stands upon their entitlements that difficulties may arise (which the Adjudicator may have to help to resolve). Adjudication has been described in specific cases as follows:

- Quasi-legal proceedings for which leave may be required as, for example, where the company against whom it is proposed to launch an adjudication is in administration (A Straume (UK) Ltd v Bradlor Developments Ltd, 7 April 1999).
- A speedy mechanism for settling disputes in construction contracts on a provisional interim basis requiring the decisions of Adjudicators to be observed pending the final determination of the dispute by agreement, arbitration or litigation (Macob Civil Engineering Ltd v Morrison Construction Ltd, 12 February 1999).
- In which it is inherent that mistakes and injustices, even insolvency, will occur (Bouygues UK Ltd v Dahl Jensen UK Ltd (CA), 31 July 2000).

Adjudication in various forms has existed in the UK for some time but its compulsory nature (described by some as a violent interference with the principle of freedom of contract) is new. The process of working this new concept into the existing framework has only just begun and has yet to become established. Although some decisions have been made at first instance (and some of those later varied, distinguished or departed from), the position remains uncertain in many respects. All that those involved in adjudication can do is seek to do their utmost to apply best practice in good faith. This book seeks to assist that process by providing a snapshot of what the position is understood to be as at 31 March 2001. It is up to the Parties to keep themselves advised of any subsequent developments and to exercise their best or professional judgement on the issues which confront them.

In an attempt to assist that process, this book looks at the position where Clause 9 alone is involved; considers the position where Option Y(UK) 2 is involved; considers the principles involved and any potential human rights points before finally considering the secondary legislation applicable and any commentary on developments in relation thereto.

Section I

What may precede the process of adjudication

Introduction

Adjudication is not necessarily automatic and, particularly within the UK, certain pertinent considerations precede the process of adjudication which we consider in this section.

Consideration can first of all be given to what may or may not happen prior to the implementation of any procedure for the resolution of claims.

Consideration can then turn to the procedure to be used for the resolution of the claim in question. This will involve a consideration of the provisions of the contract, which in this case provides for adjudication, but this in turn will involve a consideration of the territory in which the Works are being carried out which, in the territory of the United Kingdom, will then involve a consideration of whether or not what is involved falls within the definitions which confer jurisdiction under the applicable UK legislation in relation to adjudication.

Having determined within which 'framework' the claim in question is going to have to be resolved – and out of the same set of Works some claims may fall to be dealt with under one framework while other claims may fall to be dealt with under another framework – it is suggested that consideration then turns to the settlement/crystallisation of disputes and a consideration of what disputes are properly referable to adjudication.

Where the dispute has not been settled but has crystallised into a 'proper' dispute which may or may not be referable to adjudication, consideration can then turn to the precise procedures for the resolution of that dispute by adjudication. In these circumstances, the applicable UK legislation makes provision as to the terms of which adjudication procedure – contractual or statutory – will govern the adjudication. This requires matching the terms of the contract in question against the essential requirements of the UK legislation and a determination of the extent to which it is felt that the contract is compliant with the legislation. We then consider the possible consequences of the contract being found to be non-compliant and what, if anything, can be done to question the situation.

Finally, if an adjudication is to proceed, we consider what is to be done in relation to the Works pending the resolution of the dispute by adjudication.

12. What must be done in advance of adjudication

What may happen prior to the resolution of any disputes

Core Clause 9 and Option Y(UK) 2 of the NEC family of contracts, although they do not expressly say so, imply that they do not envisage anything else happening in relation to the resolution of any disputes between the Parties other than the agreed procedure for resolving disputes contained in the contract between the Parties.

The consequence of undertaking (even under an NEC contract) Works in a particular territory, however, is that the laws of that territory may be used to impinge upon the relationship between the Parties. Parties undertaking Works in these territories should be aware of what, beyond the NEC contract which they have entered into, may happen prior to the resolution of any disputes. It could, however, be considered to be contrary to the spirit of the NEC family of contracts for a Party thereto to embark upon such diligence.

The possible diligences we consider below.

England and Wales

Provisional measures in England and Wales are the Garnishee order and the Mareva injunction. However, the latter is available only from superior tribunals, requires a 'good arguable case' to be made out, and is difficult to obtain. These are rarely seen in construction matters and there does not appear to be any reported case of their use in England and Wales in relation to adjudication.

Even reaching agreement in their contract as to some compulsory procedure to precede adjudication will not do, as the case of R G Carter Limited v Edmund Nuttall Limited (21 June 2000) established that an application for adjudication in relation to a 'construction contract' could not be defeated by a clause in the contract requiring compulsory mediation in advance of adjudication and also that a contract containing such a clause was not compliant with the UK legislation.

Scotland

Scotland has a strong tradition of preliminary diligence which is almost standard, is often seen in construction matters, and has been seen in relation to adjudication. The two main types of diligence are arrestment on the dependence of the action and inhibition.

Arrestment on the dependence of an action

Arrestment is a form of diligence under which a debtor's moveable property in the custody of a third party may be attached. The diligence of arrestment may be used in the execution of a money judgment or it may be used on the dependence of an action for money as a form of security for the sum sued for. Arrestment is encountered most often in the latter respect.

For example, a Creditor (A) might be owed money by a Debtor (B) and Debtor (B) might have a Bank Account with Bank (X). By raising a Court action with a pecuniary crave against B and obtaining a warrant for arrestment on the dependence thereof, C is then in a position to have whatever moveable property of B's is to be found within B's Bank Account with Bank X 'frozen' and held there as security pending the outcome of the action.

Although regarded in the law of Scotland as an extraordinary remedy which is not to be extended further than has been sanctioned by law and usage, arrestment is commonplace in practice. The Scottish Law Commission are considering at the moment reform of the law relating to arrestments.

Law and usage sanction the use of arrestment on the dependence as a diligence where the writ contains, either in the first instance or the alternative, a crave for the payment of a sum of money. Property held jointly cannot, however, be arrested on the dependence for a debt due by only one of the joint owners.

Common practice in construction situations is, therefore, to fashion a claim in the form of a sum of money and then on that basis to raise a legal action in relation to which arrestment on the dependence is sought. The warrant to serve the writ and for arrestment will be almost automatically granted by the Court Clerk.

The Defenders will then seek to persuade the Court that Arbitration/adjudication is mandatory in which case the Court will sist the legal action to await the outcome of those proceedings. The diligence in the form of the arrestment is, however, likely to remain in place, although the Defenders can seek to have the arrestment recalled in full or restricted to a more reasonable level.

Arrestments of a very technical nature have already featured in two Scottish cases involving adjudication, namely Eastend Civil Engineering Ltd v Rentokil Ailsa Environmental Ltd (12 March 1999 (Sheriff) and 31 March 1999 (Sheriff Principal)) and Stiell Limited v Reima Control Systems Ltd (23 June 2000 (Court of Appeal)).

Inhibition

An inhibition affects the ability of the Party against whom it is being used to deal in any property which they may own in Scotland.

Scotland maintains a public Register of Property and also a Register of Inhibitions. Conveyancing practice requires the Register of Inhibitions to be searched before a property is dealt with and the conveyance of a property with an inhibition standing is invalid.

Inhibition can be obtained automatically on a Summons in the Superior Courts or can be obtained by means of a separate procedure. Inhibition may also be recalled on application to the Court.

The use of inhibition is often seen in practice in construction disputes (which usually involve property) but there does not so far appear to be any recorded use of inhibition in an adjudication case

Other provision

The English case holding that a precondition clause providing for compulsory mediation in advance of adjudication made the contract, if a 'construction contract', non-compliant in relation to the UK legislation is likely to be of persuasive authority in Scotland.

Northern Ireland

Provisional measures in Northern Ireland are also the Garnishee order and the Mareva injunction. However, the latter is available only from superior tribunals, requires a 'good arguable case' to be made out, and is difficult to obtain.

These are rarely seen in construction matters and there does not appear to be any reported case of their use in Northern Ireland in relation to adjudication.

Other provision

The English case holding that a precondition clause providing for compulsory mediation in advance of adjudication made the contract, if a 'construction contract', non-compliant in relation to the UK legislation is likely to be of persuasive authority in Northern Ireland .

What method is to be used to resolve any disputes

Core Clause 9 at Clause 90.1 states: 'Any dispute arising under or in connection with this contract is submitted to and settled by the Adjudicator ...'.

Option Y(UK) 2 states: 'The Parties and the Project Manager follow this procedure [adjudication] for the avoidance and settlement of disputes'.

The NEC family of contracts envisages that, in terms of the contract, one method and one method only will be used to resolve any disputes arising under the contract and that method is adjudication.

The consequences of undertaking (even under an NEC contract) Works in a particular territory, however, is that the laws of that territory may be used to impinge upon the relationship between the Parties. For example, it may happen that a contract does not provide for adjudication but that the law of the territory may provide for adjudication.

Here, the NEC family of contracts provides for adjudication so that where the law of the territory provides for adjudication there would appear to be no difference in principle. Where a practical difficulty arises, however, is in relation to the procedures to be used in relation to any adjudication.

It is open to the Parties to a contract to agree amongst themselves (provided that they all agree) precisely what procedure is to apply in relation to an adjudication in which they are involved. It could be considered to be in accordance with the spirit of the NEC family of contracts to come to such an agreement.

Where, however, the Parties are at arm's length then practical difficulties can result. One Party may decide to stand upon their statutory entitlements in the territory in which they are working. Those statutory entitlements are, however, tightly defined and it is by no means unusual that not all of the Works being undertaken will be covered by the applicable statute.

The result in practice may be that arising out of the same Works some disputes may have to be resolved using contractual adjudication procedures, while other disputes may have to be resolved using statutory adjudication procedures. Parties undertaking Works in these territories should be aware of what, beyond the NEC contract, may affect the method used to resolve any disputes arising.

We consider these below in relation to first, the territorial application of the legislation and then second, the other requirements which must be met before the entitlement or right – also known as 'jurisdiction' – to refer a dispute to adjudication arises, and then thirdly, the manner in which the procedures to be applied to such adjudications are determined.

Territory

England and Wales

The ruling provisions (applying Part II of the Housing, Grants, Construction and Regeneration Act 1996 which covers payments and adjudication) is section 104 of the Act, the relevant subsections of which are:

s. 104

(6)   This Part applies only to construction contracts which
   (a)   are entered into after the commencement of this Part, and
   (b)   relate to the carrying out of construction operations in England, Wales ...
(7)   This Part applies whether or not the law of England and Wales ... is otherwise the applicable law in relation to the contract.

Commentary The application of the legislation is territorial. Accordingly, if the Works are being carried out outwith the territories of England and Wales then the type of contract will be irrelevant because no matter what type of contract it is, there will be no entitlement to have any of the provisions of the HGCR Act 1996 applied.

Where the Works do fall within the territories of England and Wales, however, then the payment and adjudication provisions of the HGCR Act 1996 cannot be avoided simply by providing that the laws of another country are to regulate the contract between the Parties. No matter what the law of the contract is, the provisions of the HGCR Act 1996 will – provided the other conditions are met – apply to Works within the territories of England and Wales.

The territories of England and Wales are defined in national legislation and there has already been one adjudication case in which it was decided that because the (oil and gas) Works in question fell below the high water mark, they did not fall within the territories of England and Wales and therefore the provisions of the HGCR Act 1996 were not applicable.

Accordingly, when faced with a dispute which may lead to adjudication, the first step is to determine the territory within which the Works in question are being carried out. If that territory does not fall within the defined territory of England and Wales, then the potential provisions of the HGCR Act 1996 can be ignored and the primary concern will be the contractual adjudication provisions (as affected by any applicable laws of the territory in which the Works are in fact taking place).

Scotland

The ruling provisions (applying Part II of the Housing, Grants, Construction and Regeneration Act 1996 which covers payments and adjudication) is section 104 of the Act, the relevant subsections of which are:

s. 104

(6)   This Part applies only to construction contracts which
  (a)   are entered into after the commencement of this Part, and
  (b)   relate to the carrying out of construction operations in … Scotland
(7)   This Part applies whether or not the law of Scotland … is otherwise the applicable law in relation to the contract.

Commentary   The application of the legislation is territorial. Accordingly, if the Works are being carried out outwith the territory of Scotland then the type of contract will be irrelevant because no matter what type of contract it is, there will be no entitlement to have any of the provisions of the HGCR Act 1996 applied.

Where the Works do fall within the territory of Scotland, however, then the payment and adjudication provisions of the HGCR Act 1996 cannot be avoided simply by providing that the laws of another country are to regulate the contract between the Parties. No matter what the law of the contract is, the provisions of the HGCR Act 1996 will – provided the other conditions are met – apply to Works within the territory of Scotland.

The territory of Scotland is defined in national legislation and there has already been one adjudication case (*Homer Burgess*), a case involving work being supplied from England to the Scottish Borders, in which the territorial application had to be looked at closely. The English adjudication case is likely to be persuasive authority of the fact that Works below the high water mark will not be covered by the HGCR Act 1996.

Accordingly, when faced with a dispute which may lead to adjudication, the first step is to determine the territory within which the Works in question are being carried out. If that territory does not fall within the defined territory of Scotland, then the potential provisions of the HGCR Act 1996 can be ignored and the primary concern will be the contractual adjudication provisions (as affected by any applicable laws of the territory in which the Works are in fact taking place).

Northern Ireland

The ruling provisions (applying provisions corresponding to Part II of the Housing, Grants, Construction and Regeneration Act 1996 which covers payments and adjudication) is the Construction Contracts (Northern Ireland) Order 1997, Article 3, the relevant provisions of which are:

Article 3

(6)   This Order applies only to construction contracts which
  (a)   are entered into after the commencement of this Order, and
  (b)   relate to the carrying out of construction operations in Northern Ireland
(7)   This Part applies whether or not the law of Northern Ireland is otherwise the applicable law in relation to the contract.

Commentary   The application of the legislation is territorial. Accordingly, if the Works are being carried out outwith the territory of Northern Ireland then the type of contract will be irrelevant because no matter what type of contract it is, there will be no entitlement to have any of the provisions of the 1997 Order applied.

Where the Works do fall within the territory of Northern Ireland, however, then the payment and adjudication provisions of the 1997 Order cannot be avoided simply by providing that the laws of another country are to regulate the contract between the Parties. No matter what the law of the contract is, the provisions of the 1997 Order will – provided the other conditions are met – apply to Works within the territory of Northern Ireland.

The territory of Northern Ireland is defined in national legislation. The English adjudication case is likely to be persuasive authority of the fact that Works below the high water mark will not be covered by the 1997 Order.

Accordingly, when faced with a dispute which may lead to adjudication, the first step is to determine the territory within which the Works in question are being carried out. If that territory does not fall within the defined territory of Northern Ireland, then the potential provisions of the 1997 Order can be ignored and the primary concern will be the contractual adjudication provisions (as affected by any applicable laws of the territory in which the Works are in fact taking place).

The right (otherwise known as the 'jurisdiction') to refer a dispute for adjudication

England and Wales

When Part II of the HGCR Act 1996 c. 53 came into effect in England and Wales on 1 May 1998, it gave those who are Parties to a construction contract and who satisfy the conditions laid down the right to refer a dispute arising under the contract for adjudication under a procedure complying with the Act. The purpose of the following discussion is to consider the conditions that have to be met before that entitlement exists.

Does a contract exist?

It will be appreciated at the outset that the right to refer a dispute for adjudication is conditional upon a contract being in existence. The Act specifies that it is *a party* to a 'construction *contract*' (on which see later) who has the right to refer a *dispute arising under the contract* for adjudication.

It is, of course, highly unlikely that any major construction work would be undertaken without a contract and it is a commercial fact of life that almost all major construction contracts today involve at least a variation of one of the Standard Form Contracts. Nevertheless, if perchance no contract for the work exists, then *prima facie* there will be no right to refer any dispute relating to that work for adjudication.

Was the contract entered into after 1 May 1998?

The right to refer a dispute for adjudication is conditional upon the contract having been entered into after 1 May 1998. The Act is not intended to be retrospective and provides that the right to refer a dispute for adjudication applies only to construction contracts which are entered into after the commencement of that part of the Act (Part II) which relates to adjudication. (By Statutory Instrument the commencement date for Part II of the Act is ordered to be 1 May 1998). Accordingly, contracts entered into prior to 1 May 1998 *prima facie* do not carry the right to refer disputes arising under that contract for adjudication (see also Appendix A, judgment extract 2).

Is the contract within the (wide) definition of an 'agreement in writing'?

The right to refer a dispute for adjudication is conditional upon the contract being in writing. The Act provides that the contract, and any other agreement between the Parties as to any matter, is effective for the purposes of Part II of the Act only if it is in writing, but the definition of an 'agreement in writing' in the Act is extremely wide (a reference to anything being written or in writing covers being recorded by any means) and provides:

- if the agreement is made in writing, it does not have to be signed by the parties
- an exchange of communications in writing is sufficient
- it is sufficient if the agreement is evidenced in writing
- if the agreement is made by reference to terms in writing that is an agreement in writing
- if the agreement is made otherwise than in writing but with the authority of the Parties to the agreement and is recorded by one of the Parties or by a third party, then that is sufficient
- if in the exchange of written submissions in adjudication, arbitral or legal proceedings one Party alleges the existence of an agreement other-

wise than in writing and that is not denied by the Party against whom it is alleged, then that is sufficient.

It will be appreciated that the above definition covers most of the practical methods by which agreement is reached between Parties within the construction industry (perhaps even including e-mail) and it is now unlikely that any major work would be undertaken without some agreement along these lines. Nevertheless, if perchance any agreement is not put into writing, then *prima facie* it will not carry the right to refer any dispute relating to that matter for adjudication (see also Appendix A, judgment extracts 3 and 4).

Is the contract an excluded contract?

The right to refer a dispute for adjudication is conditional upon the contract not being one of the contracts excluded from the operation of Part II of the Act. A number of contracts are excluded from adjudication by the Act, which also gives a number of powers to the Secretary of State to add to, amend or repeal that list of exclusions. The procedure laid down (known as the 'affirmative resolution procedure') provides that no such Order shall be made unless a draft of it has been laid before and approved by a resolution of each of the Houses of Parliament and so it is unlikely that any changes to the list will take place without sufficient notice of any changes being made. Advantage has been taken of the Scheme passing through Parliament to bring in the first of these Orders and, as things stand at the moment, the contracts excluded from the operation of Part II of the Act are:

- contracts of employment (*per* the Employment Rights Act 1996) (104(3))
- construction contracts with residential occupiers (106) (see also Appendix A, judgment extract 5)
- Agreements under one of the following statutes:
    - Highways Act 1980 s. 38 (power of highways authority to adopt by agreement)
    - Highways Act 1980 s. 278 (agreements as to execution of works)
    - Town and Country Planning Act 1990 s.106 (planning obligations)
    - Town and Country Planning Act 1990 s.106A (modifying/discharging planning obligations)
    - Town and Country Planning Act 1990 s.299A (Crown planning obligations)
    - Water Industry Act 1991 s. 104 (adoption of sewer, drain or sewage disposal works)
    - National Health Service (Private Finance) Act 1997 s.1 (NHS Trust power re agreement).
- Private Finance Initiatives
    Contracts entered into under the private finance initiatives are defined as those where *all* the following conditions are fulfilled:
    (*a*) it contains a statement that it is entered into under a project under that initiative or one applying similar principles; and

(b) the consideration due under the contract is determined at least in part by reference to one or more of the following:
(i) the standards attained in the performance of a service, the provision of which is the principal purpose or one of the principal purposes for which the building or structure is constructed; or
(ii) the extent, rate or intensity of use of all or any part of the building or structure in question; or
(iii) the right to operate any facility in connection with the building or structure in question; and

(c) one of the parties to the contract is:
- A Minister of the Crown
- A Government Department (accountable Exchequer & Audits Departments Act 1866)
- Any other Authority or Body (inspectable Comptroller and Auditor General)
- Any other Authority or Body (*per* Sch 4 National Audit Act 1983)
- A body (auditable by the Accounts Commission)
- A governing body of a voluntary school (s. 31 Education Act 1996)
- A company wholly owned by any of the above bodies.

- Finance Agreements
  Contracts within that definition include any one of the following:
  (a) any contract of insurance
  (b) any contract for the formation of a company, partnership or association
  (c) any contract for the creation or transfer of any right or interest in securities
  (d) any contract the principal object of which is the lending of money
  (e) any contract of surety such as bonds of fidelity, advance payment, retention, performance.

- Development Agreements
  Contracts in which the land on which the principal construction operations are to take place is land in respect of which a relevant interest in the land (meaning ownership or a lease which will expire no earlier than 12 months after the completion of the construction operations under the contract) is to be granted or disposed of under the contract.

If the contract does *not* fall into the category of contracts that are excluded from the operation of Part II of the Act, then *prima facie* the right to refer a dispute arising under it for adjudication will apply if the other conditions are satisfied.

Is the contract a construction contract?

The right to refer a dispute for adjudication is conditional upon the contract being a 'construction contract' (which in turn involves a consideration of whether it relates to 'construction operations').

Territorially, the Act applies to the carrying out of 'construction operations' in England and Wales. Thus, domestic or foreign contractors who

satisfy the conditions and who contract to carry out 'construction operations' within those territories *prima facie* have the right to refer disputes
arising under those contracts for adjudication. Furthermore, it will not be
possible for those contractors to seek to avoid the application of the Act by
specifying that some other foreign law shall apply to the contract, for the Act
also provides that Part II of the Act is to apply whether or not the law of
England and Wales is the applicable law in relation to the contract.

Conceptually, the Act – and specifically included in this definition are
agreements to do architectural, design or surveying work, or provide advice
on building, engineering, interior or exterior decoration or on the laying-out
of landscape, and also agreements entered into by or on behalf of the Crown
– applies to a 'construction contract' which the Act defines as meaning an
agreement with a person for any of the following:

(a) the carrying out of 'construction operations'
(b) arranging for the carrying out of 'construction operations' by others,
    whether under sub-contract to him or otherwise
(c) providing his own labour, or the labour of others, for the carrying out of
    'construction operations'.

An agreement which makes provision of any kind within this definition
relates to construction operations and Part II applies. In the event that the
contract cannot be brought under one of the above definitions, then *prima
facie* it will not carry the right to refer a dispute arising under it for adjudication.

Is the construction operation an excluded construction operation?

The right to refer a dispute for adjudication is conditional upon the construction operation involved not being one of the construction operations
excluded from Part II of the Act. The Act lists a number of construction
operations that are excluded but again, and on the same basis, power is given
to the Secretary of State to add to, amend or repeal that list. As things stand at
the moment, the construction operations (and it is only these operations but
not the Works associated with them) excluded from the definition are:

(a) drilling for, or extraction of, oil or natural gas
(b) extraction (whether by underground or surface working) of minerals;
    tunnelling or boring, or construction of underground works, for this
    purpose
(c) assembly, installation or demolition of plant or machinery, or erection
    or demolition of steelwork for the purposes of supporting or providing
    access to plant or machinery, on a site where the primary activity is:
    (i) nuclear processing, power generation, or water or effluent treatment
    (ii) the production, transmission, processing or bulk storage (other than
    warehousing) of chemicals, pharmaceuticals, oil, gas, steel or food and
    drink
(d) manufacture or delivery to site of:
    (i) building and engineering components or equipment

(ii) materials, plant or machinery

(iii) components for systems of heating, lighting, air-conditioning, ventilation, power supply, drainage, sanitation, water supply or fire protection, or for security or communications systems, except under a contract which also provides for their installation

(*e*) the making, installation and repair of artistic works, being sculptures, murals and other works which are wholly artistic in nature.

If the construction operation being undertaken does not fall within one of the above categories of construction operation excluded from the operation of the Act then – if the other conditions are satisfied – for all practical purposes a *prima facie* right to have disputes arising out of that construction operation referred for adjudication is likely to exist. The Act does in fact go on to give a positive definition of a construction operation and, although it is conceivable that there could be an argument as to whether or not an operation falls within that definition, the definition itself (said to have been adopted from a taxation statute) is so all-embracing as to be likely to cover almost all the operations typically encountered in construction. The positive definition given is as follows:

(*a*) construction, alteration, repair, maintenance, extension, demolition or dismantling of buildings, or structures forming, or to form, part of the land (whether permanent or not)

(*b*) construction, alteration, repair, maintenance, extension, demolition or dismantling of any Works forming, or to form, part of the land, including (without prejudice to the foregoing) walls, roadworks, power-lines, telecommunications apparatus, aircraft runways, docks and harbours, railways, inland waterways, pipe-lines, reservoirs, water-mains, wells, sewers, industrial plant and installations for purposes of land drainage, coast protection or defence

(*c*) installation in any building or structure of fittings forming part of the land, including (without prejudice to the foregoing) systems of heating, lighting, air-conditioning, ventilation, power supply, drainage, sanitation, water supply or fire protection, or security or communications systems

(*d*) external or internal cleaning of buildings and structures, so far as carried out in the course of their construction, alteration, repair, extension or restoration

(*e*) operations which form an integral part of, or are preparatory to, or are for rendering complete, such operations as are previously described in this subsection, including site clearance, earth-moving, excavation, tunnelling and boring, laying of foundations, erection, maintenance or dismantling of scaffolding, site restoration, landscaping and the provision of roadways and other access works

(*f*) painting or decorating the internal or external surfaces of any building or structure.

Where an agreement relates to construction operations and other matters, Part II applies only insofar as it relates to the construction operations. Demarcation

disputes in this area are likely. In the unlikely event of the construction operation being undertaken not coming within one of the above definitions, then
prima facie it will not carry the right to refer any dispute relating to that matter
for adjudication. See Appendix A, judgment extract 6, for references to the
meaning of 'construction operations' and 'construction contract'.

Scotland

When Part II of the HGCR Act 1996 c. 53 came into effect in Scotland on 1
May 1998 it gave those who are Parties to a construction contract and who
satisfy the conditions laid down the right to refer a dispute arising under the
contract for adjudication under a procedure complying with the Act. The
purpose of the following discussion is to consider the conditions that have to
be met before that entitlement exists.

Does a contract exist?

It will be appreciated at the outset that the right to refer a dispute for adjudication is conditional upon a contract being in existence. The Act specifies
that it is *a party* to a 'construction *contract*' (on which see later) who has the
right to refer a *dispute arising under the contract* for adjudication.

It is, of course, highly unlikely that any major construction work would
be undertaken without a contract and it is a commercial fact of life that
almost all major construction contracts today involve at least a variation of
one of the Standard Form Contracts. Nevertheless, if perchance no contract
for the work exists, then *prima facie* there will be no right to refer any
dispute relating to that work for adjudication.

Was the contract entered into after 1 May 1998?

The right to refer a dispute for adjudication is conditional upon the contract
having been entered into after 1 May 1998. The Act is not intended to be
retrospective and provides that the right to refer a dispute for adjudication
applies only to construction contracts which are entered into after the
commencement of that part of the Act (Part II) which relates to adjudication.
(By Statutory Instrument the commencement date for Part II of the Act is
ordered to be 1 May 1998). Accordingly, contracts entered into prior to 1
May 1998 *prima facie* do not carry the right to refer disputes arising under
that contract for adjudication.

Is the contract within the (wide) definition of an 'agreement in writing'?

The right to refer a dispute for adjudication is conditional upon the contract
being in writing. The Act provides that the contract, and any other agreement between the parties as to any matter, is effective for the purposes of
Part II of the Act only if it is in writing, but the definition of an 'agreement in
writing' in the Act is extremely wide (a reference to anything being written
or in writing covers being recorded by any means) and provides:

- if the agreement is made in writing, it does not have to be signed by the Parties
- an exchange of communications in writing is sufficient
- it is sufficient if the agreement is evidenced in writing
- if the agreement is made by reference to terms in writing that is an agreement in writing
- if the agreement is made otherwise than in writing but with the authority of the Parties to the agreement and is recorded by one of the Parties or by a third Party, then that is sufficient
- if in the exchange of written submissions in adjudication, arbitral or legal proceedings one Party alleges the existence of an agreement otherwise than in writing and that is not denied by the Party against whom it is alleged, then that is sufficient.

It will be appreciated that the above definition covers most of the practical methods by which agreement is reached between Parties within the construction industry (perhaps even including e-mail) and it is now unlikely that any major work would be undertaken without some agreement along these lines. Nevertheless, if perchance any agreement is not put into writing, then *prima facie* it will not carry the right to refer any dispute relating to that matter for adjudication.

Is the contract an excluded contract?

The right to refer a dispute for adjudication is conditional upon the contract not being one of the contracts excluded from the operation of Part II of the Act. A number of contracts are excluded from adjudication by the Act, which also gives a number of powers to the Secretary of State to add to, amend or repeal that list of exclusions. The procedure laid down (known as the 'affirmative resolution procedure') provides that no such Order shall be made unless a draft of it has been laid before and approved by a resolution of each of the Houses of Parliament and so it is unlikely that any changes to the list will take place without sufficient notice of any changes being made. Advantage has been taken of the Scheme passing through Parliament to bring in the first of these Orders and, as things stand at the moment, the contracts excluded from the operation of Part II of the Act are:

- contracts of employment (*per* the Employment Rights Act 1996) (104(3))
- construction contracts with residential occupiers (106)
- Agreements under one of the following statutes:
  - An agreement under s. 48 (contributions towards expenditure on constructing and improving roads) of the Roads (Scotland) Act 1984
  - An agreement under s. 75 (agreements regulating development or use of land) or s. 246 (agreements relating to Crown land) of the Town and Country Planning (Scotland) Act 1997
  - An agreement under s. 8 (agreements as to provision of sewers etc. for new premises) of the Sewerage (Scotland) Act 1968

- An externally financed development agreement within the meaning of s. 1 (powers of NHS Trusts to enter into agreements) of the National Health Service (Private Finance) Act 1997.
- Private Finance Initiatives
  Contracts entered into under the private finance initiatives are defined as those where *all* the following conditions are fulfilled:
  (*a*) it contains a statement that it is entered into under a project under that initiative or one applying similar principles; and
  (*b*) the consideration due under the contract is determined at least in part by reference to one or more of the following:
  (i) the standards attained in the performance of a service, the provision of which is the principal purpose or one of the principal purposes for which the building or structure is constructed; or
  (ii) the extent, rate or intensity of use of all or any part of the building or structure in question; or
  (iii) the right to operate any facility in connection with the building or structure in question; and
  (*c*) one of the parties to the contract is:
  - A Minister of the Crown
  - A Government Department (accountable Exchequer & Audits Departments Act 1866)
  - Any other Authority or Body (inspectable Comptroller and Auditor General)
  - Any other Authority or Body (*per* Sch 4 National Audit Act 1983)
  - A body (auditable by the Accounts Commission for Scotland)
  - A water and sewerage authority established under s. 62 (new water and sewerage authorities) of the Local Government etc. (Scotland) Act 1994
  - A governing body of a self-governing school within the meaning of s. 1(3) (duty of Secretary of State to maintain self-governing schools) of the Self-Governing Schools etc. (Scotland) Act 1989
  - A company wholly owned by any of the above bodies.
- Finance Agreements
  Contracts within that definition include any one of the following:
  (*a*) any contract of insurance
  (*b*) any contract for the formation of a company, partnership or association
  (*c*) any contract for the creation or transfer of any right or interest in securities
  (*d*) any contract the principal object of which is the lending of money
  (*e*) any contract of surety such as bonds of fidelity, advance payment, retention, performance.
- Development Agreements
  Contracts in which the land on which the principal construction operations are to take place is land in respect of which a relevant interest in the land (meaning ownership or a lease which will expire no earlier than 12 months after the completion of the construction operations under the contract) is to be granted or disposed of under the contract.

If the contract does *not* fall into the category of contracts that are excluded from the operation of Part II of the Act, then *prima facie* the right to refer a dispute arising under it for adjudication will apply if the other conditions are satisfied.

Is the contract a construction contract?

The right to refer a dispute for adjudication is conditional upon the contract being a 'construction contract' (which in turn involves a consideration of whether it relates to 'construction operations').

Territorially, the Act applies to the carrying out of 'construction operations' in Scotland. Thus, domestic or foreign contractors who satisfy the conditions and who contract to carry out 'construction operations' within those territories *prima facie* have the right to refer disputes arising under those contracts for adjudication. Furthermore, it will not be possible for those contractors to seek to avoid the application of the Act by specifying that some other foreign law shall apply to the contract, for the Act also provides that Part II of the Act is to apply whether or not the law of Scotland is the applicable law in relation to the contract.

Conceptually, the Act – and specifically included in this definition are agreements to do architectural, design or surveying work, or provide advice on building, engineering, interior or exterior decoration or on the laying-out of landscape, and also agreements entered into by or on behalf of the Crown – applies to a 'construction contract' which the Act defines as meaning an agreement with a person for any of the following:

(*a*) the carrying out of 'construction operations'
(*b*) arranging for the carrying out of 'construction operations' by others, whether under sub-contract to him or otherwise
(*c*) providing his own labour, or the labour of others, for the carrying out of 'construction operations'.

An agreement which makes provision of any kind within this definition relates to construction operations and Part II applies. In the event that the contract cannot be brought under one of the above definitions, then *prima facie* it will not carry the right to refer a dispute arising under it for adjudication.

Is the construction operation an excluded construction operation?

The right to refer a dispute for adjudication is conditional upon the construction operation involved not being one of the construction operations excluded from Part II of the Act. The Act lists a number of construction operations that are excluded but again, and on the same basis, power is given to the Secretary of State to add to, amend or repeal that list. As things stand at the moment, the construction operations (and it is only these operations but not the Works associated with them) excluded from the definition are:

(*a*) drilling for, or extraction of, oil or natural gas

(*b*) extraction (whether by underground or surface working) of minerals, tunnelling or boring, or construction of underground works, for this purpose

(*c*) assembly, installation or demolition of plant or machinery, or erection or demolition of steelwork for the purposes of supporting or providing access to plant or machinery, on a site where the primary activity is:
(i) nuclear processing, power generation, or water or effluent treatment, or
(ii) the production, transmission, processing or bulk storage (other than warehousing) of chemicals, pharmaceuticals, oil, gas, steel or food and drink

(*d*) manufacture or delivery to site of:
(i) building and engineering components or equipment
(ii) materials, plant or machinery
(iii) components for systems of heating, lighting, air-conditioning, ventilation, power supply, drainage, sanitation, water supply or fire protection, or for security or communications systems, except under a contract which also provides for their installation

(*e*) the making, installation and repair of artistic works, being sculptures, murals and other works which are wholly artistic in nature.

If the construction operation being undertaken does not fall within one of the above categories of construction operation excluded from the operation of the Act then – if the other conditions are satisfied – for all practical purposes a *prima facie* right to have disputes arising out of that construction operation referred for adjudication is likely to exist. The Act does in fact go on to give a positive definition of a construction operation and, although it is conceivable that there could be an argument as to whether or not an operation falls within that definition, the definition itself (said to have been adopted from a taxation statute) is so all-embracing as to be likely to cover almost all the operations typically encountered in construction. The positive definition given is as follows:

(*a*) construction, alteration, repair, maintenance, extension, demolition or dismantling of buildings, or structures forming, or to form, part of the land (whether permanent or not)

(*b*) construction, alteration, repair, maintenance, extension, demolition or dismantling of any works forming, or to form, part of the land, including (without prejudice to the foregoing) walls, roadworks, power-lines, telecommunications apparatus, aircraft runways, docks and harbours, railways, inland waterways, pipe-lines, reservoirs, water-mains, wells, sewers, industrial plant and installations for purposes of land drainage, coast protection or defence

(*c*) installation in any building or structure of fittings forming part of the land, including (without prejudice to the foregoing) systems of heating, lighting, air-conditioning, ventilation, power supply, drainage, sanitation, water supply or fire protection, or security or communications systems (*d*) external or internal cleaning of buildings and structures, so far as carried out in the course of their construction, alteration, repair, extension or restoration

(*e*) operations which form an integral part of, or are preparatory to, or are for rendering complete, such operations as are previously described in this subsection, including site clearance, earth-moving, excavation, tunnelling and boring, laying of foundations, erection, maintenance or dismantling of scaffolding, site restoration, landscaping and the provision of roadways and other access works

(*f*) painting or decorating the internal or external surfaces of any building or structure.

Where an agreement relates to construction operations and other matters, Part II applies only insofar as it relates to the construction operations. Demarcation disputes in this area are likely. In the unlikely event of the construction operation being undertaken not coming within one of the above definitions, then *prima facie* it will not carry the right to refer any dispute relating to that matter for adjudication. See Appendix A, judgment extract 7, for references to the definition of 'construction operations' and 'construction contract'.

Northern Ireland

When the Construction Contracts (Northern Ireland) Order 1997 came into effect in Northern Ireland on 1 June 1999 it gave those who are Parties to a construction contract and who satisfy the conditions laid down the right to refer a dispute arising under the contract for adjudication under a procedure complying with the Order. The purpose of the following discussion is to consider the conditions that have to be met before that entitlement exists.

Does a contract exist?

It will be appreciated at the outset that the right to refer a dispute for adjudication is conditional upon a contract being in existence. The Order specifies that it is a *party* to a 'construction *contract*' (on which see later) who has the right to refer a *dispute arising under the contract* for adjudication.

It is, of course, highly unlikely that any major construction work would be undertaken without a contract and it is a commercial fact of life that almost all major construction contracts today involve at least a variation of one of the Standard Form Contracts. Nevertheless, if perchance no contract for the work exists, then *prima facie* there will be no right to refer any dispute relating to that work for adjudication.

Was the contract entered into after 1 June 1999?

The right to refer a dispute for adjudication is conditional upon the contract having been entered into after 1 June 1999. The Order is not intended to be retrospective and provides that the right to refer a dispute for adjudication applies only to construction contracts which are entered into after the coming into operation of this Order. (By Statutory Instrument the commencement date for Part II of the Act is ordered to be 1 June 1999). Accordingly, contracts entered into prior to 1 June 1999 *prima facie* do not carry the right to refer disputes arising under that contract for adjudication.

Is the contract within the (wide) definition of an 'agreement in writing'?

The right to refer a dispute for adjudication is conditional upon the contract being in writing. The Order provides that the contract, and any other agreement between the parties as to any matter, is effective for the purposes of the Order only if it is in writing, but the definition of an 'agreement in writing' in the Order is extremely wide (a reference to anything being written or in writing covers being recorded by any means) and provides:

- if the agreement is made in writing, it does not have to be signed by the parties
- an exchange of communications in writing is sufficient
- it is sufficient if the agreement is evidenced in writing
- if the agreement is made by reference to terms in writing that is an agreement in writing
- if the agreement is made otherwise than in writing but with the authority of the Parties to the agreement and is recorded by one of the Parties or by a third party, then that is sufficient
- if in the exchange of written submissions in adjudication, arbitral or legal proceedings one Party alleges the existence of an agreement otherwise than in writing and that is not denied by the Party against whom it is alleged, then that is sufficient.

It will be appreciated that the above definition covers most of the practical methods by which agreement is reached between Parties within the construction industry (perhaps even including e-mail) and it is now unlikely that any major work would be undertaken without some agreement along these lines. Nevertheless, if perchance any agreement is not put into writing, then *prima facie* it will not carry the right to refer any dispute relating to that matter for adjudication.

Is the contract an excluded contract?

The right to refer a dispute for adjudication is conditional upon the contract not being one of the contracts excluded from the operation of the Order. A number of contracts are excluded from adjudication by the Order, which also gives a number of powers to the Department of the Environment to add to, amend or repeal that list of exclusions. The first of these Orders is The Construction Contracts Exclusion Order (Northern Ireland) 1999 and, as things stand at the moment, the contracts excluded from the operation of the Order are:

- contracts of employment (*per* the Employment Rights (Northern Ireland) Order 1996) (Article 3(3))
- construction contracts with residential occupiers (Article 5)

- Agreements under one of the following statutes:
  - An agreement under Article 3(4C) (works for the improvement of a public road joined by a private street) or Article 32 (agreement for carrying out street works in a private street) of the Private Streets (Northern Ireland) Order 1980
  - An agreement under Article 122 of the Roads (Northern Ireland) Order 1993 (execution of works by Department at expense of another)
  - An agreement under Article 40 of the Planning (Northern Ireland) Order 1991 (agreements facilitating, regulating or restricting development or use of land)
  - An externally financed development agreement under Article 3 of the Health and Personal Social Services (Private Finance) (Northern Ireland) Order 1997 (powers of Health and Social Services trusts to enter into agreements)
  - An agreement under Article 17(4) of the Water and Sewerage Services (Northern Ireland) Order 1973 (applications for water or sewerage services).
- Private Finance Initiatives
  Contracts entered into under the private finance initiatives are defined as those where *all* the following conditions are fulfilled:
  (*a*) it contains a statement that it is entered into under a project under that initiative or one applying similar principles; and
  (*b*) the consideration due under the contract is determined at least in part by reference to one or more of the following:
  (i) the standards attained in the performance of a service, the provision of which is the principal purpose or one of the principal purposes for which the building or structure is constructed; or
  (ii) the extent, rate or intensity of use of all or any part of the building or structure in question; or
  (iii) the right to operate any facility in connection with the building or structure in question; and
  (*c*) one of the parties to the contract is:
  - A Minister of the Crown or the head of a Northern Ireland Department
  - A Northern Ireland Department
  - Any other authority or body whose accounts are required to be examined and certified by or are open to the inspection of the Comptroller and Audit General for Northern Ireland by virtue of an agreement entered into before the coming into operation of this Order or by virtue of any statutory provision
  - The Northern Ireland Transport Holding Company
  - A body whose accounts are subject to audit by auditors appointed under section 74 of the Local Government Act (Northern Ireland) 1972 or Article 90 of the Health and Personal Social Services (Northern Ireland) Order 1972
  - The managers or trustees of a voluntary school or the managers or trustees of a grant-maintained integrated school within the meaning of the Education and Libraries (Northern Ireland) Order 1986
  - A company wholly owned by any of the above bodies.

- Finance Agreements
  Contracts within that definition include any one of the following:
  (*a*) any contract of insurance
  (*b*) any contract for the formation of a company, partnership or association
  (*c*) any contract for the creation or transfer of any right or interest in securities
  (*d*) any contract the principal object of which is the lending of money
  (*e*) any contract of surety such as bonds of fidelity, advance payment, retention, performance.
- Development Agreements
  Contracts in which the land on which the principal construction operations are to take place is land in respect of which a relevant interest in the land (meaning ownership or a lease which will expire no earlier than 12 months after the completion of the construction operations under the contract) is to be granted or disposed of under the contract.

If the contract does *not* fall into the category of contracts that are excluded from the operation of the Order, then *prima facie* the right to refer a dispute arising under it for adjudication will apply if the other conditions are satisfied.

Is the contract a construction contract?

The right to refer a dispute for adjudication is conditional upon the contract being a 'construction contract' (which in turn involves a consideration of whether it relates to 'construction operations').

Territorially, the Act applies to the carrying out of 'construction operations' in Northern Ireland. Thus, domestic or foreign contractors who satisfy the conditions and who contract to carry out 'construction operations' within those territories *prima facie* have the right to refer disputes arising under those contracts for adjudication. Furthermore, it will not be possible for those contractors to seek to avoid the application of the Order by specifying that some other foreign law shall apply to the contract, for the Order also provides that the Order is to apply whether or not the law of Northern Ireland is the applicable law in relation to the contract.

Conceptually, the Act – and specifically included in this definition are agreements to do architectural, design or surveying work, or provide advice on building, engineering, interior or exterior decoration or on the laying-out of landscape, and also agreements entered into by or on behalf of the Crown – applies to a 'construction contract' which the Act defines as meaning an agreement with a person for any of the following:

(*a*) the carrying out of 'construction operations'
(*b*) arranging for the carrying out of 'construction operations' by others, whether under sub-contract to him or otherwise
(*c*) providing his own labour, or the labour of others, for the carrying out of 'construction operations'.

An agreement which makes provision of any kind within this definition relates to construction operations and the Order applies. In the event that the contract cannot be brought under one of the above definitions, then *prima facie* it will not carry the right to refer a dispute arising under it for adjudication.

Is the construction operation an excluded construction operation?

The right to refer a dispute for adjudication is conditional upon the construction operation involved not being one of the construction operations excluded from the Order. The Order lists a number of construction operations that are excluded but again, and on the same basis, power is given to the Department of the Environment to add to, amend or repeal that list. As things stand at the moment, the construction operations (and it is only these operations but not the Works associated with them) excluded from the definition are:

(*a*) drilling for, or extraction of, oil or natural gas

(*b*) extraction (whether by underground or surface working) of minerals, tunnelling or boring, or construction of underground works, for this purpose

(*c*) assembly, installation or demolition of plant or machinery, or erection or demolition of steelwork for the purposes of supporting or providing access to plant or machinery, on a site where the primary activity is:
(i) nuclear processing, power generation, or water or effluent treatment, or
(ii) the production, transmission, processing or bulk storage (other than warehousing) of chemicals, pharmaceuticals, oil, gas, steel or food and drink

(*d*) manufacture or delivery to site of:
(i) building and engineering components or equipment
(ii) materials, plant or machinery
(iii) components for systems of heating, lighting, air-conditioning, ventilation, power supply, drainage, sanitation, water supply or fire protection, or for security or communications systems, except under a contract which also provides for their installation

(*e*) the making, installation and repair of artistic works, being sculptures, murals and other works which are wholly artistic in nature.

If the construction operation being undertaken does not fall within one of the above categories of construction operation excluded from the operation of the Order then – if the other conditions are satisfied – for all practical purposes a *prima facie* right to have disputes arising out of that construction operation referred for adjudication is likely to exist. The Order does in fact go on to give a positive definition of a construction operation and, although it is conceivable that there could be an argument as to whether or not an operation falls within that definition, the definition itself (said to have been adopted from a taxation statute) is so all-embracing as to be likely to cover almost all the operations typically encountered in construction. The positive definition given is as follows:

(*a*) construction, alteration, repair, maintenance, extension, demolition or dismantling of buildings, or structures forming, or to form, part of the land (whether permanent or not)

(*b*) construction, alteration, repair, maintenance, extension, demolition or dismantling of any works forming, or to form, part of the land, including (without prejudice to the foregoing) walls, roadworks, power-lines, telecommunications apparatus, aircraft runways, docks and harbours, railways, inland waterways, pipe-lines, reservoirs, water-mains, wells, sewers, industrial plant and installations for purposes of land drainage, coast protection or defence

(*c*) installation in any building or structure of fittings forming part of the land, including (without prejudice to the foregoing) systems of heating, lighting, air-conditioning, ventilation, power supply, drainage, sanitation, water supply or fire protection, or security or communications systems

(*d*) external or internal cleaning of buildings and structures, so far as carried out in the course of their construction, alteration, repair, extension or restoration

(*e*) operations which form an integral part of, or are preparatory to, or are for rendering complete, such operations as are previously described in this subsection, including site clearance, earth-moving, excavation, tunnelling and boring, laying of foundations, erection, maintenance or dismantling of scaffolding, site restoration, landscaping and the provision of roadways and other access works

(*f*) painting or decorating the internal or external surfaces of any building or structure.

Where an agreement relates to construction operations and other matters, the Order applies only insofar as it relates to the construction operations. Demarcation disputes in this area are likely. In the unlikely event of the construction operation being undertaken not coming within one of the above definitions, then *prima facie* it will not carry the right to refer any dispute relating to that matter for adjudication.

What is required for the settlement/crystallisation of disputes

Having determined the territorial, jurisdictional, and procedural considerations which apply in relation to any claim which has arisen, before going on to the next stage it is convenient to consider here what is required for the settlement/crystallisation of disputes and then to consider what disputes are referable to adjudication.

The NEC family of contracts does have a procedure for the settlement/ crystallisation of disputes.

Core Clause 9

Core Clause 9 categorises disputes into different types and in the Adjudication Table distinguishes between an action or a failure to take action and any other matter and provides as follows:

Action

Notification

Core Clause 9 provides that if the [Consultant/Contractor/Subcontractor] is dissatisfied with an action by the [Employer/Project Manager or Supervisor/ Contractor], he notifies his dissatisfaction to [the relevant person] no later than four weeks after he became aware of the action.

Settlement/crystallisation

There then follows a period of grace of two weeks within which the dispute may not be submitted to the Adjudicator and during which the intention is presumably that the dissatisfaction will either be settled or will crystallise into a proper 'dispute'.

Failure to take action

Notification

Core Clause 9 provides that if the [Consultant/Contractor/Subcontractor] is dissatisfied with a failure to take action by the [Employer/Project Manager or Supervisor/Contractor], he notifies his dissatisfaction to [the relevant person] no later than four weeks after he became aware of the failure to take action.

Settlement/crystallisation

There then follows a period of grace of two weeks within which the dispute may not be submitted to the Adjudicator and during which the intention is presumably that the dissatisfaction will either be settled or will crystallise into a proper 'dispute'.

Any other matter

Notification

Core Clause 9 provides in relation to any other matter that either Party shall give notification of the dispute to the Other Party (but does not impose a time limit for doing so).

Settlement/crystallisation

There then follows a period of grace of two weeks within which the dispute may not be submitted to the Adjudicator and during which the intention is presumably that the dissatisfaction will either be settled or will crystallise into a proper 'dispute'.

Option Y(UK) 2

Option Y(UK) 2 categorises disputes into different types and distinguishes between an action or a failure to take action by the Project Manager (Clause 90.2) and any other matter (Clause 90.3) and provides as follows:

Action

Notification

Option Y(UK) 2 provides that if the Contractor is dissatisfied with an action by the Project Manager, he notifies his dissatisfaction to the Project Manager no later than four weeks after he became aware of the action.

Settlement/crystallisation

There then follows a period during which, within two weeks of such notification of dissatisfaction, the Contractor and the Project Manager attend a meeting to discuss and resolve the matter (Clause 90.2). It is also expressly provided (Clause 90.4) that the Parties are agreed that no matter shall be a dispute (which includes any difference) unless a notice of dissatisfaction has been given and the matter has not been resolved within four weeks and that the word dispute has that meaning. The intention is, presumably, that during that four-week period of grace the dissatisfaction will either be settled or will crystallise into a proper 'dispute'.

Failure to take action

Notification

Option Y(UK) 2 provides that if the Contractor is dissatisfied with a failure to take action by the Project Manager, he notifies his dissatisfaction to the Project Manager no later than four weeks after he became aware that the action had not been taken.

Settlement/crystallisation

There then follows a period during which, within two weeks of such notification of dissatisfaction, the Contractor and the Project Manager attend a meeting to discuss and resolve the matter (Clause 90.2). It is also expressly provided (Clause 90.4) that the Parties are agreed that no matter shall be a dispute (which includes any difference) unless a notice of dissatisfaction has been given and the matter has not been resolved within four weeks and that the word dispute has that meaning. The intention is, presumably, that during that four-week period of grace the dissatisfaction will either be settled or will crystallise into a proper 'dispute'.

Any other matter

Notification

Option Y(UK) 2 provides that if either Party is dissatisfied with any other matter, he notifies his dissatisfaction to the Project Manager and to the Other Party no later than four weeks after he became aware of the matter.

Settlement/crystallisation
There then follows a period during which, within two weeks of such notification of dissatisfaction, the Contractor and the Project Manager attend a meeting to discuss and resolve the matter (Clause 90.3). It is also expressly provided (Clause 90.4) that the Parties are agreed that no matter shall be a dispute (which includes any difference) unless a notice of dissatisfaction has been given and the matter has not been resolved within four weeks and that the word dispute has that meaning. The intention is, presumably, that during that four-week period of grace the dissatisfaction will either be settled or will crystallise into a proper 'dispute'.

The NEC Engineering and Construction Short Contract (where the UK legislation applies)

This contract provides (Clause 93.1UK):

Notification
If either Party is dissatisfied with an action or lack of action by the Other Party on any matter arising out of this contract, the dissatisfied Party notifies the Other Party of the dissatisfaction within four weeks of becoming aware of it.

Settlement/crystallisation
Within two weeks of the notice, the Parties meet to discuss and resolve the matter. The Parties agree that no matter shall be a dispute unless a notice of dissatisfaction has been given and the matter has not been resolved within four weeks of the notification. The word dispute (which includes a difference) has that meaning. The intention is, presumably, that during that four-week period of grace the dissatisfaction will either be settled or will crystallise into a proper 'dispute'.

Interpretation

However, the consequences of undertaking (even under an NEC contract) Works – and especially Works which fall within the definition of 'construction contracts' – in a particular territory is, however, that the laws of that territory may have an effect upon that procedure for the settlement/crystallisation of disputes and ultimately upon the disputes referable to adjudication and the very procedure to be followed in the adjudication.

Parties undertaking Works in these territories should therefore be aware of what, beyond the NEC contract which they have entered into, may affect the procedures for the settlement/crystallisation of disputes and it is proposed to consider that aspect here.

England and Wales

s. 108 of the HGCR Act 1996 c. 53 provides:

(1)   A party to a construction contract has the right to refer a dispute arising under the contract for adjudication under a procedure complying with this section. For this purpose 'dispute' includes any difference.

(2)   The contract shall
  (a)   enable a party to give notice at any time of his intention to refer a dispute to adjudication.

Commentary The significant feature of this legislation is that it provides for a Party to give notice at any time of intention to refer a dispute to adjudication. The legislation does not, however, make any provision for the settlement/crystallisation of disputes and nor (other than saying that it includes a 'difference') does the legislation define what a dispute is.

There has, however, been some interpretation of the situation in cases involving adjudication, although the resultant position is not entirely clear which is unfortunate given the importance of the issue involved.

The first of these cases is Fastback Contractors Ltd *v* Morrison Construction Ltd, which came before the Technology and Construction Court in England and Wales.

In that case His Honour Judge Thornton said: 'the "dispute" [which may be referred to adjudication] … is whatever claims, heads of claim, issues, contentions, or causes of action that are then in dispute which the Referring Party has chosen to crystallise into an adjudication reference'.

He went on to say that:

> a 'dispute' can only arise once the subject-matter of the claim, issue or other matter has been brought to the attention of the opposing party and that party has had an opportunity of considering and admitting, modifying or rejecting the claim or assertion.

He finally concluded:

> that a claim and its submission do not necessarily constitute a dispute, that a dispute only arises when a claim has been notified and rejected, that a rejection can occur when an opposing party refuses to answer the claim and that a dispute can arise when there has been a bare rejection of a claim to which there is no discernible answer in fact or in law.

It seems clear, therefore, that in England and Wales at least, even in relation to 'construction contracts' covered by the UK legislation, the principle is still being recognised that some process [a process of claim, an opportunity of considering, and either acceptance, modification or some form of rejection] of settlement/crystallisation must be gone through before a proper 'dispute' arises.

It has been pointed out that over several decades the ICE has developed procedures – which have been accepted as good practice – for identifying, defining, and resolving disputes which are reflected in both Core Clause 9, Option Y(UK) 2 and any other adjustments to the NEC family of contracts. On one interpretation of the above case, the notice of dissatisfaction procedures followed by the periods of grace in the NEC family of contracts are merely methods of settlement or crystallisation into a proper 'dispute'.

The point is not without importance, for in relation to 'construction contracts' being undertaken within the UK, the crucial question – and as we shall see in the next section the question is indeed a crucial one – is whether the above provisions are simply a contractually agreed method of settlement/crystallisation for arriving at a properly defined 'dispute' which is then capable of being referred for adjudication (in which case the above provisions would be compliant with the applicable UK legislation and their procedures will govern the adjudication), or whether the above provisions are not compliant with the applicable UK legislation (in which case the statutory adjudication procedures may govern the adjudication).

The point of significance is, perhaps, whether or not – where 'construction contracts' within the UK are involved – the Parties are entitled to define in their contracts when a 'dispute' arises.

In this respect, another adjudication case is of relevance. The case of John Mowlem & Company plc *v* Hydra-Tight Ltd came before the Technology and Construction Court in England and Wales. The contract in that case was an NEC Engineering and Construction Sub-contract in which the Parties had adopted and incorporated Option Y(UK) 2. The Parties, through their representatives, were agreed in submitting to the Court that the contractual adjudication provisions of Option Y(UK) 2 should not apply and that the statutory adjudication procedures of the Scheme for Construction Contracts (England and Wales) Regulations should apply. His Honour Judge Toulmin remarked, which on the basis of the foregoing may be regarded as an *obiter* remark:

> This contract does not comply with subsection (1) and subsection 1(a) [of s. 108 of HGCR Act 1996] since, under Clauses 90.1 to 90.4 [of Option Y(UK) 2] the Parties have no immediate right to refer at any time or to give notice of an intention to refer a dispute to adjudication.

Upon one interpretation of this case, a number of attacks could be launched against the extent to which the provisions of the NEC family of contracts are compliant with the applicable legislation as follows:

The nature of the disputes
The NEC family of contracts distinguishes between various categories of dispute. While Parties are clearly entitled to name any claim, head of claim, issue, contention or cause of action in any way they like – including as an 'action' a 'failure to take action' or 'any other matter' – the UK legislation does not distinguish between categories of disputes and allows each and every type of dispute (unless otherwise disqualified) to be referred to adjudi-

cation. The NEC family of contracts may, therefore, be non-compliant in that respect, particularly when allied with the other considerations referred to below.

The parties entitled to refer the disputes

The NEC family of contracts only allows one of the Parties [the Consultant/ Contractor/ Sub-contractor as the case may be] to submit a dispute in relation to an action or failure to take an action. The Other Party is not given the right in the NEC contract to submit that type of dispute to the Adjudicator. The UK legislation, on the other hand, allows *any* Party to refer any dispute to adjudication. The NEC family of contracts may, therefore, be non-compliant in that respect, particularly when allied with the other considerations referred to below.

Time limits for notification of disputes

The NEC family of contracts requires, for actions or failure to take an action, that the relevant Party makes notification of that event within four weeks of becoming aware of that event. By implication (although this is not expressly stated) a failure to give that notification within the four weeks disentitles that Party from submitting that dispute to adjudication. The UK legislation, on the other hand, requires the contract to allow a Party to give notice *at any time* of his intention to refer a dispute to adjudication. The NEC family of contracts may, therefore, be non-compliant in that respect, particularly when allied with the other considerations referred to below.

Time limits for submission of disputes

The NEC family of contracts, in their various forms, provides various periods of grace within which disputes are not to be submitted for adjudication and presumably during which settlement/crystallisation is to take place. The UK legislation, on the other hand, requires the contract to allow a Party to give notice *at any time* of his intention to refer a dispute to adjudication. The NEC contracts also provide, in some cases, a 'window' of between two and four weeks when a dispute may be submitted to adjudication. By implication (although this is not expressly stated) a failure to make that submission within the four weeks disentitles that Party from submitting that dispute to adjudication. The UK legislation, on the other hand, requires the contract to allow a Party to give notice *at any time* of his intention to refer a dispute to adjudication. The NEC family of contracts may, therefore, be non-compliant in that respect, particularly when allied with the other considerations referred to below.

Summary

As earlier noted, adjudication is a new concept in the UK construction industry which is only beginning to evolve. The cases – which are at first instance – of John Mowlem & Company plc *v* Hydra-Tight Ltd and Fastrack Contractors Ltd *v* Morrison Construction Ltd were decided for the first time within a short period of each other without, so far as is known, the one case being cited in the other.

To a certain extent, the cases are in conflict but could be reconciled if it were to be recognised that a proper 'dispute' does not arise until after a settlement/crystallisation procedure (if necessary provided for in the contract) has been gone through. On that interpretation, some of the NEC family could be interpreted as compliant in that the delays built in for settlement/crystallisation would not be in conflict with the legislation and that after a proper 'dispute' has been arrived at by those means the contracts are thereafter compliant with the legislation.

It may be that other decisions at first instance will be arrived at which will place a different interpretation upon one or other of these cases. It may be that a similar case will go to appeal where the cases may be reconciled or distinguished, upheld or overturned.

In the meantime, however, due regard will require to be paid to these decisions which are significant in relation to the way in which any adjudications may be conducted.

Scotland

s. 108 of the HGCR Act 1996 c. 53 provides:

(1)   A party to a construction contract has the right to refer a dispute arising under the contract for adjudication under a procedure complying with this section. For this purpose 'dispute' includes any difference.

(2)   The contract shall
 (a)   enable a party to give notice at any time of his intention to refer a dispute to adjudication.

Commentary The English authorities referred to above are likely to be regarded as being of persuasive authority in Scotland although the issue has not so far been examined and conclusively determined in Scotland.

Northern Ireland

Article 7 of the Construction Contracts (Northern Ireland) Order 1997 No 274 (NI 1) provides:

(1)   A party to a construction contract has the right to refer a dispute arising under the contract for adjudication under a procedure complying with this Article. For this purpose 'dispute' includes any difference.

(2)   The contract shall
 (a)   enable a party to give notice at any time of his intention to refer a dispute to adjudication.

Commentary The English authorities referred to above are likely to be regarded as being of persuasive authority in Northern Ireland, although the issue has not so far been examined and conclusively determined in Northern Ireland.

What disputes are referable to adjudication

The nature of any disagreement should be examined in the settlement/ crystallisation process and one of the considerations which may be brought to bear is likely to be the fact that not every dispute is referable to adjudication.

The NEC family of contracts places few barriers in the way of the disputes which may be referred to adjudication but the consequences of undertaking Works – especially those which fall within the definition of 'construction contracts' – within a particular territory is that it may have an effect upon the nature of the disputes which are referable to adjudication. It is proposed to consider that aspect here.

Core Clause 9

Core Clause 9 begins (Clause 90.1) with the statement that 'Any dispute arising under or in connection with this contract is submitted to and settled by the Adjudicator as follows.'

Core Clause 9 then categorises disputes and in the Adjudication Table distinguishes between an action or a failure to take action and any other matter and provides as follows:

Action

Core Clause 9 provides that if the [Consultant/Contractor/Subcontractor] is dissatisfied with an action by the [Employer/Project Manager or Supervisor/ Contractor], he notifies his dissatisfaction to [the relevant person] no later than four weeks after he became aware of the action. There is then imposed a period of grace of two weeks within which the dispute may not be submitted to the Adjudicator, a period of between two and four weeks within which the dispute may be submitted to the Adjudicator and, by implication, a bar upon submitting to the Adjudicator disputes which are more than four weeks older than the notification.

Failure to take action

Core Clause 9 provides that if the [Consultant/Contractor/Subcontractor] is dissatisfied with a failure to take action by the [Employer/Project Manager or Supervisor/Contractor], he notifies his dissatisfaction to [the relevant person] no later than four weeks after he became aware of the failure to take action. There is then imposed a period of grace of two weeks within which the dispute may not be submitted to the Adjudicator, a period of between two and four weeks within which the dispute may be submitted to the Adjudicator and, by implication, a bar upon submitting to the Adjudicator disputes which are more than four weeks older than the notification.

Any other matter

Core Clause 9 provides in relation to any other matter that either Party shall give notification of the dispute to the Other Party (but does not impose a time limit for doing so). There is then imposed a period of grace of two weeks within which the dispute may not be submitted to the Adjudicator, a period of between two and four weeks within which the dispute may be submitted to the Adjudicator and, by implication, a bar upon submitting to the Adjudicator disputes which are more than four weeks older than the notification.

Option Y(UK) 2

Option Y(UK) 2 begins (Clause 90.1) with the bold statement that 'The Parties and the Project Manager follow this procedure for the avoidance and settlement of disputes.'

Option Y(UK) 2 then categorises disputes and distinguishes between an action or a failure to take action by the Project Manager (Clause 90.2) and any other matter (Clause 90.3) and provides as follows:

Action

Option Y(UK) 2 provides that if the Contractor is dissatisfied with an action by the Project Manager, he notifies his dissatisfaction to the Project Manager no later than four weeks after he became aware of the action and that within two weeks of such notification of dissatisfaction, the Contractor and the Project Manager attend a meeting to discuss and resolve the matter (Clause 90.2).

Failure to take action

Option Y(UK) 2 provides that if the Contractor is dissatisfied with a failure to take action by the Project Manager, he notifies his dissatisfaction to the Project Manager no later than four weeks after he became aware that the action had not been taken and that within two weeks of such notification of dissatisfaction, the Contractor and the Project Manager attend a meeting to discuss and resolve the matter (Clause 90.2).

Any other matter

Option Y(UK) 2 provides that if either Party is dissatisfied with any other matter, he notifies his dissatisfaction to the Project Manager and to the Other Party no later than four weeks after he became aware of the matter and that within two weeks of such notification of dissatisfaction, the Parties and the Project Manager attend a meeting to discuss and seek to resolve the matter (Clause 90.3).

Generally

Option Y(UK) 2 then goes on to expressly provide that 'The Parties agree that no matter shall be a dispute unless a notice of dissatisfaction has been given and the matter has not been resolved within four weeks. The word dispute (which includes a difference) has that meaning.'

The NEC Engineering and Construction Short Contract (where the UK legislation applies)

This contract provides:

If either Party is dissatisfied with an action or lack of action by the other Party on any matter arising out of this contract, the dissatisfied

Party notifies the other Party of the dissatisfaction within four weeks of becoming aware of it. Within two weeks of the notice, the Parties meet to discuss and resolve the matter. The Parties agree that no matter shall be a dispute unless a notice of dissatisfaction has been given and the matter has not been resolved within four weeks of the notification. The word dispute (which includes a difference) has that meaning.

Interpretation

Although the position regarding disputes referable to adjudication seems relatively clear-cut under the NEC family of contracts, national legislation – particularly where the Works fall within the definition of 'construction contracts' – could have a significant effect in relation to the disputes referable to adjudication.

England and Wales

Time limits for referring disputes

On one interpretation, where the Works fall within the definition of 'construction contracts', the applicable legislation – which enables a Party to give notice of intention to refer a dispute to adjudication *at any time* – means that any difference or dispute may be immediately referred to adjudication without regard to the periods of grace for settlement/crystallisation built into the NEC family of contracts.

s. 108 of the HGCR Act 1996 c. 53 provides:

(2)   The contract shall
    (a) enable a party to give notice at any time of his intention to refer a dispute to adjudication.

The definition of disputes

Where the Works fall within the definition of 'construction contracts', it could be argued that the applicable legislation – which enables a Party to give notice of intention to refer a dispute to adjudication – means that any difference or dispute may be referred to adjudication without regard to the categorisation of disputes built into the NEC family of contracts (see also Appendix A, judgment extracts 8–11).

s. 108 of the HGCR Act 1996 c. 53 provides:

(1)   A party to a construction contract has the right to refer a dispute arising under the contract for adjudication under a procedure complying with this section.

For this purpose 'dispute' includes any difference.

Paragraph 1 of the Scheme for Construction Contracts (England and Wales) Regulations 1998 SI No 649 provides:

(1)   Any party to a construction contract (the 'referring party') may give written notice (the 'notice of adjudication') of his intention to refer any dispute arising under the contract, to adjudication.

The Parties to disputes

The NEC family of contracts categorises the disputes and then provides that only certain Parties may refer certain disputes to adjudication. The legislation, on the other hand, allows any Party to refer a dispute to adjudication.

Accordingly, where the Works fall within the definition of 'construction contracts', it could be argued that the applicable legislation – which enables any Party to give notice of intention to refer a dispute to adjudication – means that the restrictions on which a Party may refer which disputes to adjudication built into the NEC family of contracts may no longer be applicable.

s. 108 of the HGCR Act 1996 c. 53 provides:

(1)   A party to a construction contract has the right to refer a dispute arising under the contract for adjudication under a procedure complying with this section.

For this purpose 'dispute' includes any difference.

Paragraph 1of the Scheme for Construction Contracts (England and Wales) Regulations 1998 SI No 649 provides:

(1)   Any party to a construction contract (the 'referring party') may give written notice (the 'notice of adjudication') of his intention to refer any dispute arising under the contract, to adjudication.

Matters relating to the contract

The definition of what, by reference to the contract containing it, may or may not be referred to a dispute resolution procedure has been the subject of extensive litigation in other areas. Matters such as the validity of the contract itself or the extent to which the contract itself was induced by fraudulent misrepresentation and the like may or may not be considered to fall within the dispute resolution clause contained in the contract itself. Much of the interpretation has revolved around the precise words used in the contract such as 'arising under the contract' or arising 'in connection with the contract'. In something of a 'belt-and-braces' approach the NEC family of contracts uses the term 'arising under or in connection with this contract'. The legislation, on the other hand, confines itself to the use of the term 'arising under the contract'. Unusually, therefore, where the Works fall within the definition of 'construction contracts', it could be argued that the applicable legislation is more restrictive than the NEC contract.

s. 108 of the HGCR Act 1996 c. 53 provides:

(1)   A party to a construction contract has the right to refer a dispute *arising under the contract* for adjudication under a procedure complying with this section.

For this purpose 'dispute' includes any difference.

Paragraph 1 of the Scheme for Construction Contracts (England and Wales) Regulations 1998 SI No 649 provides:

(1)   Any party to a construction contract (the 'referring party') may give written notice (the 'notice of adjudication') of his intention to refer any dispute *arising under the contract*, to adjudication.

Certificates

There has been substantial litigation in relation to the power of the Courts to review certificates. In Northern Regional Health Authority *v* Derek Crouch Construction Ltd (1984) 2 WLR 676, the Court of Appeal held that where a contract confers the power on a third party certifier to make substantive determination of rights, then the Courts have no power to review any certificates issued in that respect. However, in the case of Beauford Developments (NI) Ltd *v* Gilbert-Ash (NI) Ltd, the House of Lords distinguished Crouch on the grounds that certificates other than final certificates should not be regarded as having that effect.

Certificates are used in the NEC family of contracts but no attempt appears to have been made to attach excessive or final significance to such certificates. Accordingly, the application, where applicable, of UK legislation in this respect could – unusually – actually be restrictive in relation to the type of disputes referable to adjudication where Works falling within the definition of 'construction contracts' are being carried out under NEC contracts within the territories of the UK, in that certificates which are stated to be final and conclusive may not be referable to adjudication.

Paragraph 20 of the Scheme for Construction Contracts (England and Wales) Regulations 1998 SI No 649 provides:

[The Adjudicator] may

(a)   open up, revise and review any decision taken or any certificate given by any person referred to in the contract *unless the contract states that the decision or certificate is final and conclusive*.

Payment cases

As with any similar contract, under the NEC family of contracts payment is a matter of agreement between the Parties which is generally of only peripheral effect in relation to any disputes or adjudications.

The introduction of payment provisions in the UK legislation is, however, likely to have a significant practical effect upon adjudications relating to Works which fall within the definition of 'construction contracts'. While a Party would not be denied an adjudication if they wanted one, a failure to issue a proper and timeous notice of intention to withhold payment might have the practical effect of making any adjudication a mere formality (see also Appendix A, judgment extracts 12 and 13).

The Scottish case of payment is likely to be of persuasive value in England and Wales.

Sections 109 to 113

The Housing Grants, Construction and Regeneration Act 1996 c.53

Part II – Payment Paragraphs 1 to 12

The Scheme for Construction Contracts (England and Wales) Regulations 1998 SI No 649

Insolvency

Adjudication and insolvency appear to be developing a close practical relationship which is not, perhaps, surprising in that adjudication often takes place at the end of a project when the success or failure of the project is often reflected in the success or failure of the businesses involved.

In the case of Staume *v* Bradlor (7 April 1999) Straume wished to commence adjudication proceedings against Bradlor who were in administration but in an application of the Insolvency Act 1996, His Honour Judge Behrens held that adjudication was a 'quasi-legal process' in respect of which the consent of the Court (refused in this case) was required before such proceedings could be commenced against an insolvent company.

The issue of insolvency also featured large in the decision of the Court of Appeal (only) in the case of Bouygues *v* Dahl-Jensen.

Scotland

Time limits for referring disputes

On one interpretation, where the Works fall within the definition of 'construction contracts', the applicable legislation – which enables a Party to give notice of intention to refer a dispute to adjudication *at any time* – means that any difference or dispute may be immediately referred to adjudication without regard to the periods of grace for settlement/crystallisation built into the NEC family of contracts.

s. 108 of the HGCR Act 1996 c. 53 provides:

(2)   The contract shall
  (a)   enable a party to give notice at any time of his intention to refer a dispute to adjudication.

The definition of disputes

Where the Works fall within the definition of 'construction contracts', it could be argued that the applicable legislation – which enables a Party to give notice of intention to refer a dispute to adjudication – means that any difference or dispute may be referred to adjudication without regard to the categorisation of disputes built into the NEC family of contracts.

s. 108 of the HGCR Act 1996 c. 53 provides:

(1)   A party to a construction contract has the right to refer a dispute arising under the contract for adjudication under a procedure complying with this section.

For this purpose 'dispute' includes any difference.

Paragraph 1 of the Scheme for Construction Contracts (Scotland) Regulations 1998 SI No 687 provides:

(1)   Any party to a construction contract (the 'referring party') may give written notice (the 'notice of adjudication') of his intention to refer *any* dispute arising under the contract, to adjudication.

The Parties to disputes

The NEC family of contracts categorises the disputes and then provides that only certain Parties may refer certain disputes to adjudication. The legislation, on the other hand, allows any Party to refer a dispute to adjudication.

Accordingly, where the Works fall within the definition of 'construction contracts', it could be argued that the applicable legislation – which enables any Party to give notice of intention to refer a dispute to adjudication – means that the restrictions on which Party may refer which disputes to adjudication built into the NEC family of contracts may no longer be applicable.

s. 108 of the HGCR Act 1996 c. 53 provides:

(1)   A party to a construction contract has the right to refer a dispute arising under the contract for adjudication under a procedure complying with this section.

For this purpose 'dispute' includes any difference.

Paragraph 1 of the Scheme for Construction Contracts (Scotland) Regulations 1998 SI No 687 provides:

(1)   Any party to a construction contract (the 'referring party') may give written notice (the 'notice of adjudication') of his intention to refer any dispute arising *under the contract*, to adjudication.

Matters relating to the contract

The definition of what, by reference to the contract containing it, may or may not be referred to a dispute resolution procedure has been the subject of extensive litigation in other areas. Matters such as the validity of the contract itself or the extent to which the contract itself was induced by fraudulent misrepresentation and the like may or may not be considered to fall within the dispute resolution clause contained in the contract itself. Much of the interpretation has revolved around the precise words used in the contract such as 'arising under the contract' or arising 'in connection with the contract'. In something of a 'belt-and-braces' approach the NEC family of contracts uses the term 'arising under or in connection with this contract'. The legislation, on the other hand, confines itself to the use of the term 'arising under the contract'. Unusually, therefore, where the Works fall within the definition of 'construction contracts', it could be argued that the applicable legislation is more restrictive than the NEC contract.

s. 108 of the HGCR Act 1996 c. 53 provides:

(1)   A party to a construction contract has the right to refer a dispute *arising under the contract* for adjudication under a procedure complying with this section.

For this purpose 'dispute' includes any difference.

Paragraph 1 of the Scheme for Construction Contracts (Scotland) Regulations 1998 SI No 687 provides:

(1)   Any party to a construction contract (the 'referring party') may give written notice (the 'notice of adjudication') of his intention to refer any dispute *arising under the contract*, to adjudication.

Certificates

There has been substantial litigation in relation to the power of the Courts to review certificates. In Northern Regional Health Authority *v* Derek Crouch Construction Ltd (1984) 2 WLR 676, the Court of Appeal held that where a contract confers the power on a third party certifier to make substantive determination of rights, then the Courts have no power to review any certificates issued in that respect. However, in the case of Beauford Developments (NI) Ltd *v* Gilbert-Ash (NI) Ltd, the House of Lords distinguished Crouch on the grounds that certificates other than final certificates should not be regarded as having that effect. This principle is recognised in Scotland.

Certificates are used in the NEC family of contracts but no attempt appears to have been made to attach excessive or final significance to such certificates. Accordingly, the application, where applicable, of UK legislation in this respect could – unusually – actually be restrictive in relation to the type of disputes referable to adjudication where Works falling within the definition of 'construction contracts' are being carried out under NEC contracts within the territories of the UK, in that certificates which are stated to be final and conclusive may not be referable to adjudication.

Paragraph 20 of the Scheme for Construction Contracts (Scotland) Regulations 1998 SI No 687 provides:

[The Adjudicator] may

(a)   open up, revise and review any decision taken or any certificate given by any person referred to in the contract *unless the contract states that the decision or certificate is final and conclusive.*

Payment cases

As with any similar contract, under the NEC family of contracts payment is a matter of agreement between the Parties which is generally of only peripheral effect in relation to any disputes or adjudications.

The introduction of payment provisions in the UK legislation is, however, likely to have a significant practical effect upon adjudications relating to Works which fall within the definition of 'construction contracts'. While a Party would not be denied an adjudication if they wanted one, a failure to issue a proper and timeous notice of intention to withhold payment might have the practical effect of making any adjudication a mere formality (see also Appendix A, judgment extracts 14 and 15).

This has been illustrated recently in the Scottish case of Strathmore Building Services Limited *v* Colin Scott Greig t/a Hestia Fireside Design (18 May 2000) where in respect of a construction claim a Court action for payment was raised but a sist for arbitration/adjudication was refused on the basis that in the absence of a valid notice of intention to withhold payment there was justiciable dispute.

Sections 109 to 113

The Housing Grants, Construction and Regeneration Act 1996 c.53

Part II – Payment Paragraphs 1 to 12

Insolvency

Adjudication and insolvency appear to be developing a close practical relationship which is not, perhaps, surprising in that adjudication often takes place at the end of a project when the success or failure of the project is often reflected in the success or failure of the businesses involved.

The English cases on insolvency are likely to be of persuasive value in Scotland.

Northern Ireland

Time limits for referring disputes

On one interpretation, where the Works fall within the definition of 'construction contracts', the applicable legislation – which enables a Party to give notice of intention to refer a dispute to adjudication *at any time* – means that any difference or dispute may be immediately referred to adjudication without regard to the periods of grace for settlement/crystallisation built into the NEC family of contracts.

Article 7 of the Construction Contracts (Northern Ireland) Order 1997 provides:

(2)   The contract shall
  (a)   enable a party to give notice at any time of his intention to refer a dispute to adjudication.

The definition of disputes

Where the Works fall within the definition of 'construction contracts', it could be argued that the applicable legislation – which enables a Party to give notice of intention to refer a dispute to adjudication – means that any difference or dispute may be referred to adjudication without regard to the categorisation of disputes built into the NEC family of contracts.

Article 7 of the Construction Contracts (Northern Ireland) Order 1997 provides:

(1)   A party to a construction contract has the right to refer a dispute arising under the contract for adjudication under a procedure complying with this section.

For this purpose 'dispute' includes any difference.

Paragraph 1 of the Scheme for Construction Contracts in Northern Ireland Regulations (Northern Ireland) 1999 provides:

(1)   Any party to a construction contract (the 'referring party') may give written notice (the 'notice of adjudication') of his intention to refer any dispute arising under the contract, to adjudication.

The Parties to disputes

The NEC family of contracts categorises the disputes and then provides that only certain Parties may refer certain disputes to adjudication. The legislation, on the other hand, allows any Party to refer a dispute to adjudication.

Accordingly, where the Works fall within the definition of 'construction contracts', it could be argued that the applicable legislation – which enables any Party to give notice of intention to refer a dispute to adjudication – means that the restrictions on which Party may refer which disputes to adjudication built into the NEC family of contracts may no longer be applicable.

Article 7 of the Construction Contracts (Northern Ireland) Order 1997 provides that:

(1)   A party to a construction contract has the right to refer a dispute arising under the contract for adjudication under a procedure complying with this section.

For this purpose 'dispute' includes any difference.

Paragraph 1 of the Scheme for Construction Contracts in Northern Ireland Regulations (Northern Ireland) 1999 provides:

(1)   Any party to a construction contract (the 'referring party') may give written notice (the 'notice of adjudication') of his intention to refer any dispute arising under the contract, to adjudication.

Matters relating to the contract

The definition of what, by reference to the contract containing it, may or may not be referred to a dispute resolution procedure has been the subject of extensive litigation in other areas. Matters such as the validity of the contract itself or the extent to which the contract itself was induced by fraudulent misrepresentation and the like may or may not be considered to fall within the dispute resolution clause contained in the contract itself. Much of the interpretation has revolved around the precise words used in the contract such as 'arising under the contract' or arising 'in connection with the contract'. In something of a 'belt-and-braces' approach the NEC family of contracts uses the term 'arising under or in connection with this contract'.

The legislation, on the other hand, confines itself to the use of the term 'arising under the contract'. Unusually, therefore, where the Works fall within the definition of 'construction contracts', it could be argued that the applicable legislation is more restrictive than the NEC contract.

Article 7 of the Construction Contracts (Northern Ireland) Order 1997 provides:

(1)   A party to a construction contract has the right to refer a dispute *arising under the contract* for adjudication under a procedure complying with this section.

For this purpose 'dispute' includes any difference.

Paragraph 1 of the Scheme for Construction Contracts in Northern Ireland Regulations (Northern Ireland) 1999 provides:

(1)   Any party to a construction contract (the 'referring party') may give written notice (the 'notice of adjudication') of his intention to refer any dispute *arising under the contract*, to adjudication.

Certificates

There has been substantial litigation in relation to the power of the Courts to review certificates. In Northern Regional Health Authority *v* Derek Crouch Construction Ltd (1984) 2 WLR 676, the Court of Appeal held that where a contract confers the power on a third party certifier to make substantive determination of rights, then the Courts have no power to review any certificates issued in that respect. However, in the case of Beauford Developments (NI) Ltd *v* Gilbert-Ash (NI) Ltd the House of Lords distinguished Crouch on the grounds that certificates other than final certificates should not be regarded as having that effect. This principle is recognised in Northern Ireland.

Certificates are used in the NEC family of contracts but no attempt appears to have been made to attach excessive or final significance to such certificates.

Accordingly, the application, where applicable, of UK legislation in this respect could – unusually – actually be restrictive in relation to the type of disputes referable to adjudication where Works falling within the definition of 'construction contracts' are being carried out under NEC contracts within the territories of the UK, in that certificates which are stated to be final and conclusive may not be referable to adjudication.

Paragraph 20 of the Scheme for Construction Contracts in Northern Ireland Regulations (Northern Ireland) 1999 provides:

[The Adjudicator] may

(a)   open up, revise and review any decision taken or any certificate given by any person referred to in the contract *unless the contract states that the decision or certificate is final and conclusive.*

Payment cases

As with any similar contract, under the NEC family of contracts payment is a matter of agreement between the Parties which is generally of only peripheral effect in relation to any disputes or adjudications.

The introduction of payment provisions in the UK legislation is, however, likely to have a significant practical effect upon adjudications relating to Works which fall within the definition of 'construction contracts'. While a Party would not be denied an adjudication if they wanted one, a failure to issue a proper and timeous notice of intention to withhold payment might have the practical effect of making any adjudication a mere formality.

The Scottish case on payments is likely to be of persuasive value in Northern Ireland.

Articles 8 to 12

The Construction Contracts (Northern Ireland) Order 1997

Part II – Payment Paragraphs 1 to 12

The Scheme for Construction Contracts in Northern Ireland Regulations (Northern Ireland) 1999

Insolvency

Adjudication and insolvency appear to be developing a close practical relationship which is not, perhaps, surprising in that adjudication often takes place at the end of a project when the success or failure of the project is often reflected in the success or failure of the businesses involved.

The English cases on insolvency are likely to be of persuasive value in Northern Ireland.

13. What procedure is to govern the adjudication

Having ascertained that the Works in question are being carried out within the territories of the United Kingdom and that the Works satisfy the other requirements and fall within the definition of 'construction contracts' and having settlement/crystallisation procedures and ascertained that the dispute is one which is referable to adjudication, the next step is to determine the procedure which is to govern that adjudication.

It bears mentioning here that what the UK legislation confers in these circumstances is an entitlement but not an obligation and therefore, provided *all* Parties are in agreement, then it is open to them to choose whatever procedure they like for their adjudication. The decision is theirs (and not, it is suggested, up to the Adjudicator to decide). The Parties could, for example, decide that no matter what their entitlements are, the adjudication will be conducted using the NEC adjudication procedures. The Parties could also, for example, decide that no matter what their entitlements are, the adjudication will be conducted using the statutory adjudication procedures.

Where, however, one Party is standing on their rights or entitlements then it may become necessary to take a more formal approach to the selection of the adjudication procedure. Where the Works fall within the definition of 'construction contracts' and the other requirements are satisfied then the legislation determines the procedure to be applied as follows.

England and Wales

(1) A Party to a construction contract has the right to refer a dispute (which includes any difference) arising under the contract for adjudication under a procedure complying with this [section/article].

Commentary The provisions contained in the section/article with which the contract procedure must comply are as follows:

(2) The contract shall
(a) enable a Party to give notice at any time of his intention to refer a dispute to adjudication
(b) provide a timetable with the object of securing the appointment of the adjudicator and referral of the dispute to him within seven days of such notice

(c) require the adjudicator to reach a decision within 28 days of referral or such longer period as is agreed by the Parties after the dispute has been referred

(d) allow the adjudicator to extend the period of 28 days by up to 14 days, with the consent of the Party by whom the dispute was referred

(e) impose a duty on the adjudicator to act impartially

(f) enable the adjudicator to take the initiative in ascertaining the facts and the law.

(3) The contract shall provide that the decision of the adjudicator is binding until the dispute is finally determined by legal proceedings, by arbitration (if the contract provides for arbitration or the Parties otherwise agree to arbitration) or by agreement. The Parties may agree to accept the decision of the adjudicator as finally determining the dispute.

(4) The contract shall also provide that the adjudicator is not liable for anything done or omitted in the discharge or purported discharge of his functions as adjudicator unless the act or omission is in bad faith, and that any employee or agent of the adjudicator is similarly protected from liability. [England and Wales – HGCR Act 1996 s. 108; Scotland – HGCR Act 1996 s. 108; Northern Ireland – The Construction Contracts (Northern Ireland) Order 1997 Article 7]

Commentary Provided that the contract complies with the above then the adjudication procedures set out in the contract will apply in the adjudication (and a Party has no right or entitlement to utilise the statutory adjudication procedures unless all of the Parties agree so to do).

Where, however, any one of the above has not been met in the contract then:

(5) If the contract does not comply with the requirements of subsections (1) to (4), the adjudication procedures of [the applicable Scheme] apply. [England and Wales – HGCR Act 1996 s. 108(5); Scotland – HGCR Act 1996 s. 108(5); Northern Ireland – The Construction Contracts (Northern Ireland) Order 1997 Article 7(5)]

Commentary The way in which those procedures are to apply is also provided for:

Where any provisions of [the applicable Scheme] apply by virtue of this [Part/Order] in default of contractual provision agreed by the parties, they have effect as implied terms of the contract concerned. [England and Wales – HGCR Act 1996 s. 114(4); Scotland – HGCR Act 1996 s. 114(4); Northern Ireland – The Construction Contracts (Northern Ireland) Order 1997 Article 13(3)].

What the legislation does not make clear, however, is how a non-complying contract is to interrelate with the applicable Scheme. Parliament might well have had its reasons for not doing so, but it would have been relatively easy for the legislation to have expressly provided that, in the event of non-compliance, the contractual adjudication procedures shall be of no effect and that the sole applicable adjudication procedures shall be those set out in the applicable Scheme.

The fact is that there is no such provision and therefore it is necessary to interpret the position. It should be borne in mind that it was necessary, particularly in the early stages, to envisage a situation where the contract made no provision for adjudication whatsoever and where the applicable Scheme needed to provide a full set of adjudication procedures.

What is less clear, however, is where the contract provides adjudication procedures and the applicable Scheme provides adjudication procedures and one of the essential requirements of the Act (say providing for the immunity of the Adjudicator's agent) has been omitted from the contract. It would appear, on the face of it, to be unreasonable in those circumstances where a simple small omission has been made to apply the applicable Scheme *in toto*. That would result, for example, in the introduction of the provision that the Adjudicator may take into account any other matters which the Parties to the dispute agree should be within the scope of the adjudication or which are matters under the contract which he or she considers are necessarily connected with the dispute. This would apply even where the contractual procedures expressly provide that the Adjudicator may not take into account any matter beyond the dispute referred to him or her and may not take into account any matter not referred to him or her.

The result of such an interpretation would be that the Adjudicator would have to juggle between the adjudication provisions in the applicable Scheme and the adjudication procedures in the applicable contract to work out which procedures from the applicable Scheme he or she should imply into the applicable contract so as to satisfy the minimum requirements set out in the legislation. That is, of course, what the legislation says, for it does not say 'when *the* provisions of [the applicable Scheme] apply' but instead says 'where *any* provisions of [the applicable Scheme] apply'. It is also provided in the Schemes themselves that 'The adjudicator shall – act impartially in carrying out his duties and shall do so *in accordance with any relevant terms of the contract*'.

Of course, it would make life easier for the Adjudicator if it were necessary to have regard to one set of adjudication procedures only. It would in fact be open to *the Parties* to agree that the adjudication should proceed solely under the adjudication procedures of the applicable Scheme. What appears to have happened, according to the reports of some of the earlier cases, is that the Adjudicator has informed the Parties of his decision to proceed under the adjudication procedures of the applicable Scheme. It is submitted that while the Adjudicator has the power to 'case manage', it is beyond the Adjudicator's powers to decide which complete set of adjudication procedures shall apply and that that is a matter for the Parties alone.

It should be pointed out that there is some authority to the effect that the Scheme should be applied *in toto* but the remarks were made *obiter* and without full argument. It has to be borne in mind, also, that the interpretation of the new Schemes is at a relatively early stage.

The submission which is made in this book is that, where necessary, the contract and the Scheme require to be read together. On that basis, Parties using one of the NEC family of contracts on Works which are construction contracts within the United Kingdom face three possible scenarios:

- The NEC contract provides only for Clause 9 which must be read in conjunction with the applicable Scheme
- The NEC contract adopts Option Y(UK) 2 which must be read in conjunction with the applicable Scheme
- The applicable Scheme is to apply in isolation.

It is proposed to consider these next.

Core Clause 9

9   Disputes and termination

Settlement of disputes   90

90.1   Any dispute arising under or in connection with this contract is submitted to and settled by the *Adjudicator* as follows.

ADJUDICATION TABLE

Dispute about:	*Which Party may submit it to the Adjudicator?*	*When may it be submitted to the Adjudicator?*
An action of the *Project Manager* or the *Supervisor*	The *Contractor*	Between two and four weeks after the *Contractor's* notification of the dispute to the *Project Manager*, the notification itself being made not more than four weeks after the *Contractor* becomes aware of the action
The *Project Manager* or *Supervisor* not having taken an action	The *Contractor*	Between two and four weeks after the *Contractor's* notification of the dispute to the *Project Manager*, the notification itself being made not more than four weeks after the *Contractor* becomes aware that the action was not taken
Any other matter	Either Party	Between two and four weeks after notification of the dispute to the other Party and the *Project Manager*

90.2   The *Adjudicator* settles the dispute by notifying the Parties and the *Project Manager* of his decision together with his reasons within the time allowed by this contract. Unless and until there is such a settlement, the Parties and the *Project Manager* proceed as if the action, inaction or other matter disputed were not disputed. The decision is final and binding unless and until revised by the *tribunal*.

The adjudication   91

91.1   The Party submitting the dispute to the *Adjudicator* includes with his submission information to be considered by the *Adjudicator*. Any further information from a Party to be considered by the *Adjudicator* is provided within four weeks from the submission. The *Adjudicator* notifies his decision within four weeks of the end of the period for providing information. The four week periods in this clause may be extended if requested by the *Adjudicator* in view of the nature of the dispute and agreed by the Parties.

91.2   If a matter disputed under or in connection with a subcontract is also a matter disputed under or in connection with this contract, the *Contractor* may submit the subcontract dispute to the *Adjudicator* at the same time as the main contract submission. The *Adjudicator* then settles the two disputes together and references to the Parties for the purposes of the dispute are interpreted as including the Subcontractor.

The Adjudicator   92

92.1   The *Adjudicator* settles the dispute as independent adjudicator and not as arbitrator. His decision is enforceable as a matter of contractual obligation between the Parties and not as an arbitral award. The *Adjudicator*'s powers include the power to review and revise any action or inaction of the *Project Manager* or *Supervisor* related to the dispute. Any communication between a Party and the *Adjudicator* is communicated also to the other Party. If the *Adjudicator*'s decision includes assessment of additional cost or delay caused to the *Contractor*, he makes his assessment in the same way as a compensation event is assessed.

92.2   If the *Adjudicator* resigns or is unable to act, the Parties choose a new adjudicator jointly. If the Parties have not chosen a new adjudicator jointly within four weeks of the *Adjudicator* resigning or becoming unable to act, a Party may ask the person stated in the Contract Data to choose a new adjudicator and the Parties accept his choice. The new adjudicator is appointed as *Adjudicator* under the NEC Adjudicator's Contract. He has power to settle disputes that were currently submitted to his predecessor but had not been settled at the time when his predecessor resigned or became unable to act. The date of his appointment is the date of submission of these disputes to him as *Adjudicator*.

Review by the tribunal   93

93.1   If after the *Adjudicator* notifies his decision or fails to do so within
the time provided by this contract a Party is dissatisfied, that Party
notifies the other Party of his intention to refer the matter which he
disputes to the *tribunal*. It is not referable to the *tribunal* unless the
dissatisfied Party notifies his intention within four weeks of notification of the *Adjudicator*'s decision or the time provided by this
contract for this notification if the *Adjudicator* fails to notify his decision within that time whichever is the earlier. The *tribunal* proceedings are not started before Completion of the whole of the *works* or
earlier termination.

93.2   The *tribunal* settles the dispute referred to it. Its powers include the
power to review and revise any decision of the *Adjudicator* and any
action or inaction of the *Project Manager* or the *Supervisor* related to
the dispute. A Party is not limited in the *tribunal* proceedings to the
information, evidence or arguments put to the *Adjudicator*.

Termination   94

94.1   If either Party wishes to terminate, he notifies the *Project Manager*
giving details of his reason for terminating. The *Project Manager*
issues a termination certificate promptly if the reason complies with
this contract.

94.2   The *Contractor* may terminate only for a reason identified in the
Termination Table. The *Employer* may terminate for any reason. The
procedures followed and the amounts due on termination are in
accordance with the Termination Table.

TERMINATION TABLE

Terminating Party	Reason	Procedure	Amount due
The *Employer*	A reason other than R1–R21	P1 and P2	A1, A2 and A4
	R1–R15, R19	P1, P2 and P3	A1 and A3
	R17, R18, R21	P1 and P3	A1, A2 and A5
The *Contractor*	R1–R10, R16, R20	P1 and P4	A1, A2 and A4
	R17, R18, R21	P1 and P4	A1, A2 and A5

94.3   The procedures for termination are implemented immediately after
the *Project Manager* has issued a termination certificate.

94.4   Within thirteen weeks of termination, the *Project Manager* certifies a final payment to or from the *Contractor* which is the *Project Manager*'s assessment of the amount due on termination less the total of previous payments.

94.5   After a termination certificate has been issued, the *Contractor* does no further work necessary to complete the *works*.

Reasons for termination   95

95.1   Either Party may terminate if the other Party has done one of the following or its equivalent.

(1) If the other Party is an individual and has
- presented his petition for bankruptcy (R1),
- had a bankruptcy order made against him (R2),
- had a receiver appointed over his assets (R3) or
- made an arrangement with his creditors (R4).

(2) If the other Party is a company or partnership and has
- had a winding-up order made against it (R5),
- had a provisional liquidator appointed to it (R6),
- passed a resolution for winding-up (other than in order to amalgamate or reconstruct) (R9),
- had an administration order made against it (R8),
- had a receiver, receiver and manager, or administrative receiver appointed over the whole or a substantial part of its undertaking or assets (R7) or
- made an arrangement with its creditors (R10).

95.2   The *Employer* may terminate if the *Project Manager* has notified that the *Contractor* has defaulted in one of the following ways and not put the default right within four weeks of the notification.
- Substantially failed to comply with his obligations (R11).
- Not provided a bond or guarantee which this contract requires (R12).
- Appointed a Subcontractor for substantial work before the *Project Manager* has accepted the Subcontractor (R13).

95.3   The *Employer* may terminate if the *Project Manager* has notified that the *Contractor* has defaulted in one of the following ways and not stopped defaulting within four weeks of the notification.
- Substantially hindered the *Employer* or Others (R14).
- Substantially broken a health or safety regulation (R15).

95.4   The *Contractor* may terminate if the *Employer* has not paid an amount certified by the *Project Manager* within thirteen weeks of the date of the certificate (R16).

95.5   Either Party may terminate if
- war or radioactive contamination has substantially affected the *Contractor*'s work for 26 weeks (R17) or
- the Parties have been released under the law from further performance of the whole of this contract (R18).

95.6 If the *Project Manager* has instructed the *Contractor* to stop or not to start any substantial work or all work and an instruction allowing the work to restart or start has not been given within thirteen weeks,
- the *Employer* may terminate if the instruction was due to a default by the *Contractor* (R19),
- the *Contractor* may terminate if the instruction was due to a default by the *Employer* (R20) and
- either Party may terminate if the instruction was due to any other reason (R21).

Procedures on termination 96

96.1 On termination, the *Employer* may complete the *works* himself or employ other people to do so and may use any Plant and Materials to which he has title (P1).

96.2 The procedure on termination also includes one or more of the following as set out in the Termination Table.
P2 The *Employer* may instruct the *Contractor* to leave the Site, remove any Equipment, Plant and Materials from the Site and assign the benefit of any subcontract or other contract related to performance of this contract to the *Employer*.
P3 The *Employer* may use any Equipment to which he has title.
P4 The *Contractor* leaves the Working Areas and removes the Equipment.

Payment on termination 97

97.1 The amount due on termination includes (A1)
an amount due assessed as for normal payments,
the Actual Cost for Plant and Materials
- within the Working Areas or
- to which the *Employer* has title and of which the *Contractor* has to accept delivery,
- other Actual Cost reasonably incurred in expectation of completing the whole of the *works*,
- any amounts retained by the *Employer* and
- a deduction of any unrepaid balance of an advanced payment.

97.2 The amount due on termination also includes one or more of the following as set out in the Termination Table.
A2 The forecast Actual Cost of removing the Equipment.
A3 A deduction of the forecast of the additional cost to the *Employer* of completing the whole of the *works*.
A4 The *fee percentage* applied to
- for Options A, B, C and D, any excess of the total of the Prices at the Contract Date over the Price for Work Done to Date or
- for Options E and F, any excess of the first forecast of the Actual Cost for the *works* over the Price for Work Done to Date less the Fee.
A5 Half of A4.

The extent to which Clause 9 standing alone complies with the minimum requirements

When faced with a potential dispute to which, firstly, the territorial requirements apply and secondly, the Works in question fall within the definition of 'construction operations' and therefore of 'construction contracts' , it will then be necessary to determine the extent to which the contract in question complies with the minimum standards set down in the legislation.

Whether by accident or design, Parties to a contract may find themselves in that position where the NEC contract between them contains only Core Clause 9 standing alone. We consider below the extent to which that (Clause 9) provision of the relevant NEC contract is likely to be interpreted as complying with the minimum standards of the applicable legislation.

(1) The requirement that a party to a construction contract has the right to refer a dispute (defined for this purpose to include any difference) arising under the contract for adjudication under a procedure complying with this section.

Commentary It can hardly be disputed that Clause 9 complies with this requirement in that Clause 90.1 provides 'Any dispute arising under or in connection with this contract is submitted to and settled by the Adjudicator as follows.'

(2) The requirement that the contract shall enable a party to give notice at any time of his intention to refer a dispute to adjudication.

Commentary Compliance with this requirement is more difficult to interpret. If the notification procedure is regarded as simply a means of arriving at a proper 'dispute' which the Party is then free to submit to adjudication then it could be argued that Clause 9 complies to that extent. However, it can hardly be disputed that Clause 9 is non-compliant in that the imposition of a time limit of four weeks on the submission of disputes to the Adjudicator does not meet the essential requirement that notice of intention to refer a dispute to adjudication at any time.

(3) The requirement that the contract provide a timetable with the object of securing the appointment of the adjudicator and referral of the dispute to him within 7 days of such notice.

Commentary Again, compliance with this requirement is difficult to interpret. Clause 9 does not provide for 'adjudication notices' and 'referral notices' as such. On one view (if the applicable legislation is interpreted as directory), it could be argued that once the notification procedure has been gone through to arrive at a proper 'dispute' then where the Adjudicator is named in the contract there is nothing to prevent a Party submitting (or referring) that dispute to the Adjudicator within seven days and that Clause 9 complies with the object of the timetable to that extent. On another view (if the applicable legislation is interpreted as mandatory), it could be argued that if the legislation requires the contract to have a separate procedure for notice of intention to refer a dispute to adjudication and a separate procedure for referral of the dispute and a contractual requirement that the latter take place within seven days of the former, then Clause 9 is non-compliant in that respect. Of course, where Option Z is used to allow the Adjudicator to be appointed at the time when the dispute arises then that appointment clause could be made compliant with this requirement.

(4) The requirement that the contract provide that the adjudicator reach a decision within 28 days of referral or such longer period as is agreed by the parties after the dispute has been referred.

Commentary On one view (if the applicable legislation is interpreted as mandatory), it could be argued that if the legislation requires there to be a separate procedure known as 'referral' and (unless an exception applies) that there be a contractual requirement placed upon the Adjudicator to reach a decision within twenty-eight days of the referral, then Clause 9 is non-compliant in that respect. On another view (if the applicable legislation is interpreted as directory), then it could be argued that since in Clause 9 the Parties have agreed a longer period, the contract is compliant in that respect. However, the legislation appears to provide that the Parties can only agree a longer period after the dispute has been referred, and since the basic requirement of Clause 90.2 allows for the submission, and then four weeks for any further information, and then four weeks from the end of that period for the decision, it would appear that Clause 9 is non-compliant in that respect.

(5) The requirement that the contract allow the adjudicator to extend the period of 28 days by up to 14 days, with the consent of the party by whom the dispute was referred.

Commentary On one view (if the applicable legislation is interpreted as directory), it could be argued that the Clause 90.2 does broadly provide for this. However, on another view (if the applicable legislation is interpreted as mandatory), it could be argued that since the legislation requires there to be a basic contractual requirement upon the Adjudicator to produce a decision within twenty-eight days and that any extension can only be with the consent of the Submitting or Referring Party, then Clause 9 is non-compliant. However, the thrust of the legislation appears to be aimed at capping any extension in this respect at fourteen days and since Clause 9 does not provide for that and also provides that any extension may be granted only if requested by the Adjudicator in view of the nature of the dispute and agreed by [all] Parties, Clause 9 must be regarded as non-compliant in that respect.

(6) The requirement that the contract impose a duty on the adjudicator to act impartially.

Commentary Again, this is a difficult requirement to interpret. On the one hand, Clause 9 nowhere mentions the word 'impartially'. However, Clause 92.1 does provide that the Adjudicator settles the dispute as independent Adjudicator. Independence and impartiality are distinct but related concepts and it could be argued that the former is greater than and includes the latter. On that basis, it could be argued that Clause 9 complies with this requirement.

On another view, it could be argued that Clause 9 is non-compliant in this respect in that the word 'impartiality' appears nowhere.

(7) The requirement that the contract enable the adjudicator to take the initiative in ascertaining the facts and the law.

Commentary Clause 9 is entirely silent as to how the Adjudicator should go about his or her task. Clause 9 is therefore clearly non-compliant in this respect and only the brave could suggest that such an enablement should be inferred in a contract containing Clause 9.

(8) The requirement that (although the parties may agree to accept the decision of the adjudicator as finally determining the dispute) the contract shall provide that the decision of the adjudicator is binding until the dispute is finally determined by legal proceedings, by arbitration (if the contract provides for arbitration or the parties otherwise agree to arbitration) or by agreement.

Commentary Again, this is a difficult requirement to interpret. Clause 9 makes no express reference to litigation, Arbitration or agreement (leaving it to the Employer to determine the tribunal). On a strict view, it could be argued that Clause 9 is therefore non-compliant in that respect. On another view, however, Clause 90.2 provides that the decision [of the Adjudicator] is final and binding unless and until revised by the tribunal and it could be argued that Clause 9 is therefore to that extent compliant.

(9) The requirement that the contract shall also provide that the adjudicator is not liable for anything done or omitted in the discharge or purported discharge of his functions as Adjudicator unless the act or omission is in bad faith, and that any employee or agent of the Adjudicator is similarly protected from liability.

Commentary There is no express reference to this in Clause 9 itself. On a strict view, it could therefore be argued that Clause 9 is non-compliant in that respect. However, where the Adjudicator is named in the contract or later appointed under the contract and an NEC Adjudicator's Contract is entered into at the same time, then it could be argued that the Adjudicator's Contract is so closely associated as to be a part of the main contract between the Parties.

Since the Adjudicator's Contract provides in Clause 4.1 that 'The Adjudicator, his employees and agents are not liable to the Parties for any action or failure to take action in an adjudication unless the action or failure to take action is in bad faith', it could be argued that the Parties' contract is compliant in that respect.

Summary

It must, it is submitted, be accepted that Clause 9 standing alone does not comply with a number of the essential requirements of the UK legislation and that therefore a contract containing Core Clause 9 standing alone is non-compliant in relation to 'construction contracts' which satisfy the other conditions and are within the United Kingdom.

Option Y(UK) 2

Contract

Option Y(UK)2: The Housing Grants, Construction and Regeneration Act 1996

Y2.1   In this Option
- the Act means The Housing Grants, Construction and Regeneration Act 1996 and
- periods of time stated in days are reckoned in accordance with Section 116 of the Act.

Y2.2   Clause 51 is amended as follows:

Clause 51.1 the first sentence is deleted and replaced with the following sentence:

> "The Contractor certifies a payment on or before the date on which a payment becomes due."

Clause 51.2 the first sentence is deleted and replaced with the following sentence:

> "Each certified payment is made on or before the final date for payment."

Y2.3   The following clauses are added

Dates for Payment 56

56.1   For the purpose of Sections 109 and 110 of the Act,
- the Contractor's certificate is the notice of payment to the Subcontractor specifying the amount (if any) of the payment made or proposed to be made, and the basis on which that amount was calculated,
- the date on which a payment becomes due is fourteen days after the assessment date and
- the final date for payment is
- twenty one days or
- if a different period for payment is stated in the Subcontract Data, the period stated

after the date on which the payment becomes due.

56.2   If the Contractor intends to withhold payment after the final date for payment of a sum due under this contract, he notifies the Subcontractor not later than seven days (the prescribed period) before the final date for payment by specifying
- the amount proposed to be withheld and the ground for withholding payment or
- if there is more than one ground, each ground and the amount attributable to it.

Y2.4   The following is added to clause 60

60.7   Suspension of performance is a compensation event if the Subcontractor exercises his right to suspend performance under the Act.

Y2.5   Clause 90 is deleted and replaced by the following:

Avoidance and settlement of disputes 90

90.1   The Parties follow this procedure for the avoidance and settlement of disputes.

90.2   If a Party is dissatisfied with an action, a failure to take action, or any other matter, he notifies his dissatisfaction to the other Party no later than
- four weeks after he became aware of the action,
- four weeks after he became aware that the action had not been taken or
- four weeks after he became aware of the matter he is dissatisfied with.

90.3   Within two weeks of such notification of dissatisfaction, the Parties attend a meeting to discuss and seek to resolve the matter.

90.4   The Parties agree that no matter shall be a dispute unless a notice of dissatisfaction has been given and the matter has not been resolved within four weeks. The word dispute (which includes a difference) has that meaning.

90.5   Either Party may give notice to the other Party at any time of his intention to refer a dispute to adjudication. The notifying Party refers the dispute to the Adjudicator within seven days of the notice.

90.6   The Party referring the dispute to the Adjudicator includes with his submission information to be considered by the Adjudicator. Any further information from a Party to be considered by the Adjudicator is provided within fourteen days of referral.

90.7   Unless and until the Adjudicator has given his decision on the dispute, the Parties proceed as if the action, failure to take action or other matters were not disputed.

90.8   The Adjudicator acts impartially. The Adjudicator may take the initiative in ascertaining the facts and the law.

90.9   The Adjudicator reaches a decision within twenty eight days of referral or such longer period as is agreed by the Parties after the dispute has been referred. The Adjudicator may extend the period of twenty eight days by up to fourteen days with the consent of the notifying Party.

90.10   The Adjudicator provides his reasons to the Parties with his decision.

90.11   The decision of the Adjudicator is binding until the dispute is finally determined by the tribunal or by agreement

90.12   The Adjudicator is not liable for anything done or omitted in the discharge or purported discharge of his functions as adjudicator unless the act or omission is in bad faith and any employee or agent of the Adjudicator is similarly protected from liability.

Y2.6   Clause 91 is amended as follows:

Side heading "The adjudication" is replaced with "Combining procedures"

Clause 91.1 is deleted and replaced by the following:

> 91.1   If a matter causing dissatisfaction under or in connection with a subsubcontract is also a matter causing dissatisfaction under or in connection with this contract, the subsubcontractor may attend the meeting between the Parties to discuss and seek to resolve the matter.

Clause 91.2 line 4 "settles" is replaced with "gives his decision on"

Clause 91.3 is renumbered to clause 91.4 and a new clause 91.3 inserted as follows:

> 91.3   If the main contract provides for the Subcontractor to attend a meeting to discuss and seek to resolve a matter of dissatisfaction under or in connection with the main contract which is also a matter causing dissatisfaction under or in connection with this subcontract, the Subcontractor attends the meeting.

> renumbered clause 91.4 line 10 "settles" is replaced with "gives his decision on"

Y2.7   Clause 92 is amended as follows:

> Clause 92.1 line 1 "settles" is replaced with "gives his decision on"

> Clause 92.2 line 6 "settle" is replaced with "decide on"

> Clause 92.2 line 7 "had not been settled" is replaced with "a decision had not been given"

Y2.8   Subcontract Data Part 1 – Optional statements

The fifth optional statement is deleted and replaced by the following:

> "If the period for payment is not twenty one days

> • The period within which payments are made is ..... days"

Subcontract

Option Y(UK)2: The Housing Grants, Construction and Regeneration Act 1996

Y2.1   In this Option

- the Act means The Housing Grants, Construction and Regeneration Act 1996 and
- periods of time stated in days are reckoned in accordance with Section 116 of the Act.

Y2.2   Clause 51 is amended as follows:

Clause 51.1 the first sentence is deleted and replaced with the following sentence:

> "The Project Manager certifies a payment on or before the date on which a payment becomes due."

Clause 51.2 the first sentence is deleted and replaced with the following sentence:

"Each certified payment is made on or before the final date for payment."

Y2.3   The following clauses are added

Dates for Payment 56

56.1   For the purpose of Sections 109 and 110 of the Act,
- the Project Manager's certificate is the notice of payment from the Employer to the Contractor specifying the amount (if any) of the payment made or proposed to be made, and the basis on which that amount was calculated,
- the date on which a payment becomes due is seven days after the assessment date and
- the final date for payment is
  - twenty one days or
  - if a different period for payment is stated in the Contract Data, the period stated

  after the date on which the payment becomes due.

56.2   If the Employer intends to withhold payment after the final date for payment of a sum due under this contract, he notifies the Contractor not later than seven days (the prescribed period) before the final date for payment by specifying
- the amount proposed to be withheld and the ground for withholding payment or
- if there is more than one ground, each ground and the amount attributable to it.

Y2.4   The following is added to clause 60

60.7   Suspension of performance is a compensation event if the Contractor exercises his right to suspend performance under the Act.

Y2.5   Clause 90 is deleted and replaced by the following:

Avoidance and settlement of disputes 90

90.1   The Parties and the Project Manager follow this procedure for the avoidance and settlement of disputes.

90.2   If the Contractor is dissatisfied with an action or a failure to take action by the Project Manager, he notifies his dissatisfaction to the Project Manager no later than
- four weeks after he became aware of the action or
- four weeks after he became aware that the action had not been taken.

Within two weeks of such notification of dissatisfaction, the Contractor and the Project Manager attend a meeting to discuss and seek to resolve the matter.

90.3   If either Party is dissatisfied with any other matter, he notifies his dissatisfaction to the Project Manager and to the other Party no later than four weeks after he became aware of the matter. Within two weeks of such notification of dissatisfaction, the Parties and the Project Manager attend a meeting to discuss and seek to resolve the matter.

90.4   The Parties agree that no matter shall be a dispute unless a notice of dissatisfaction has been given and the matter has not been resolved within four weeks. The word dispute (which includes a difference) has that meaning.

90.5   Either Party may give notice to the other Party at any time of his intention to refer a dispute to adjudication. The notifying Party refers the dispute to the Adjudicator within seven days of the notice.

90.6   The Party referring the dispute to the Adjudicator includes with his submission information to be considered by the Adjudicator. Any further information from a Party to be considered by the Adjudicator is provided within fourteen days of referral.

90.7   Unless and until the Adjudicator has given his decision on the dispute, the Parties and the Project Manager proceed as if the action, failure to take action or other matters were not disputed.

90.8   The Adjudicator acts impartially. The Adjudicator may take the initiative in ascertaining the facts and the law.

90.9   The Adjudicator reaches a decision within twenty eight days of referral or such longer period as is agreed by the Parties after the dispute has been referred. The Adjudicator may extend the period of twenty eight days by up to fourteen days with the consent of the notifying Party.

90.10   The Adjudicator provides his reasons to the Parties and to the Project Manager with his decision.

90.11   The decision of the Adjudicator is binding until the dispute is finally determined by the tribunal or by agreement.

90.12   The Adjudicator is not liable for anything done or omitted in the discharge or purported discharge of his functions as adjudicator unless the act or omission is in bad faith and any employee or agent of the Adjudicator is similarly protected from liability.

Y2.6   Clause 91 is amended as follows:

Side heading "The adjudication" is replaced with "Combining procedures"

Clause 91.1 is deleted and replaced by the following:

91.1   If a matter causing dissatisfaction under or in connection with a subcontract is also a matter causing dissatisfaction under or in connection with this contract, the subcontractor may attend the meeting between the Parties and the Project Manager to discuss and seek to resolve the matter.

Clause 91.2 line 4 "settles" is replaced with "gives his decision on"

Y2.7   Clause 92 is amended as follows:

Clause 92.1 line 1 "settles" is replaced with "gives his decision on"

Clause 92.2 line 6 "settle" is replaced with "decide on"

Clause 92.2 line 7 "had not been settled" is replaced with "a decision had not been given"

Y2.8   Contract Data Part 1 – Optional statements

The fifth optional statement is deleted and replaced by the following:

"If the period for payment is not twenty one days

• The period within which payments are made is ..... days"

The extent to which option Y(UK) 2 complies with the minimum requirements of the UK legislation

Option Y(UK) 2 is specifically aimed at complying with the minimum requirements of the UK legislation. Where, therefore, anticipating working within the territory of the United Kingdom on Works falling within the definition of 'construction operations' and therefore of 'construction contracts', the Parties have incorporated Option Y(UK) 2 into their NEC contract, it will then be necessary to take a view on the extent to which that contract complies with the minimum standards set down in the UK legislation.

(1) The requirement that a party to a construction contract has the right to refer a dispute (defined for this purpose to include any difference) arising under the contract for adjudication under a procedure complying with this section.

Commentary It can hardly be disputed that Option Y(UK) 2 complies with this requirement in that it gives Parties the right to refer disputes arising under a contract containing that Option to adjudication.

(2) The requirement that the contract shall enable a party to give notice at any time of his intention to refer a dispute to adjudication.

Commentary Compliance with this requirement is more difficult to interpret. If the notification of dissatisfaction procedure is regarded as simply a means of arriving at a proper 'dispute' which the Party is then free to submit to adjudication then it could be argued that Option Y(UK) 2 complies to that extent, particularly as Clause 90.5 expressly provides that either Party may give notice to the other Party at any time of his intention to refer a dispute for adjudication. However, at least one decision at first instance has suggested that the notification of dissatisfaction procedure in Option Y(UK) 2 is incompatible with the minimum legislative requirement to refer a dispute to adjudication at any time. It is possible that other decisions at first instance or an appeal may later clarify this issue.

(3) The requirement that the contract provide a timetable with the object of securing the appointment of the adjudicator and referral of the dispute to him within 7 days of such notice.

Commentary Compliance with this requirement is easier to interpret in that Option Y(UK) 2 does provide for separate 'notices of intention to refer a dispute to adjudication' and 'referral notices' . Clause 90.6 then goes on to expressly provide that 'The notifying Party refers the dispute to the Adjudicator within seven days of the notice'. To that extent, therefore, Option Y(UK) 2 is clearly compliant in that respect. Option Y(UK) 2 envisages, of course, that the Adjudicator is named in the contract. Where Option Z is used to allow the Adjudicator to be appointed at the time when the dispute arises, then that appointment clause could be made compliant with this requirement, particularly as regards both appointment and referral taking place within seven days of the notice of intention to refer a dispute to adjudication.

(4) The requirement that the contract provide that the adjudicator reach a decision within 28 days of referral or such longer period as is agreed by the parties after the dispute has been referred.

Commentary Option Y(UK) 2 is clearly compliant in that Clause 90.9 expressly provides that 'The Adjudicator reaches a decision within twenty eight days of referral or such longer period as is agreed by the Parties after the dispute has been referred'.

(5) The requirement that the contract allow the adjudicator to extend the period of 28 days by up to 14 days, with the consent of the party by whom the dispute was referred.

Commentary Option Y(UK) 2 is clearly compliant in that Clause 90.9 expressly provides that 'The Adjudicator may extend the period of twenty eight days by up to fourteen days with the consent of the notifying Party.'

(6) The requirement that the contract impose a duty on the adjudicator to act impartially.

Commentary Option Y(UK) 2 is clearly compliant in that Clause 90.8 expressly provides that 'The Adjudicator acts impartially.'

(7) The requirement that the contract enable the adjudicator to take the initiative in ascertaining the facts and the law.

Commentary Option Y(UK) 2 is clearly compliant in that Clause 90.8 expressly provides that 'The Adjudicator may take the initiative in ascertaining the facts and the law'.

(8) The requirement that (although the parties may agree to accept the decision of the adjudicator as finally determining the dispute) the contract shall provide that the decision of the adjudicator is binding until the dispute is finally determined by legal proceedings, by arbitration (if the contract provides for arbitration or the parties otherwise agree to arbitration) or by agreement.

Commentary Again, this is a difficult requirement to interpret. Option Y(UK) 2 makes no express reference to litigation or Arbitration (leaving it to the Employer to determine the tribunal). On a strict view, it could be argued that Option Y(UK) 2 is therefore non-compliant in that respect. On another view, however, since Clause 90.11 provides that 'The decision of the Adjudicator is binding until the dispute is finally determined by the tribunal or by agreement' it could be argued that Option Y(UK) 2 is therefore to that extent compliant.

(9) The requirement that the contract shall also provide that the Adjudicator is not liable for anything done or omitted in the discharge or purported discharge of his functions as Adjudicator unless the act or omission is in bad faith, and that any employee or agent of the Adjudicator is similarly protected from liability.

Commentary Option Y(UK) 2 is clearly compliant in that Clause 90.12 expressly provides that 'The Adjudicator is not liable for anything done or omitted in the discharge or purported discharge of his functions as Adjudicator unless the act or omission is in bad faith and any employee or agent of the Adjudicator is similarly protected from liability.'

Summary

It could be argued that Option Y(UK) 2 does, in fact, comply with the essential requirements of the UK legislation. However, regard must be had to the persuasive authority of the decision in John Mowlem & Company plc *v* Hydra-Tight Ltd to the effect that it does not.

The consequences of this decision, as we shall see later, are not inconsiderable. It may be that the Parties are able to resolve the matter by agreement amongst themselves failing which, if the decision that Option Y(UK) 2 is non-compliant is to be challenged, then that Party will require to be prepared for litigation.

Clauses 93UK to 95UK of the NEC Engineering and Construction Short Contract

Settlement of disputes   93

The simple adjudication procedure provided in this clause is designed to be appropriate for the type of work likely to be undertaken under the ECSC, wherever the site is located.

93.1   This clause establishes the principle, followed in other NEC contracts, that any dispute which cannot be resolved by the Parties themselves must be decided by the Adjudicator who is independent of the Parties and is required to act impartially (cl. 94.1). In order to ensure the early declaration of a dispute and expedite its resolution, time limits are stated for:

• notification between the Parties of the existence of the dispute,

and

• submission of the dispute to the Adjudicator after two weeks. This period is intended to allow and encourage the Parties to resolve the dispute themselves.

93.2 &   These clauses state further time limits after the submission within
93.3   which:

- the Parties can provide information to the Adjudicator, and
- the Adjudicator decides the dispute and notifies the Parties giving reasons.

The Adjudicator   94

94.1   The person appointed as Adjudicator is named in the Contract Data. The Adjudicator's impartiality and independence must be ensured. It is recommended that possible names are suggested by the Employer in the invitation to tender so that the Contractor can agree a name for inclusion in the final Contract Data (see examples A2 and C3). Acceptance of the Contractor's Offer signifies agreement to the named Adjudicator.

The Adjudicator should be a person with practical experience of the kind of work to be provided by the Contractor. The Adjudicator should be able to:

- understand the procedures embodied in the ECSC,
- understand the roles of both the Employer and the Contractor in the ECSC,
- act impartially and in a spirit of independence of the Parties,
- understand and have access to costs at current market rates,
- understand and have access to information on planning times and productivities,
- appreciate risks and how allowances for them should be set and
- obtain other specialist advice when required.

The Adjudicator's charges (fees and expenses) are shared equally between the Parties, regardless of the Adjudicator's decision.

It is important for achieving a successful adjudication that the Adjudicator should not be concerned that a disappointed Party may pursue the Adjudicator personally over the decision and that the Adjudicator is protected from legal action by a third party arising out of the decision. It is strongly recommended that the Parties jointly appoint the Adjudicator under the latest edition of the NEC Adjudicator's Contract. The Adjudicator's Contract limits the Adjudicator's liability to the Parties and includes an indemnity by the Parties concerning action by a third party.

In the UK, the Construction Industry Council and the Professional Institutions have lists of adjudicators from which the Adjudicator may be selected.

The second and third sentences of cl. 94.1 state the legal status of the Adjudicator's decision.

94.2   The first sentence requires openness of communications during a reference to the Adjudicator. The second makes use of the assessment procedures established for compensation events in cl. 63.

Reference to the tribunal 95

95.1   Under cl. 93.4 the Adjudicator's decision is binding until it is "finally determined by the tribunal or by agreement". A dispute cannot be referred to the tribunal unless it has first been referred to the Adjudicator (cl. 93.1). Cl. 95.1 states the circumstances in which a referral can be made with a time limit for notifying a Party's intention to do so.

The Employer identifies the tribunal in the Contract Data (see example A2). The choice will normally be between arbitration and the courts, either being competent to give a legally final and binding decision on the dispute.

It is important to be aware of the different choices that are available when making the decision about the tribunal. Different laws and arbitration procedures exist in different countries whilst in some countries no arbitration exists at all. If the tribunal is arbitration, the arbitration procedure to be used is also stated in the Contract Data (see example A2).

The UK Housing Grants, Construction and Regeneration Act 1996

If the UK Housing Grants, Construction and Regeneration Act 1996 (referred to as "the Act" in the following notes) applies to the contract, clauses 93 to 95 are replaced by clauses 93UK to 95UK.

The provisions of cls. 93 to 95 do not comply with the Act although the principle of independent adjudication of disputes has been a key feature of the NEC family since its first publication in 1991. An objective in all NEC contracts is to overcome, where possible, the causes of disputes and, where they still arise, to motivate their clear definition and early resolution.

Avoidance and settlement of disputes   93UK

The intention of cls. 93.1UK to 93.5UK is to retain the principles of the adjudication provisions in cls. 93.1 to 93.5 for the management of disputes and, at the same time, comply with the Act so that the "Scheme for Construction Contracts" does not apply.

The Adjudicator   94UK

This clause is broadly equivalent to cl. 94 but has additions and changes to reflect the Act.

Reference to the tribunal   95UK

95.1UK This clause has the same wording as cl. 95.1.

Joining subcontract disputes with main contract disputes

The following notes apply whether cls. 93 to 95 or cls. 93UK to 95UK are used.

Under cl. 21.1, the Contractor is responsible for all subcontractors. It is recommended that the Adjudicator named in the main contract is also appointed to act in all subcontracts subject, of course, to the agreement of the subcontractor concerned.

If the Contractor wishes to have any matter arising under or in connection with a subcontract that impinges on a main contract matter decided with the main contract matter, the following clause should be included in the main contract.

The extent to which clauses 93UK to 95UK of the NEC Engineering and Construction Short Contract comply with the minimum requirements of the UK legislation

Clauses 93UK to 95UK of this NEC contract are specifically aimed at complying with the minimum requirements of the UK legislation. It will, therefore, be necessary to take a view on the extent to which that contract then complies with the minimum standards set down in the UK legislation.

(1) The requirement that a party to a construction contract has the right to refer a dispute (defined for this purpose to include any difference) arising under the contract for adjudication under a procedure complying with this section.

Commentary It can hardly be disputed that Clauses 93UK to 95UK comply with this requirement in that they give Parties the right to refer disputes arising under a contract containing those Clauses to adjudication.

(2) The requirement that the contract shall enable a party to give notice at any time of his intention to refer a dispute to adjudication.

Commentary Compliance with this requirement is more difficult to interpret. If the notification of dissatisfactión procedure is regarded as simply a means of arriving at a proper 'dispute' which the Party is then free to submit to adjudication then it could be argued that Clauses 93UK to 95UK comply to that extent, particularly as Clause 93.2UK expressly provides that either Party may give notice to the other Party at any time of his intention to refer a dispute for adjudication. However, at least one decision at first instance has suggested that the notification of dissatisfaction procedure used in Clauses 93UK to 95UK is incompatible with the minimum legislative requirement to refer a dispute to adjudication at any time. It is possible that other decisions at first instance or an appeal may later clarify this issue.

(3) The requirement that the contract provide a timetable with the object of securing the appointment of the adjudicator and referral of the dispute to him within 7 days of such notice.

Commentary Compliance with this requirement is easier to interpret in that Clauses 93UK to 95UK do provide for separate 'notices of intention to refer a dispute to adjudication' and 'referral notices'. Clause 93.2UK then goes on to expressly provide that 'The notifying Party refers the dispute to the Adjudicator within seven days of the notice'. To that extent, therefore, Clauses 93UK to 95UK are clearly compliant in that respect. Clauses 93UK to 95UK envisage, of course, that the Adjudicator is named in the contract. Where Option Z is used to allow the Adjudicator to be appointed at the time when the dispute arises then that appointment clause could be made compliant with this requirement, particularly as regards both appointment and referral taking place within seven days of the notice of intention to refer a dispute to adjudication.

(4) The requirement that the contract provide that the adjudicator reach a decision within 28 days of referral or such longer period as is agreed by the parties after the dispute has been referred.

Commentary Clauses 93UK to 95UK may be compliant in that Clause 93UK expressly provides that 'The Adjudicator gives a decision on the dispute by notifying the Parties of the decision and of the reasons for it within four weeks of referral ...'.

(5) The requirement that the contract allow the adjudicator to extend the period of 28 days by up to 14 days, with the consent of the party by whom the dispute was referred.

Commentary Clauses 93UK to 95UK may be compliant in that Clause 93.4UK expressly goes on to provide 'or a longer period if agreed by the Parties after the dispute has been referred.'

(6) The requirement that the contract impose a duty on the adjudicator to act impartially.

Commentary Clauses 93UK to 95UK are clearly compliant in that Clause 94.1UK expressly provides that 'The Adjudicator acts impartially.'

(7) The requirement that the contract enable the adjudicator to take the initiative in ascertaining the facts and the law.

Commentary Clauses 93UK to 95UK are clearly compliant in that Clause 94.1UK expressly provides that 'The Adjudicator may take the initiative in ascertaining the facts and the law.'

(8) The requirement that (although the parties may agree to accept the decision of the adjudicator as finally determining the dispute) the contract shall provide that the decision of the adjudicator is binding until the dispute is finally determined by legal proceedings, by arbitration (if the contract provides for arbitration or the parties otherwise agree to arbitration) or by agreement.

Commentary Again, this is a difficult requirement to interpret. Clauses 93UK to 95UK make no express reference to litigation or Arbitration (leaving it to the Employer to determine the tribunal). On a strict view, it could be argued that Clauses 93UK to 95UK are therefore non-compliant in that respect. On another view, however, since Clause 93.5UK provides that 'The decision of the Adjudicator is binding until the dispute is finally determined by the tribunal or by agreement' it could be argued that Clauses 93UK to 95UK are therefore to that extent compliant.

(9) The requirement that the contract shall also provide that the adjudicator is not liable for anything done or omitted in the discharge or purported discharge of his functions as Adjudicator unless the act or omission is in bad faith, and that any employee or agent of the Adjudicator is similarly protected from liability.

Commentary Clauses 93UK to 95UK are clearly compliant in that Clause 94.4UK expressly provides that ' The Adjudicator is not liable for anything done or omitted in the discharge or purported discharge of his functions as Adjudicator unless the act or omission is in bad faith and any employee or agent of the Adjudicator is similarly protected from liability'.

Summary

It could be argued that Clauses 93UK to 95UK do, in fact, comply with the essential requirements of the UK legislation. However, regard must be had to the persuasive authority in relation to Option Y(UK) 2 of the decision in John Mowlem & Company plc *v* Hydra-Tight Ltd which might suggest that it does not.

The consequences of this decision, as we shall see later, are not inconsiderable. It may be that the Parties are able to resolve the matter by agreement amongst themselves failing which, if the suggestion that Clauses 93UK to 95UK are non-compliant is to be challenged, then that Party may require to be prepared for litigation.

What the consequences are of the NEC contract being non-compliant

It is clearly arguable that the NEC family of contracts does comply with the essential requirements of the UK legislation in some respects but may or may not comply with the essential requirements of the UK legislation in certain other respects.

What the legislation does not make clear, however, is what is to happen in such a situation and, in particular, how a non-complying contract is to inter-relate with the applicable Scheme.

It was open to Parliament to make clear provision in that respect and, although Parliament might well have had its reasons for not doing so, it would have been relatively easy for the legislation to have expressly provided that, in the event of non-compliance, the contractual adjudication procedures shall be of no effect and that the sole applicable adjudication procedures shall be those set out in the applicable Scheme.

The fact is that there is no such provision and therefore it is necessary to interpret the position. It should be borne in mind that it was necessary, particularly in the early stages, to envisage a situation where the contract made no reference to adjudication whatsoever and therefore to cope with that eventuality, the applicable Scheme needed to provide a full set of adjudication procedures.

What is less clear, however, is the situation where the Works satisfy all the requirements and fall within the definition of 'construction contracts' but, while the contract provides detailed adjudication procedures, because one of the essential requirements of the Act (say providing for the immunity of the Adjudicator's agent) has been omitted from the contract, that opens the door to the statutory adjudication procedures of the applicable Scheme.

On one interpretation, it could be argued that all that is necessary is to take from the applicable statutory Scheme only that provision which is necessary to meet the essential requirements of the legislation and imply only that into the contractual adjudication procedures.

On another interpretation, it could be argued that, although the legislation does not expressly say so, a failure in respect of *any* of the essential requirements of the applicable UK legislation shuts out all of the contractual adjudication provisions and opens the door to the wholesale introduction of the applicable statutory adjudication procedures.

The consequences of the latter interpretation are not inconsiderable in that the consequences would be, for example, where the contract omitted immunity for the agents of the Adjudicator, that no matter what provision to the contrary the Parties had made in their contract (and the NEC family of contracts does make provision in these respects), they would now, on one interpretation, find themselves in the situation where they:

- require that the notice of adjudication was in a particular form
- require that the referral notice be in a particular form
- ask the Adjudicator to adjudicate at the same time on more than one dispute
- ask the Adjudicator to adjudicate at the same time on related disputes
- require the Adjudicator to avoid incurring unnecessary expense
- have adverse inferences drawn from perceived failures to comply with the Adjudicator
- have representation in any hearing limited to one person
- face a fresh adjudication in the event of the Adjudicator failing to reach a decision
- have any certificate marked final and conclusive excluded from the adjudication
- face being ordered to comply peremptorily with the Adjudicator's decision
- face having s. 42 of AA 1996 applied against them in England and Wales
- face having to pay an allocation of the Adjudicator's fees and expenses.

Disregarding provision which the Parties have made in their contract against any of the above eventualities is clearly unfortunate, particularly as paragraph

12 of the applicable Scheme provides that as well as acting impartially in carrying out his duties, the Adjudicator shall do so in accordance with any relevant terms of the contract.

On the other hand, it has to be admitted that in practical terms it would be easier to concentrate upon one set of procedures rather than having to juggle between the adjudication provisions in the applicable Scheme and the adjudication procedures in the applicable contract to work out which procedures from the applicable Scheme he or she should imply into the applicable contract so as to satisfy the minimum requirements set out in the legislation. Adjudicators have not been slow to pick up on this point in that in a number of reported decisions, Adjudicators have 'directed' that the applicable statutory Scheme is to apply to their adjudication. That certainly seems to be happening in practice at the moment. While Adjudicators clearly have 'case management' powers it is, however, strongly suggested that the power to decide the overall procedure applicable to an adjudication rests not with the Adjudicator but with the Parties.

This issue has to a certain extent been considered by the Courts. In the adjudication case of John Mowlem & Co plc *v* Hydra-Tight Ltd which came before the Technology and Construction Court in England and Wales, His Honour Judge Toulmin said:

> I have considered whether, if some parts of the subcontract comply with the Act, they can be retained and the Act can be used in substitution for or to fill in those parts of the subcontract which are contrary to the Act. But the words of the Act are clear. Either a party complies in its terms and conditions with the requirements of sections 108(1) to (4) of the Act or the provisions of the Scheme apply.

Of course, in that case both Parties, through their representatives, had submitted to the Court that they were in agreement that the contractual adjudication procedures should not apply and that the applicable adjudication procedures should apply, so that no argument was put up on the point and the remarks of His Honour Judge Toulmin might be regarded as *obiter*.

The wording used in the legislation – s. 114(4) of the HGCR Act 1996 or Article 13(3) of the Northern Ireland Order is as follows: 'Where any provisions of [the applicable Scheme] apply by virtue of this [Part/Order] in default of contractual provision agreed by the parties, they have effect as implied terms of the contract concerned' and the reference to '*any* provision' could be taken as an indication that Parliament intended that there be a certain amount of picking and choosing amongst the provisions.

Summary

Adjudication is a new and radical process which is at an early stage in its development. It may be that as other cases emerge and move on to appeal the position or another position will become clearer. In the meantime, practice appears to be favouring the wholesale selection of one procedure or another and due regard should be had to the *obiter* decision in the above case. Parties who wish to face their own route and stand by their contract may have to be prepared to face litigation.

Other considerations

What can be done to question the progress towards an adjudication

Clearly, there are a number of stages along the line of discovering territorial application, applying the definition of 'construction contracts', applying the settlement/crystallisation procedure, determining which disputes are referable to adjudication and settling upon the procedure which is to apply to the adjudication in question, at which objection could be raised to the way in which matters are proceeding.

The NEC family of contracts does not, however, provide any procedure for the initial determination of jurisdiction and neither does the applicable legislation or secondary legislation in the form of the Schemes.

In these circumstances, resort would require to be had to the Courts under the applicable *lex mercatoria* but the prospects of doing something at this stage (as opposed to later in answer to enforcement proceedings) appear to be limited. Where there is an objection to jurisdiction, however, the most important thing at this stage is not to lose that right to maintain the objection to jurisdiction and we consider that aspect at the end of this section (see also Appendix A, judgment extracts 16–21).

England and Wales

Injunction

In theory, it should be possible for a Party convinced that there is clearly no jurisdiction for a statutory adjudication to apply to the Courts for an injunction or interdict (as the case may be) to forestall an adjudication and all the cost and time that goes with it. In practice, however, this appears to be quite difficult to achieve.

An attempt to obtain an injunction against an adjudication has in fact been made in England and Wales (Workplace Technologies plc *v* E Squared Ltd TCC 16 February 2000).

Workplace Technologies plc had entered into a sub-contract (the date of which was uncertain) with E Squared Ltd. The Works proceeded but then E Squared Ltd intimated their intention to seek adjudication under the HGCR Act 1996 and asked the Royal Institution of Chartered Surveyors to appoint an Adjudicator. Mr Riches was appointed as the Adjudicator and began the adjudication.

Workplace Technologies plc then applied to the Queen's Bench Division (Technology and Construction Court) of the High Court of Justice and, joining the Adjudicator into the proceedings, applied for, *inter alia*, Declaration that the contract came into existence on 9 October 1997, Declaration that the Adjudicator therefore had no jurisdiction (the contract pre-dating the Act) and an Injunction restraining E Squared Ltd from continuing the adjudication.

The matter came before His Honour Judge Wilcox QC, initially as an *ex parte* application for interim injunction at which it was decided the application for interim injunction would be dropped on the basis that the Court would make time available to hear the substantive point within a matter of days. At that substantive hearing, His Honour Judge Wilcox held that on the facts of the case the contract was entered into after the Act had come into force (which disposed of the substantive point) but also added a number of *obiter* remarks relating to injunctions and adjudications.

In relation to interim injunctions, His Honour Judge Wilcox indicated that in his judgment the balance of convenience favoured allowing an adjudication process to continue, on the basis that if a Court were to grant an injunction without determining an issue such as the date of the contract, then it would inexorably follow that the Court may be interfering in a valid judgment to its detriment and the statutory Scheme of the giving of an early decision as to who shall hold the money pending litigation or Arbitration would then have been frustrated.

In relation to injunctions generally, His Honour Judge Wilcox was not persuaded that there was power to grant an injunction to restrain a Party initiating a void reference and pursuing proceedings which themselves are void and which may give rise to a void and, thus, unenforceable adjudication decision. There did not appear to His Honour Judge Wilcox to be any legal or equitable interest that such an injunction would protect and while, doubtless, the initiation of such proceedings may be conceived to be a source of harassment, pressure or needless expense, mere harassment by unfair or futile proceedings does not found a remedy – the Party must be harassed by the infringement of a legal or equitable right. His Honour Judge Wilcox held that the instant proceedings did not assert or identify any such infringement.

In the analogous field of Arbitration, injunctions have proved difficult (North London Railway Company *v* Great Northern Railway Company (1988) 11 QBD 30, approved in Siskina *v* Distos [1979] AC 210).

The matter does not appear to have been tested elsewhere as there appears to be no record of an interdict against an adjudication being applied for in Scotland and no record of an injunction against an adjudication being applied for in Northern Ireland.

On the persuasive authority of Workplace Technologies plc, however, it seems that an application for an injunction or interdict (as the case may be) to prevent an adjudication proceeding is unlikely to succeed except in the clearest of cases.

Declarator

Declarator, where the substantive objection to jurisdiction is argued out and decided, is a much more fertile area for dealing with jurisdictional objections to adjudication.

In principle, however, in such situations the adjudication and the action for Declaration are likely to proceed side-by-side unless the Parties agree to suspend the adjudication until the outcome of the action for Declaration is known (which is unlikely but has happened) or an injunction or interdict is granted restraining the adjudication pending the outcome of the action of Declaration (which, on the basis of Workplace Technologies plc *v* E Squared Ltd, is unlikely to be granted).

The difficulty in practice is that an adjudication (with its 28-days-unless-extended) is likely to have concluded and any binding decision required to be observed long before an action for a Declaration could make its normal progress through the lists.

The Courts have shown a willingness to co-operate (in the Workplace case, for example, the substantive point relating to the Declaration sought was, with the co-operation of the Court, heard within a matter of days) but that will in practice not always be possible in every case (see also Appendix A, judgment extract 22).

The matter does not appear to have been tested elsewhere in advance of an adjudication as there appears to be no record of proceedings akin to a Declaration in either Scotland or Northern Ireland.

Seeking a Declaration is certainly a solution to a jurisdictional objection to adjudication but obtaining it in practice may be the difficulty.

Scotland

Interdict

There does not seem to have been any reported case of an attempt to interdict an adjudication (other than an unreported case in Glasgow Sheriff Court which failed).

Other proceedings

There does not seem to have been any reported case of any other attempt to prevent an adjudication (which in practice would be very difficult to achieve before any adjudication was due to start).

Northern Ireland

Injunction

There do not appear to have been any reported instances.

Declaration

There do not appear to have been any reported instances.

Maintaining an objection to the Adjudication

In many instances, therefore, even though a jurisdictional objection to adjudication may exist (at least in the minds of one of the Parties) there will be little practical alternative other than to proceed with the adjudication in the meantime.

The Courts may be relatively sanguine about that situation in that an adjudication produces a decision which is only temporarily binding and in relation to which the issues involved (including any jurisdictional points) can be later resolved when the dispute is finally determined. That will, of course, be little comfort to a Party obliged to make a payment under the temporarily binding decision of an Adjudicator who later finds that the recovery of that money to which the Party is later determined to be properly entitled is impossible due to the insolvency of the recipient (as has already happened several times).

The most important point to note (as a number of cases have already illustrated) in this situation where the adjudication requires to be proceeded with over an objection to jurisdiction, is that it is vital to maintain the objection to jurisdiction.

The immediate consequences of maintaining the objection appear to vary. As we shall see in Section II under Seizing the Jurisdiction, Scotland appears to recognise a power on the part of the Adjudicator to rule upon his or her own jurisdiction, whereas England and Wales appears to consider that there is no power on the part of the Adjudicator to rule upon his or her own jurisdiction. Northern Ireland would appear likely to follow the line shown in England and Wales. The immediate consequence of *not* maintaining the objection, however, is likely to be the creation of an *ad hoc* adjudication in which the Parties will be taken to have given the Adjudicator the necessary authority.

What is to happen while the dispute is resolved by Adjudication

Core Clause 9

Clause 90.2

Unless and until [the Adjudicator settles the dispute by notifying the Parties and the Project Manager of his decision], the Parties and the Project Manager proceed as if the action, inaction or other matter disputed were not disputed.

Option Y(UK) 2

Clause 90.7

Unless and until [the Adjudicator settles the dispute by notifying the Parties and the Project Manager of his decision], the Parties proceed as if the action, failure to take action or other matter disputed were not disputed.

Interpretation

It is clearly desirable that matters should proceed pending the resolution of the dispute. Both Clause 9 and Option Y(UK) 2 make specific provision in this respect.

Perhaps surprisingly, the applicable Schemes do not make any express provision in this respect but it is to be expected that the same principle will apply there also.

England and Wales

There is no specific provision in the Scheme in this respect.

Scotland

There is no specific provision in the Scheme in this respect.

Northern Ireland

There is no specific provision in the Scheme in this respect.

Summary

Accordingly – and this is one of the aims and intentions of the very process of adjudication – a Party faced with an adjudication and unable to prevent its process must (preserving any objection to jurisdiction if they so wish) proceed with the Works and allow the adjudication to proceed.

We consider what is involved in an adjudication proceeding in the following Section II. Any objections may be dealt with after the adjudication has been completed and we consider the position there in Section III.

Section II

The process of adjudication

14. The appointment and referral of the dispute to the Adjudicator

Introduction

In this chapter, it is proposed to consider what is involved in the appointment of the Adjudicator and the referral of the dispute to the Adjudicator.

For those contracts which fall within the definition of 'construction contracts' and which are being carried out within the territories of the United Kingdom, the relevant legislation regards the appointment of the Adjudicator and the referral of the dispute to the Adjudicator as a *unum quid* (a single process). This involves the giving of a notice of intention to refer a dispute to adjudication, the appointment of an Adjudicator (who is sent a copy of that notice of adjudication) and then the referral (in writing) of the dispute to the Adjudicator, all not later than seven days from the date of the notice of adjudication. It is proposed, therefore, to begin with an overview of the whole process.

Thereafter, it is proposed to consider what is involved in the notice to refer a dispute to adjudication.

We shall then consider the various procedures which can be adopted for the appointment of the Adjudicator, including making the appointment by agreement of the Parties, by naming in the contract, by a Nominating Body or by an Adjudicator Nominating Body. We shall also consider how the appointment of the Adjudicator is confirmed.

We shall also consider what is involved in the referral (in writing) of the dispute to the Adjudicator.

Finally, we shall seek to summarise what is involved in the appointment and referral of a dispute to the Adjudicator.

Overview

Clause 9	*Option Y(UK) 2*
	Notice of intention to refer a
Notification	*dispute to adjudication*
	Clause 90.5

The Party gives notification of the dispute to the relevant person within four weeks of becoming aware of that event (except for disputes involving 'any other matter')	Either Party may give notice to the Other Party at any time of his intention to refer a dispute to adjudication

Appointment	*Appointment*
Unamended NEC contract	Unamended NEC contract
The Adjudicator will have been named in the contract as follows:	The Adjudicator will have been named in the contract as follows:
Contract Data:	Contract Data:
The Adjudicator is	The Adjudicator is
Name [.....]	Name [.....]
Address [.....]	Address [.....]
Amended NEC contract	Amended NEC contract
The Adjudicator will have been appointed in accordance with the agreed procedure at the time when the dispute arises	The Adjudicator will have been appointed in accordance with the agreed procedure at the time when the dispute arises

Referral	*Referral*
	Clause 90.5
The Party submits the dispute to the Adjudicator between two and four weeks after notification of the dispute	The notifying Party refers the dispute to the Adjudicator within seven days of the notice

NEC PRINCIPLES

Appointment and referral of dispute to Adjudicator (within a timetable of seven days)

When the NEC contract involved relates to Works falling within the definition of 'construction contracts' being carried out within the territories of the United Kingdom and the other conditions are satisfied, then where the Other Party is standing upon their entitlement regard will require to be had to the applicable UK legislation.

The relevant UK legislation in this respect makes it an essential requirement (essential requirement 2) that – on pain of having the statutory provisions of the Scheme for Construction Contracts applied to the contract by way of an implied term – the contract in question shall provide a procedure which has the object of securing *both* the appointment of the Adjudicator *and* the referral of the dispute to him or her within a timetable of seven days.

The statutory scheme, which applies in default, envisages a two-stage process. Firstly, there is a notice of intention to refer a dispute to adjudication (the 'Notice of Adjudication' in relation to which provision is made as to its contents). Following upon the giving of that Notice of Adjudication, the matter of the appointment of the Adjudicator (and the various methods for achieving that appointment) are considered, which appointment is accompanied by the Notice of Adjudication. Where an Adjudicator has been selected then, secondly, the dispute is referred (in writing) to the Adjudicator by way of a notice of referral (the 'referral notice' in relation to which provision is made as to its contents) and this requires to be done not later than seven days from the date of the Notice of Adjudication.

It is hardly surprising, and entirely in keeping with the objective of providing a process for the resolution of disputes within the UK which will be both speedy and susceptible to the minimum of interference and delay, that the UK legislation should make provision – in the form of an essential requirement – for *both* the appointment of the Adjudicator *and* the referral of the dispute to him or her within a timetable of seven days. What seems clear is that the contract in question must provide a timetable with the object of securing the appointment of the Adjudicator and the referral of the dispute to him or her within seven days of the giving of notice of intention to refer the dispute to adjudication. What is not so clear, however, and what does not appear to have been tested in Court yet, is the extent to which that essential requirement is mandatory (such that a failure to so comply by, say, extending to eight days, would make any resulting decision null and void) or directory (such that any slippage in the timetable will not affect the validity of the adjudication).

We shall consider here the extent to which, an NEC contract having been entered into in relation to which it is subsequently established that it falls within the definition of 'construction contracts' being carried out within the territories of the United Kingdom and the other conditions are satisfied, those requirements will have to be complied with.

Timetable with object of securing the appointment of Adjudicator and the referral of the dispute to him or her within seven days

Where Clause 9 is standing alone

Leaving to one side considerations about when a 'dispute' has truly arisen (which we considered in the previous section), the difficulty with Clause 9 standing alone is that it does *not* provide a timetable with the object of securing the appointment of the Adjudicator and the referral of the dispute to him or her within seven days of the giving of notice of intention to refer the dispute to adjudication.

Clause 9 (although it provides for 'notification') does not, as such, provide for a formal 'notice of adjudication' or indeed for anything formally called a 'timetable' but assuming that these are not made *vox signata* by the legislation, the difficulty with Clause 9 lies in is its prohibition on submitting the dispute to the Adjudicator within the period of two weeks following notification of the dispute. That is clearly contradictory to the essential requirement of the UK legislation that the contract in question must provide a timetable with the object of securing the appointment of the Adjudicator and the referral of the dispute to him or her within seven days of the giving of notice of intention to refer the dispute to adjudication. Accordingly, Clause 9 standing alone is clearly non-compliant in that it involves not a timetable of seven days but a period, after 'notification', of at least two weeks and one day before the dispute can be submitted to adjudication.

As a result, when a dispute arises a Party to such a contract with Clause 9 standing alone has the entitlement (but not any obligation) to demand that the essential requirements of the applicable UK legislation be complied with.

As discussed earlier, it has perhaps not yet been conclusively decided whether in these circumstances the entire statutory adjudication scheme falls to be implied as a whole or whether it is only necessary to imply sufficient of the statutory scheme to provide the missing essential requirement.

If the latter is the case, then much of what might have gone before could be preserved and, preserving the relatively informal notification procedures of Clause 9, it would be open to the Party standing upon their entitlement to say to the Other Party that, notwithstanding the provision in Clause 9 prohibiting the referral of the dispute to the Adjudicator later than four weeks or earlier than two weeks from the date of such notification, by implication from the applicable statutory adjudication scheme the dispute will in fact be referred to the Adjudicator within seven days of that notification.

If the former is the case, however, then it would be open to the Party standing upon their entitlement to insist upon the incorporation by implication of the wholesale provisions of the applicable statutory scheme. Anything which has gone before would, in these circumstances, require to be abandoned. Matters would require to be commenced anew. Within a timetable of seven days fresh notification would require to be given in the form of a formal Notice of Adjudication (with its specified contents), formal procedures for appointment of the Adjudicator and the serving on him or her of the Notice of Adjudication would require to be gone through and a formal referral notice (with its specified contents) served.

Where Option Y(UK) 2 has been adopted

Where Parties to an NEC Contract have foreseen themselves working within the territory of the United Kingdom on Works which fall within the definition of a 'construction contract' and have adopted into their contract Option Y(UK) 2, then it is suggested that their contract is compliant with the UK legislation.

Leaving to one side considerations about when a 'dispute' has truly arisen (which we considered in the previous section) and looking at appointment and referral alone, Option Y(UK) 2, it is suggested, complies with the essential legislative requirements in that Clause 90.5 specifically provides that the notifying Party refers the dispute to the Adjudicator within seven days of the notice of intention to refer a dispute to adjudication.

On that basis, a contract containing Option Y(UK) 2 complies with the essential legislative requirement and nothing requires to be implied from any applicable statutory adjudication scheme.

Potential UK human rights points

Insofar as it is likely to impact upon adjudication, the main thrust of the human rights legislation is likely to relate to the fair and proper procedures adopted under the process of adjudication.

The procedures used to achieve notification of the dispute, the appointment of the Adjudicator, and the referral of that dispute to the Adjudicator – albeit within a relatively short timescale of seven days – seem unlikely to be seen as objectionable.

The main thrust of any human rights considerations are likely to relate to the procedures following thereon and the timescale relating to them and these we touch upon next.

England and Wales

The essential requirement:

The HGCR Act 1996 c. 53 provides:

s. 108(2) The contract shall

(b) provide a timetable with the object of securing the appointment of the adjudicator and referral of the dispute to him within 7 days of such notice.

The provisions

The Scheme for Construction Contracts (England and Wales) Regulations 1998 SI No 649 provides:

Paragraph 1

(1)   Any party to a construction contract (the 'referring party') may give written notice (the 'notice of adjudication') of his intention to refer any dispute arising under the contract, to adjudication …

Paragraph 2

(1)1   Following upon the giving of a notice of adjudication …
[Paragraphs 2, 5 and 6 then provide in detail for the appointment of an Adjudicator]

Paragraph 7

(1)   Where an adjudicator has been selected in accordance with paragraphs 2, 5 or 6 the referring party shall, not later than seven days from the date of the notice of adjudication, refer the dispute in writing (the 'referral notice') to the adjudicator.

Scotland

The essential requirement:

The HGCR Act 1996 c. 53 provides:

s. 108(2) The contract shall

(b)   provide a timetable with the object of securing the appointment of the adjudicator and referral of the dispute to him within 7 days of such notice.

The provisions

The Scheme for Construction Contracts (Scotland) Regulations 1998 SI No 687 provides:

Paragraph 1

(1)   Any party to a construction contract (the 'referring party') may give written notice (the 'notice of adjudication') of his intention to refer any dispute arising under the contract, to adjudication …

Paragraph 2

(1)   Following upon the giving of a notice of adjudication …
[Paragraphs 2, 5 and 6 then provide in detail for the appointment of an Adjudicator]

Paragraph 7

(1)   Where an adjudicator has been selected in accordance with paragraphs 2, 5 or 6 the referring party shall, not later than seven days from the date of the notice of adjudication, refer the dispute in writing (the 'referral notice') to the adjudicator.

Northern Ireland

The essential requirement:

The Construction Contracts (Northern Ireland) Order 1997 SI No 274 (NI) provides:

Article 7(2) The contract shall

(b)   provide a timetable with the object of securing the appointment of the adjudicator and referral of the dispute to him within 7 days of such notice.

The provisions

The Scheme for Construction Contracts in Northern Ireland Regulations (Northern Ireland) 1999 Statutory Rule 1999 No 32 provides:

Paragraph 1

(1)   Any party to a construction contract (the 'referring party') may give written notice (the 'notice of adjudication') of his intention to refer any dispute arising under the contract, to adjudication …

Paragraph 2

(1)   Following upon the giving of a notice of adjudication …
        [Paragraphs 2, 5 and 6 then provide in detail for the appointment of an Adjudicator]

Paragraph 7

(1)   Where an adjudicator has been selected in accordance with paragraphs 2, 5 or 6 the referring party shall, not later than seven days from the date of the notice of adjudication, refer the dispute in writing (the 'referral notice') to the adjudicator.

Notification of the dispute

Clause 9	*Option Y(UK) 2*
	Clause 90.5
Provision is made for notification of a dispute but no specific provision is made as to the form and content of such notification	Either Party may give notice to the other Party at any time of his intention to refer a dispute to adjudication but no specific provision is made as to the form and content of such notification

NEC PRINCIPLES

When the NEC contract involved relates to Works falling within the definition of 'construction contracts' and is being carried out within the territories of the United Kingdom in circumstances where all the other conditions are satisfied, then where the Other Party is standing upon their entitlements, regard will require to be had to the applicable UK legislation.

The relevant UK legislation [which concentrates upon the appointment of the Adjudicator and the referral of the dispute to the Adjudicator] does *not* make it an *essential* requirement that there should be a 'notice of intention to refer a dispute to adjudication' nor that it should be in any particular form. Nor is there any legislative requirement that a document should exist carrying a heading such as 'Notice of Adjudication' (although it might have been convenient had the legislation so provided as it can sometimes be quite difficult, in practice, to distinguish between a letter relating to negotiation or availability and a letter relating to actual submission for adjudication).

Nevertheless, in litigation following upon the bare bones of the adjudication legislation the notice of intention to refer a dispute to adjudication (the 'Notice of Adjudication') has assumed considerable significance in the respect that the dispute which the Adjudicator is to decide is essentially stated in the Notice of Adjudication and the Courts have not allowed the Parties to change or alter the nature of the dispute in the subsequent referral notice. In practice, therefore, Parties involved in any form of adjudication would be well advised to pay particular attention to the format of any Notice of Adjudication and the requirements relating thereto.

We shall consider here the extent to which, an NEC contract having been entered into in relation to which, the other conditions having been satisfied, it is subsequently determined to be a contract which falls within the definition of 'construction contracts' being carried out within the territories of the United Kingdom, those requirements will have to be complied with.

The format of a notice of intention to refer a dispute to adjudication

Where Clause 9 is standing alone

As noted above, Clause 9 standing alone has no specific provision relating to the form which any such notification has to take. The drafters of the NEC family of contracts appear to have been content to leave that as a matter of practice of the Parties.

If the view is taken that it is only necessary to imply in from the applicable Scheme that which is necessary to satisfy an individual *essential* requirement of the legislation, then since the format of any Notice of Adjudication is not an essential requirement, it could be argued that the implication of the provisions of the applicable Scheme relating to the content of the Notice of Adjudication is not a requirement and that the existing Clause 9 notification is sufficient.

If, however, the view is taken that in that particular case (perhaps for other reasons of non-compliance) the law requires the applicable Scheme to be applied in its entirety or the Parties have agreed between themselves that the applicable Scheme is to apply in its entirety to their adjudication, then consideration will have to be given to the requirements of the applicable Scheme relating to the format of any Notice of Adjudication. In these circumstances, anything which has gone before in the way of notification may require to be abandoned and a fresh notice issued headed (even though not *vox signata*) 'Notice of Adjudication', the contents of which comply with the requirements of the applicable secondary legislation (the Schemes) set out below.

It is perhaps worth mentioning, however, that given the importance which precedent is giving to the definition of the dispute in the original notification, even where not strictly a requirement, it might be advisable for best 'notification' practice of the Parties under the NEC family of the contracts to match as closely as possible the requirements for the contents set out below of the Notice of Adjudication.

Where Option Y(UK) 2 has been adopted

Where Parties to an NEC contract have foreseen themselves working within the territory of the United Kingdom on Works which fall within the definition of a 'construction contract' and have adopted into their contract Option Y(UK) 2 then it is suggested that their contract is compliant with the UK legislation.

As such, Option Y(UK) 2 makes provision for a notice of intention to refer a dispute to adjudication (Clause 90.5) but makes no provision as to the specific format which its Notice of Adjudication must follow.

On that basis, a contract containing Option Y(UK) 2 complies with the essential legislative requirement and nothing requires to be implied from any applicable statutory adjudication scheme.

Again, however, given the importance which precedent has given to this matter, consideration could be given to incorporating into any notice of intention to refer a dispute to adjudication a format along the lines suggested by the applicable statutory Schemes set out below.

Potential UK human rights points

As earlier noted, the main thrust of the human rights legislation is likely to relate to the fair and proper procedures adopted under the process of adjudication.

As such, fair notice and warning of the nature of the dispute to be adjudicated upon is clearly a vital requirement. This has already been considered to be so in domestic precedent and is even more likely to be considered so in relation to human rights considerations. Any attempt to depart from what turn out to be the minimum standards of proper notification is likely to be a matter upon which human rights considerations may arise.

England and Wales

The Scheme for Construction Contracts (England and Wales) Regulations 1998 SI No 649 provides:

Paragraph 1

(3)   The notice of adjudication shall set out briefly
  (a) the nature and a brief description of the dispute and of the parties involved
  (b) details of where and when the dispute has arisen
  (c) the nature of the redress which is sought
  (d) the names and addresses of the parties to the contract (including, where appropriate, the addresses which the parties have specified for the giving of notices).

Scotland

The Scheme for Construction Contracts (Scotland) Regulations 1998 SI No 687 provides:

Paragraph 1

(3)   The notice of adjudication shall set out briefly
  (a) the nature and a brief description of the dispute and of the parties involved
  (b) details of where and when the dispute has arisen
  (c) the nature of the redress which is sought
  (d) the names and addresses of the parties to the contract (including, where appropriate, the addresses which the parties have specified for the giving of notices).

Northern Ireland

The Scheme for Construction Contracts in Northern Ireland Regulations (Northern Ireland) 1999 Statutory Rule 1999 No 32 provides:

Paragraph 1

(3)   The notice of adjudication shall set out briefly
  (a) the nature and a brief description of the dispute and of the parties involved
  (b) details of where and when the dispute has arisen
  (c) the nature of the redress which is sought
  (d) the names and addresses of the parties to the contract (including, where appropriate, the addresses which the parties have specified for the giving of notices).

The appointment of the Adjudicator

Introduction

As noted in Book I, the preferred approach adopted by the drafters of the NEC family of contracts is to name the Adjudicator in the contract at the time of contracting.

As also noted, however, it is possible for the Parties to one of the NEC family of contracts to amend that contract so as to provide for the appointment of the Adjudicator in another way or at a later stage.

In addition, problems could arise even in relation to the provision made which may necessitate the use of any alternative provision made for the appointment of a replacement Adjudicator.

Finally, if all else fails, where the Schemes are applicable then they have fall-back provisions aimed at achieving the appointment of an Adjudicator if all else fails.

We consider in detail under the following headings the means by which the appointment of an Adjudicator may be made.

Making the appointment
- By agreement of the parties
    - By contract
    - Unamended NEC contract
- By naming in the contract
- By nominating
- Amended NEC contract
- By an Adjudicator Nominating Body
- By 'bespoke' provision in the contract

Once the appointment of the Adjudicator has been arrived at then this is normally confirmed by the Adjudicator and the Parties entering into an Adjudicator's Contract. The drafters of the NEC family of contracts envisage this being done at the time of contracting but it could also be done later. We consider here as well the way in which the appointment of the Adjudicator is confirmed.

Confirming the appointment
- By an Adjudicator's Contract

Making the appointment by agreement of the Parties

Clause 9	*Option Y(UK) 2*
This would be a matter for the agreement of the Parties outwith the strict terms of their contract	This would be a matter for the agreement of the Parties outwith the strict terms of their contract

NEC PRINCIPLES

As has been emphasised throughout this book, the guiding principle of adjudication is that it is essentially consensual. Accordingly, provided that *all* of the Parties concerned are in agreement, no matter what might be expressly provided for elsewhere (including the identity of the Adjudicator who should be appointed), the Parties are in a position to make their own agreement prevail in relation to the selection of an Adjudicator to adjudicate upon any dispute between them (although they should, of course, formally amend their contract to reflect this).

This principle has been preserved under the UK legislation and therefore, whether the contract in question is compliant or not, it should be possible for the Parties to make their will prevail so far as the selection of the Adjudicator is concerned provided that *all* of the Parties concerned are in agreement.

The agreement of the Parties to an Adjudicator

Where Clause 9 is standing alone

Notwithstanding the fact than an NEC contract exists which incorporates Clause 9 and names the Adjudicator in the contract, it would be open to *all* of the Parties (agreeing suitable compensation if necessary to the named Adjudicator) to agree that some other person should act as the Adjudicator in relation to their dispute.

Even where Clause 9 is non-compliant and the Works in question being undertaken in the UK fall within the definition of 'construction contracts' and an entitlement to use one of the applicable Schemes arises, the same principle applies in relation to the Schemes which recognise this fact in that the sections dealing with the appointment of an Adjudicator specifically state that they are 'subject to any agreement between the parties as to the dispute as to who shall act as Adjudicator.'

Where Option Y(UK) 2 has been adopted

Notwithstanding the fact than an NEC contract exists which incorporates Option Y(UK) 2 and names the Adjudicator in the contract, it would be open to *all* of the Parties (agreeing suitable compensation if necessary to the named Adjudicator) to agree that some other person should act as the Adjudicator in relation to their dispute.

Even where Option Y(UK) 2 is seen as being non-compliant and the Works in question being undertaken in the UK fall within the definition of 'construction contracts' and an entitlement to use one of the applicable Schemes arises, the same principle applies in relation to the Schemes which recognise this fact in that the sections dealing with the appointment of an Adjudicator specifically state that they are 'subject to any agreement between the parties as to the dispute as to who shall act as Adjudicator.'

Potential UK human rights points

The status of any Adjudicator appointed is likely to become one of the major areas of contention in relation to human rights principles.

Where, however, all of the Parties have agreed the appointment of the Adjudicator, then it seems unlikely that any major human rights considerations will arise.

England and Wales

The Scheme for Construction Contracts (England and Wales) Regulations 1998 SI No 649 provides:

Paragraph 2

(1)   Following the giving of a notice of adjudication and subject to any agreement between the parties to the dispute as to who shall act as adjudicator …

Scotland

The Scheme for Construction Contracts (Scotland) Regulations 1998 SI No 687 provides:

Paragraph 2

(1)   Following the giving of a notice of adjudication and subject to any agreement between the parties to the dispute as to who shall act as adjudicator ...

Northern Ireland

The Scheme for Construction Contracts in Northern Ireland Regulations (Northern Ireland) 1999 Statutory Rule 1999 No 32 provides:

Paragraph 2

(1)   Following the giving of a notice of adjudication and subject to any agreement between the parties to the dispute as to who shall act as adjudicator ...

Procedure for the appointment of the Adjudicator by agreement of the Parties

This procedure has traditionally been initiated by one of the Parties writing to the Other Parties with the name or names of persons suggested as suitable to act as Adjudicator in relation to the particular dispute (normally after first checking that the persons so named are willing to act).

The Other Party will either signal their agreement to the name put forward or to selecting one of the names put forward and signifying their agreement thereto. Alternatively, that Party, if not approving of any of the names put forward, will sometimes respond with their own list of the name or names of persons suggested as suitable to act as Adjudicator to which the original Party might agree. This procedure is followed in an attempt to reach agreement between the Parties as to the identity of the person who is going to be the Adjudicator in their dispute. Agreement will either be reached or it will not.

If agreement is reached, then confirmation should then be obtained that the person agreed upon is willing to act as the Adjudicator (something which will usually have been checked in advance).

Where the adjudication is being treated as running under the NEC adjudication procedures then a simple consent communicated in any form and within a reasonable time will presumably suffice.

In either event, consent on the part of the Adjudicator to act will normally lead to the Parties and the Adjudicator entering into an Adjudicator's Contract. That might be a 'bespoke' Adjudicator's Contract or the NEC Adjudicator's Contract might be used for that purpose.

If no agreement can be reached or the Adjudicator which the Parties have agreed upon fails for any reason, then alternative procedures will be required for the appointment of an Adjudicator.

If the contract is compliant then in the absence of any supervening agreement of the Parties as to the identity of the Adjudicator, resort could be had to the provisions of the contract for the appointment of an Adjudicator.

Where the adjudication is being treated as running under one of the applicable Schemes, then in accordance with the provisions of paragraph 2(1) [which includes agreement between the Parties to the dispute as to who shall act as Adjudicator] the person agreed upon shall indicate whether or not he or she is willing to act within two days of receiving the request. It is not entirely clear what is to happen should that person fail to reply or reply in the negative (presumably the Parties could try to reach another agreement as to the identity of a person willing to act as Adjudicator) but on a broad interpretation of the Schemes, where applicable they would allow the Referring Party to adopt the other Adjudicator-appointing provisions of the applicable Scheme, such as requesting another person (if any) named in the contract to act as Adjudicator, requesting the nominating body (if any) referred to in the contract to select a person to act as Adjudicator or requesting any other Adjudicator Nominating Body to act as Adjudicator. We consider these provisions below.

Making the appointment by unamended NEC Contract

By naming in the contract

Clause 9   *Option Y(UK) 2*

Contract Data   *Contract Data*

The Adjudicator is   The Adjudicator is

  Name [.....]   Name [.....]

  Address [.....]   Address [.....]

NEC PRINCIPLES

It is open to the Parties, at the time of contracting, to agree upon the identity of an Adjudicator at that time and to reflect that agreement by inserting in their NEC contract (in the Contract Data section) the name of the person who is to act as Adjudicator in the event of any dispute later arising under the contract.

That principle has been preserved under the UK legislation and, even where the Works in question are a 'construction contract' being carried out within the territories of the UK, the right of the Parties to name their Adjudicator in the contract will be respected under the Schemes.

Naming the Adjudicator in the contract

Where Clause 9 is standing alone

Where Clause 9 stands alone and the Adjudicator is named in the contract the appointment of the Adjudicator in the contract is likely to be respected.

Even where Clause 9 is non-compliant and the Works in question being undertaken within the UK fall within the definition of 'construction contract' so that one of the Schemes applies, the appointment of the Adjudicator in the contract is likely to be respected.

Where Option Y(UK) 2 has been adopted

Where the Parties have anticipated working on 'construction contracts' within the UK and Option Y(UK) 2 has been adopted and incorporated into their contract, where the Adjudicator is named in the contract, the appointment of the Adjudicator in the contract is likely to be respected.

Even where Option Y(UK) 2 is regarded as non-compliant in some respect, so that one of the Schemes is being treated as applicable, it is likely that the appointment of the Adjudicator in the contract will be respected.

Potential UK human rights points

The status of any Adjudicator appointed is likely to become one of the major areas of contention in relation to human rights principles.

Where, however, the Parties have agreed upon and named the Adjudicator in their contract then it is unlikely that any major human rights considerations will arise.

England and Wales

The Scheme for Construction Contracts (England and Wales) Regulations 1998 SI No 649 provides:

Paragraph 2(1)

(1)   Following the giving of a notice of adjudication …
   (a)   the referring party shall request the person (if any) specified in the contract to act as adjudicator

Commentary Where the person named in the contract has *already* indicated non-availability

Paragraph 2(1)

(1)
   (b)   if … the person named in the contract has already indicated that he is unwilling to act, and the contract provides for a specified nominating body to select a person, the referring party shall request the nominating body named in the contract to select a person to act as adjudicator.

Commentary Where the person named in the contract *later* indicates non-availability

Paragraph 2(2)

(2)   A person requested to act as adjudicator in accordance with the provisions of paragraph 1 shall indicate whether or not he is willing to act within two days of receiving the request.

Paragraph 6

(1)   Where an adjudicator who is named in the contract indicates to the parties that he is unable or unwilling to act, or where he fails to respond in accordance with paragraph 2(2) the referring party may

(a) request another person (if any) specified in the contract to act as adjudicator, or

(b) request the nominating body (if any) referred to in the contract to select a person to act as adjudicator, or

(c) request any other adjudicator nominating body to select a person to act as adjudicator.

Scotland

The Scheme for Construction Contracts (Scotland) Regulations 1998 SI No 687 provides:

Paragraph 2(1)

Following the giving of a notice of adjudication …

(a) the referring party shall request the person (if any) specified in the contract to act as adjudicator.

Commentary Where the person named in the contract has *already* indicated non-availability

Paragraph 2(1)

(b) if … the person named in the contract has already indicated that he is unwilling to act, and the contract provides for a specified nominating body to select a person, the referring party shall request the nominating body named in the contract to select a person to act as adjudicator.

Commentary Where the person named in the contract *later* indicates non-availability

Paragraph 2(2)

A person requested to act as adjudicator in accordance with the provisions of paragraph 1 shall indicate whether or not he is willing to act within two days of receiving the request.

Paragraph 6

(1)   Where an adjudicator who is named in the contract indicates to the parties that he is unable or unwilling to act, or where he fails to respond in accordance with paragraph 2(2) the referring party may

(a) request another person (if any) specified in the contract to act as adjudicator, or

(b) request the nominating body (if any) referred to in the contract to select a person to act as adjudicator, or

(c) request any other adjudicator nominating body to select a person to act as adjudicator.

Northern Ireland

The Scheme for Construction Contracts in Northern Ireland Regulations (Northern Ireland) 1999 Statutory Rule 1999 No 32 provides:

Paragraph 2(1)

Following the giving of a notice of adjudication ...

(a) the referring party shall request the person (if any) specified in the contract to act as adjudicator

Commentary Where the person named in the contract has *already* indicated non-availability

Paragraph 2(1)

(b) If ... the person named in the contract has already indicated that he is unwilling to act, and the contract provides for a specified nominating body to select a person, the referring party shall request the nominating body named in the contract to select a person to act as adjudicator.

Commentary Where the person named in the contract *later* indicates non-availability

Paragraph 2(2)

A person requested to act as adjudicator in accordance with the provisions of paragraph 1 shall indicate whether or not he is willing to act within two days of receiving the request.

Paragraph 6

(1) Where an adjudicator who is named in the contract indicates to the parties that he is unable or unwilling to act, or where he fails to respond in accordance with paragraph 2(2) the referring party may

(a) request another person (if any) specified in the contract to act as adjudicator, or

(b) request the nominating body (if any) referred to in the contract to select a person to act as adjudicator, or

(c) request any other adjudicator nominating body to select a person to act as adjudicator.

Procedure in relation to naming the Adjudicator in the contract

Under the NEC family of contracts this procedure is initiated by the Employer suggesting one or more Adjudicator by inserting their name(s) in the 'Information to be supplied by the Employer' part of the Contract Data section of the contract. The intention is that this suggestion will be negotiated and agreed by the Other Party with the agreement arrived at being reflected by having the Adjudicator chosen named in Contract Data section of the contract which the Parties sign.

Should the Adjudicator named be available when a dispute later arises then there is unlikely to be any difficulty in this respect.

Where difficulties are likely to arise, however, is where, between the contract being signed (with the Adjudicator named therein) and a dispute later arising, the Adjudicator named turns out no longer to be available.

The NEC family of contracts appears to envisage that it will be open to the Parties to reach agreement as to a replacement Adjudicator and the NEC family of contracts also provides for a nomination procedure in this eventuality which we consider in the next section. It is where agreement cannot be reached and provision has not been made or does not work that difficulties may arise.

Where however, the Works fall within the definition of 'construction contracts' being carried out within the UK and the other conditions are satisfied then no difficulties should arise and the entitlement of the Parties should not be defeated because the applicable Schemes make full provision in this respect.

The Schemes provide that a person requested to act as Adjudicator in accordance with the provisions of paragraph (1) [which includes a person specified in the contract to act as Adjudicator] shall indicate whether or not he is willing to act within two days of receiving the request.

Where the person approached responds affirmatively (within two days) then it is usually at this stage [where an Adjudicator's Contract has not already been completed] that the Parties and the Adjudicator enter into a 'bespoke' adjudicator's contract (or perhaps, at that stage, the NEC Adjudicator's Contract).

The applicable Schemes appear to envisage two situations – either the named Adjudicator indicates in advance that he or she is not available or it is when called upon to adjudicate that the Adjudicator indicates he or she is unable to act – although there seems to be little difference in effect.

In relation to the first of these situations, where the Adjudicator has indicated non-availability in advance, the Referring Party can either:

(a)   if … the contract provides for a specified nominating body to select a person (as an NEC contract usually will), the referring party shall request the nominating body named in the contract to select a person to act as Adjudicator

or

(b)   where [(a) above does not apply] request an Adjudicator Nominating Body to select a person to act as Adjudicator.

In relation to the second of these situations, where, at the point of referring the dispute, the person named as Adjudicator in the contract when approached either does not respond at all or responds to the effect that he or she is unable or unwilling to act, then in that circumstance – the Parties have named an Adjudicator in their contract and the Adjudicator has been approached but declined to act or failed to reply within two days – the Schemes give the *Referring Party* (alone) a choice:

(a)   on the basis that some contracts may provide as Adjudicator for something along the lines of 'A whom failing B', request another person (if any) specified in the contract to act as Adjudicator [in which case matters would again proceed as indicated above]

or

(b)   request the nominating body (if any) referred to in the contract (and there usually will be such a provision in NEC contracts) to select a person to act as Adjudicator

or

(c)   request any other Adjudicator Nominating Body to select a person to act as Adjudicator.

We shall consider the options of Nominating Bodies or Adjudicator Nominating Bodies next.

It should be noted that if the Referring Party is coming to the use of the Adjudicator named in the contract having failed to reach agreement with the Other Party upon an Adjudicator, or is abandoning the Adjudicator named in the contract to attempt one of the other options, then so much time is likely to have elapsed after service of the original notice of intention to refer a dispute for adjudication that the seven-day timetable laid down by the legislation as an essential requirement is likely to have expired. In these circumstances, in order to comply with the essential requirements of the legislation, the Referring Party may need to consider serving a fresh Notice of Adjudication.

By nominating

Clause 9	*Option Y(UK) 2*
Contract Data	*Contract Data*
9. Disputes and termination	9. Disputes and termination
The person who will choose a new adjudicator if the Parties cannot agree a choice is [.....]	The person who will choose a new adjudicator if the Parties cannot agree a choice is [.....]

NEC PRINCIPLES

The NEC family of contracts favours naming the Adjudicator in the contract at the time of the contract (but allows amendment providing for the appointment of the Adjudicator at the time of the dispute). In either eventuality, to cater for the original Adjudicator no longer being available, the NEC family of contracts allows for provision to be made for a procedure – nomination – under which in the absence of agreement a replacement Adjudicator will be appointed.

The UK legislation also allows for the provision by the Parties for a procedure allowing for a (named) Nominating Body to nominate an Adjudicator, although that would normally be regarded as being for the purposes of appointing an original Adjudicator rather than a replacement Adjudicator (see also Appendix A, judgment extract 23).

Appointing the Adjudicator by Nominating Body

Where Clause 9 is standing alone

Where Clause 9 stands alone and in the contract both the section naming the Adjudicator and the section naming the person to choose a new Adjudicator have been completed, then where there has been a failure in relation to the person named as Adjudicator in the contract (and the Parties cannot agree), the nomination of the replacement Adjudicator by the person chosen in the contract to so nominate is likely to be respected.

Even where Clause 9 is non-compliant, in the eventuality of any named Adjudicator not being available, then (in the absence of any agreement of the Parties) the applicable Scheme is likely to respect the procedure of the contract containing Clause 9 for nominating a replacement Adjudicator.

Where Option Y(UK) 2 has been adopted

Where Option Y(UK) 2 has been adopted and in the contract both the section naming the Adjudicator and the section naming the person to choose a new Adjudicator have been completed, then where there has been a failure in relation to the person named as Adjudicator in the contract (and the Parties cannot agree), the nomination of the replacement Adjudicator by the person chosen in the contract to so nominate is likely to be respected.

Even where Option Y(UK) 2 is seen as being non-compliant, in the eventuality of any named Adjudicator not being available, then (in the absence of any agreement of the Parties) the applicable Scheme is likely to respect the procedure of the contract containing Option Y(UK) 2 for nominating a replacement Adjudicator.

Potential UK human rights points

The status of any Adjudicator appointed is likely to become one of the major areas of contention in relation to human rights principles.

This is likely to become more important where nominations are being made outwith the agreement of the Parties, and Nominating Persons or Bodies, if challenges under human rights principles are to be avoided, ought to be aware of what is called for (both independence and impartiality) in an Adjudicator.

England and Wales

The Scheme for Construction Contracts (England and Wales) Regulations 1998 SI No 649 provides:

Paragraph 2(1)

> Following the giving of a notice of adjudication …
>
> (a) …
>
> (b) if no person is named in the contract or the person named in the contract has already indicated that he is unwilling or unable to act, and the contract provides for a specified nominating body to select a person, the referring party shall request the nominating body named in the contract to select a person to act as adjudicator.

Paragraph 5

(1)   The nominating body referred to in paragraph 2(1)(b) … must communicate the selection of an adjudicator to the referring party within five days of receiving a request to do so

(2)   Where the nominating body … fails to comply with paragraph (1), the referring party may-

  (a) agree with the other party to the dispute to request a specified person to act as adjudicator, or

  (b) request any other adjudicator nominating body to select a person to act as adjudicator

(3)   The person requested to act as adjudicator in accordance with the provisions of paragraph (1) … shall indicate whether or not he is willing to act within two days of receiving the request.

Paragraph 2(2)

> A person requested to act as adjudicator in accordance with the provisions of paragraph 1 shall indicate whether or not he is willing to act within two days of receiving the request.

Repeating the loop in the event of a paragraph 2(2) failure

Paragraph 6

(1)   Where an adjudicator … fails to respond in accordance with paragraph 2(2) the referring party may-

  (a) request another person (if any) specified in the contract to act as adjudicator, or

  (b) request the nominating body (if any) referred to in the contract to select a person to act as adjudicator, or

  (c) request any other adjudicator nominating body to select a person to act as adjudicator.

Paragraph 5

(1)   The nominating body referred to in paragraph 6(1)(b) … must communicate the selection of an adjudicator to the referring party within five days of receiving a request to do so

(2)   Where the nominating body … fails to comply with paragraph (1), the referring party may-

  (a) agree with the other party to the dispute to request a specified person to act as adjudicator, or

  (b) request any other adjudicator nominating body to select a person to act as adjudicator

(3)   The person requested to act as adjudicator in accordance with the provisions of paragraph (1) … shall indicate whether or not he is willing to act within two days of receiving the request.

Scotland

The Scheme for Construction Contracts (Scotland) Regulations 1998 SI No 687 provides:

Paragraph 2(1)

Following the giving of a notice of adjudication …

  (a) …
  (b) if no person is named in the contract or the person named in the contract has already indicated that he is unwilling or unable to act, and the contract provides for a specified nominating body to select a person, the referring party shall request the nominating body named in the contract to select a person to act as adjudicator.

Paragraph 5

(1)   The nominating body referred to in paragraph 2(1)(b) … must communicate the selection of an adjudicator to the referring party within five days of receiving a request to do so
(2)   Where the nominating body … fails to comply with paragraph (1), the referring party may-
  (a) agree with the other party to the dispute to request a specified person to act as adjudicator, or
  (b) request any other adjudicator nominating body to select a person to act as adjudicator
(3)   The person requested to act as adjudicator in accordance with the provisions of paragraph (1) … shall indicate whether or not he is willing to act within two days of receiving the request.

Paragraph 2(2)

A person requested to act as adjudicator in accordance with the provisions of paragraph 1 shall indicate whether or not he is willing to act within two days of receiving the request.

Repeating the loop in the event of a paragraph 2(2) failure

Paragraph 6

(1)   Where an adjudicator … fails to respond in accordance with paragraph 2(2) the referring party may-
  (a) request another person (if any) specified in the contract to act as adjudicator, or
  (b) request the nominating body (if any) referred to in the contract to select a person to act as adjudicator, or
  (c) request any other adjudicator nominating body to select a person to act as adjudicator.

Paragraph 5

(1)   The nominating body referred to in paragraph 6(1)(b) ... must communicate the selection of an adjudicator to the referring party within five days of receiving a request to do so

(2)   Where the nominating body ... fails to comply with paragraph (1), the referring party may-

   (a) agree with the other party to the dispute to request a specified person to act as adjudicator, or

   (b) request any other adjudicator nominating body to select a person to act as adjudicator

(3)   The person requested to act as adjudicator in accordance with the provisions of paragraph (1) ... shall indicate whether or not he is willing to act within two days of receiving the request.

Northern Ireland

The Scheme for Construction Contracts in Northern Ireland Regulations (Northern Ireland) 1999 Statutory Rule 1999 No 32 provides:

Paragraph 2(1)

Following the giving of a notice of adjudication ...

   (a) ...

   (b) if no person is named in the contract or the person named in the contract has already indicated that he is unwilling or unable to act, and the contract provides for a specified nominating body to select a person, the referring party shall request the nominating body named in the contract to select a person to act as adjudicator.

Paragraph 5

(1)   The nominating body referred to in paragraph 2(1)(b) ... must communicate the selection of an adjudicator to the referring party within five days of receiving a request to do so

(2)   Where the nominating body ... fails to comply with paragraph (1), the referring party may-

   (a) agree with the other party to the dispute to request a specified person to act as adjudicator, or

   (b) request any other adjudicator nominating body to select a person to act as adjudicator

(3)   The person requested to act as adjudicator in accordance with the provisions of paragraph (1) ... shall indicate whether or not he is willing to act within two days of receiving the request.

Paragraph 2(2)

A person requested to act as adjudicator in accordance with the provisions of paragraph 1 shall indicate whether or not he is willing to act within two days of receiving the request.

Repeating the loop in the event of a paragraph 2(2) failure

Paragraph 6

(1)   Where an adjudicator … fails to respond in accordance with paragraph 2(2) the referring party may-
  (a) request another person (if any) specified in the contract to act as adjudicator, or
  (b) request the nominating body (if any) referred to in the contract to select a person to act as adjudicator, or
  (c) request any other adjudicator nominating body to select a person to act as adjudicator.

Paragraph 5

(1)   The nominating body referred to in paragraph 6(1)(b) … must communicate the selection of an adjudicator to the referring party within five days of receiving a request to do so
(2)   Where the nominating body … fails to comply with paragraph (1), the referring party may-
  (a) agree with the other party to the dispute to request a specified person to act as adjudicator, or
  (b) request any other adjudicator nominating body to select a person to act as adjudicator
(3)   The person requested to act as adjudicator in accordance with the provisions of paragraph (1) … shall indicate whether or not he is willing to act within two days of receiving the request.

Procedure in relation to a Nominating Body or Person in the contract

This nomination procedure is utilised in the NEC family of contracts for the appointment of a replacement Adjudicator in the absence of the agreement of the Parties. It is clearly dependent upon the Parties completing that section of the Contract Data which calls for the details of the Nominating Person or Body to be inserted.

Where the Parties have nominated such a person in their contract then, in the absence of any agreement, the Parties (or technically the Submitting Party whose task it is) will simply request that nominated person to choose a new Adjudicator.

Where, however, the other conditions also being satisfied and the Works fall within the definition of 'construction contracts' and are being carried out within the UK, then the applicable Schemes will also recognise that nominating procedure.

The applicable Schemes envisage that this will be used for the appointment of an original Adjudicator, but where the contract provides for a nominating procedure for the appointment of a replacement Adjudicator then that is likely to be recognised and respected under any applicable Scheme.

The person nominated will (or ought to) be aware of the requirement that, where work on a 'construction contract' is to be carried out under an NEC contract within the UK, the Schemes require the person nominated to be a natural person acting in his personal capacity [i.e. not a firm] and not to be an employee of any of the Parties to the dispute. They ought also to be aware of the requirements imposed by human rights considerations. The consequences where the Nominating Body or Person breaches this provision of the Scheme have not yet been tested.

The requirements of the applicable Scheme – which may be taken to apply where the contract is, in whole or in part, considered to be non-compliant – is that the Nominating Body (or Person) must communicate the selection of an Adjudicator to the Referring Party within five days of receiving a request (accompanied by a Notice of Adjudication) to do so.

Where the Nominating Body (or Person) fails to comply with that requirement then the Schemes give the Referring Party (alone) a choice. The Referring Party can either:

(*a*) agree with the other party to the dispute to request a specified person to act as adjudicator [on which see the preceding section] or

(*b*) request any other adjudicator nominating body to select a person to act as adjudicator.

Where, however, the Nominating Body (or Person) does nominate an Adjudicator then the person so requested to act as adjudicator shall indicate whether or not he is willing to act within two days of receiving the request.

Where the person approached responds affirmatively (within two days) then it is usually at this stage [if the Adjudicator's Contract has not already been completed] that the Parties and the Adjudicator enter into a 'bespoke' adjudicator's contract (or perhaps, at that stage, the NEC Adjudicator's Contract).

Where, however, the person so nominated either does not respond at all or responds to the effect that he or she is unable or unwilling to act, then in that circumstance the Schemes allow the *Referring Party* (alone) to request any other Adjudicator Nominating Body to select a person to act as Adjudicator.

Where, however, that section of the Contract Data has not been completed then, on the failure of the original Adjudicator, it may not (unless the *lex mercatoria* can help) be possible to proceed to an adjudication. Where, however, the other conditions also being satisfied and the Works fall within the definition of 'construction contracts' and are being carried out within the UK, then that will not be allowed to happen and resort will instead be made to the use of Adjudicator Nominating Bodies which we consider next.

It should be noted that if the Referring Party is coming to the use of the Nominating Body (or Person) named in the contract having failed to reach agreement with the Other Party upon an Adjudicator or in abandoning the Adjudicator named in the contract to attempt one of the other options, then so much time is likely to have elapsed after service of the original notice of intention to refer a dispute for adjudication that the seven-day timetable laid down by the legislation as an essential requirement is likely to have expired. In these circumstances, in order to comply with the essential requirements of the legislation, the Referring Party may need to consider serving a fresh Notice of Adjudication.

By an Adjudicator Nominating Body

Clause 9   *Option Y(UK) 2*

No provision is made in this respect No provision is made in this respect

NEC PRINCIPLES

As drafted, the NEC family of contracts does not make any provision for the use of Adjudicator Nominating Bodies. As earlier noted, it is possible to amend such contracts so as to provide for the use of Adjudicator Nominating Bodies.

Where no amendment has been made to the NEC contracts then a failure on the part of both the Adjudicator named in the contract and any person nominated to choose an Adjudicator could, in the absence of any agreement between the Parties, bring the process of adjudication to a premature conclusion.

However, where the Works fall within the definition of a 'construction contract' within the territories of the UK, then the Party with a dispute has the entitlement to see to it that this does not happen and that will be done by implying into the contract from the applicable statutory scheme provisions which will allow for the appointment of an Adjudicator through the use of Adjudicator Nominating Bodies.

Appointing the Adjudicator by an Adjudicator Nominating Body

Where Clause 9 is standing alone

Where Clause 9 is standing alone but the provisions in the contract to which it relates have failed as regards the Adjudicator named and any person nominated to choose an Adjudicator, then a failure of the Parties to agree will not necessarily bring the adjudication process to a premature end where the Works are being carried out within the UK and fall within the definition of 'construction contracts'. In these circumstances, the Party with a dispute may be entitled to insist that at least sufficient provisions are implied into the contract from the applicable Scheme (if not the whole Scheme) which will allow for the appointment of an Adjudicator through the use of an Adjudicator Nominating Body.

Where Option Y(UK) 2 has been adopted

Where Option Y(UK) 2 has been adopted but the provisions in the contract to which it relates have failed as regards the Adjudicator named and any person nominated to choose an Adjudicator, then a failure of the Parties to agree will not necessarily bring the adjudication process to a premature end where the Works are being carried out within the UK and fall within the definition of 'construction contracts'. In these circumstances, the Party with a dispute may be entitled to insist that at least sufficient provisions are implied into the contract from the applicable Scheme (if not the whole Scheme) which will allow for the appointment of an Adjudicator through the use of an Adjudicator Nominating Body.

Potential UK human rights points

The status of any Adjudicator appointed is likely to become one of the major areas of contention in relation to human rights principles.

This is particularly important where nominations are being made outwith the agreement of the Parties.

Adjudicator Nominating Bodies ought, therefore, to be aware of the human rights principles which may apply to Adjudicators (both independence and impartiality) if challenges are to be avoided in this area.

England and Wales

The Scheme for Construction Contracts (England and Wales) Regulations 1998 SI No 649 provides:

Paragraph 2(1)

Following the giving of a notice of adjudication ...

    (a) ...
    (b) ...
    (c) where neither paragraph (a) nor (b) above applies, or where the person referred to in (a) has already indicated that he is unwilling or unable to act and (b) does not apply, the referring party shall request an adjudicator nominating body to select a person to act as adjudicator.

Paragraph 3

The request referred to in paragraph 2 ... shall be accompanied by a copy of the notice of adjudication.

Paragraph 5

(1)   The adjudicator nominating body referred to in paragraph 2(1)(c) ... must communicate the selection of an adjudicator to the referring party within five days of receiving a request to do so

(2)   Where the nominating body ... fails to comply with paragraph (1), the referring party may-

   (a) agree with the other party to the dispute to request a specified person to act as adjudicator, or

   (b) request any other adjudicator nominating body to select a person to act as adjudicator

(3)   The person requested to act as adjudicator in accordance with the provisions of paragraph (1) ... shall indicate whether or not he is willing to act within two days of receiving the request.

Paragraph 5

(1)   The adjudicator nominating body referred to in paragraph 5(2)(b) ... must communicate the selection of an adjudicator to the referring party within five days of receiving a request to do so

(2)   Where the nominating body ... fails to comply with paragraph (1), the referring party may-

(a)   agree with the other party to the dispute to request a specified person to act as adjudicator, or

(b)   request any other adjudicator nominating body to select a person to act as adjudicator

(3)   The person requested to act as adjudicator in accordance with the provisions of paragraph (1) … shall indicate whether or not he is willing to act within two days of receiving the request.

Paragraph 2(2)

A person requested to act as adjudicator in accordance with the provisions of paragraph 1 shall indicate whether or not he is willing to act within two days of receiving the request.

Repeating the loop in the event of paragraph 2(2) failure

Paragraph 6

(1)   Where an adjudicator … fails to respond in accordance with paragraph 2(2) the referring party may

(a)   request another person (if any) specified in the contract to act as adjudicator, or

(b)   request the nominating body (if any) referred to in the contract to select a person to act as adjudicator, or

(c)   request any other adjudicator nominating body to select a person to act as adjudicator

Paragraph 5

(1)   The adjudicator nominating body referred to in paragraph 6(1)(c) … must communicate the selection of an adjudicator to the referring party within five days of receiving a request to do so

(2)   Where the nominating body … fails to comply with paragraph (1), the referring party may-

(a)   agree with the other party to the dispute to request a specified person to act as adjudicator, or

(b)   request any other adjudicator nominating body to select a person to act as adjudicator

(3)   The person requested to act as adjudicator in accordance with the provisions of paragraph (1) … shall indicate whether or not he is willing to act within two days of receiving the request.

Scotland

The Scheme for Construction Contracts (Scotland) Regulations 1998 SI No 687 provides:

Paragraph 2(1)

Following the giving of a notice of adjudication …

(a)   …
(b)   …

(c)   where neither paragraph (a) nor (b) above applies, or where the person referred to in (a) has already indicated that he is unwilling or unable to act and (b) does not apply, the referring party shall request an adjudicator nominating body to select a person to act as adjudicator

Paragraph 3

The request referred to in paragraph 2 ... shall be accompanied by a copy of the notice of adjudication.

Paragraph 5

(1)   The adjudicator nominating body referred to in paragraph 2(1)(c) ... must communicate the selection of an adjudicator to the referring party within five days of receiving a request to do so

(2)   Where the nominating body ... fails to comply with paragraph (1), the referring party may-

  (a)   agree with the other party to the dispute to request a specified person to act as adjudicator, or

  (b)   request any other adjudicator nominating body to select a person to act as adjudicator

(3)   The person requested to act as adjudicator in accordance with the provisions of paragraph (1) ... shall indicate whether or not he is willing to act within two days of receiving the request.

Paragraph 5

(1)   The adjudicator nominating body referred to in paragraph 5(2)(b) ... must communicate the selection of an adjudicator to the referring party within five days of receiving a request to do so

(2)   Where the nominating body ... fails to comply with paragraph (1), the referring party may-

  (a)   agree with the other party to the dispute to request a specified person to act as adjudicator, or

  (b)   request any other adjudicator nominating body to select a person to act as adjudicator

(3)   The person requested to act as adjudicator in accordance with the provisions of paragraph (1) ... shall indicate whether or not he is willing to act within two days of receiving the request.

Paragraph 2(2)

A person requested to act as adjudicator in accordance with the provisions of paragraph 1 shall indicate whether or not he is willing to act within two days of receiving the request.

Repeating the loop in the event of paragraph 2(2) failure

Paragraph 6

(1)   Where an adjudicator ... fails to respond in accordance with paragraph 2(2) the referring party may-

  (a)   request another person (if any) specified in the contract to act as adjudicator, or

   (b) request the nominating body (if any) referred to in the contract to select a person to act as adjudicator, or

   (c) request any other adjudicator nominating body to select a person to act as adjudicator

Paragraph 5

(1)   The adjudicator nominating body referred to in paragraph 6(1)(c) … must communicate the selection of an adjudicator to the referring party within five days of receiving a request to do so

(2)   Where the nominating body … fails to comply with paragraph (1), the referring party may-

   (a) agree with the other party to the dispute to request a specified person to act as adjudicator, or

   (b) request any other adjudicator nominating body to select a person to act as adjudicator

(3)   The person requested to act as adjudicator in accordance with the provisions of paragraph (1) … shall indicate whether or not he is willing to act within two days of receiving the request.

Northern Ireland

The Scheme for Construction Contracts in Northern Ireland Regulations (Northern Ireland) 1999 Statutory Rule 1999 No 32 provides:

Paragraph 2(1)

Following the giving of a notice of adjudication …

   (a) …

   (b) …

   (c) where neither paragraph (a) nor (b) above applies, or where the person referred to in (a) has already indicated that he is unwilling or unable to act and (b) does not apply, the referring party shall request an adjudicator nominating body to select a person to act as adjudicator

Paragraph 3

The request referred to in paragraph 2 … shall be accompanied by a copy of the notice of adjudication.

Paragraph 5

(1)   The adjudicator nominating body referred to in paragraph 2(1)(c) … must communicate the selection of an adjudicator to the referring party within five days of receiving a request to do so

(2)   Where the nominating body … fails to comply with paragraph (1), the referring party may-

   (a) agree with the other party to the dispute to request a specified person to act as adjudicator, or

   (b) request any other adjudicator nominating body to select a person to act as adjudicator

(3)   The person requested to act as adjudicator in accordance with the provisions of paragraph (1) … shall indicate whether or not he is willing to act within two days of receiving the request.

Paragraph 5

(1)   The adjudicator nominating body referred to in paragraph 5(2)(b) … must communicate the selection of an adjudicator to the referring party within five days of receiving a request to do so

(2)   Where the nominating body … fails to comply with paragraph (1), the referring party may-

  (a) agree with the other party to the dispute to request a specified person to act as adjudicator, or

  (b) request any other adjudicator nominating body to select a person to act as adjudicator

(3)   The person requested to act as adjudicator in accordance with the provisions of paragraph (1) … shall indicate whether or not he is willing to act within two days of receiving the request.

Paragraph 2(2)

A person requested to act as adjudicator in accordance with the provisions of paragraph 1 shall indicate whether or not he is willing to act within two days of receiving the request.

Repeating the loop in the event of paragraph 2(2) failure

Paragraph 6

(1)   Where an adjudicator … fails to respond in accordance with paragraph 2(2) the referring party may-

  (a) request another person (if any) specified in the contract to act as adjudicator, or

  (b) request the nominating body (if any) referred to in the contract to select a person to act as adjudicator, or

  (c) request any other adjudicator nominating body to select a person to act as adjudicator

Paragraph 5

(1)   The adjudicator nominating body referred to in paragraph 6(1)(c) … must communicate the selection of an adjudicator to the referring party within five days of receiving a request to do so

(2)   Where the nominating body … fails to comply with paragraph (1), the referring party may-

  (a) agree with the other party to the dispute to request a specified person to act as adjudicator, or

  (b) request any other adjudicator nominating body to select a person to act as adjudicator

(3)   The person requested to act as adjudicator in accordance with the provisions of paragraph (1) … shall indicate whether or not he is willing to act within two days of receiving the request.

Procedure in relation to an Adjudicator Nominating Body in the contract

There is no obligation upon a qualifying Party with a dispute to use Adjudicator Nominating Bodies but it is their entitlement to do so if they so wish.

A person so wishing will normally simply select a body holding itself out publicly as an Adjudicator Nominating Body (for example, the Royal Institution of Chartered Surveyors or the Institute of Chartered Arbitrators).

Adjudicator Nominating Bodies will (or ought to) be aware of the requirement that, where work on a 'construction contract' is to be carried out under an NEC contract within the UK, the Schemes require the person nominated to be a natural person acting in his personal capacity [i.e. not a firm] and not to be an employee of any of the Parties to the dispute. The consequences where the Adjudicator Nominating Body breaches this provision of the Scheme have not yet been tested.

The Schemes provide that the Adjudicator Nominating Body must communicate the selection of an Adjudicator to the Referring Party within five days of receiving a request (accompanied by a Notice of Adjudication) to do so.

Where the Adjudicator Nominating Body fails to comply with that requirement then the Schemes give the Referring Party (alone) a choice. The Referring Party can either:

(a) agree with the Other Party to the dispute to request a specified person to act as Adjudicator [on which see the preceding section] or
(b) request any other Adjudicator Nominating Body to select a person to act as Adjudicator.

Where, however, the Adjudicator Nominating Body does nominate an Adjudicator then the person so requested to act as Adjudicator shall indicate whether or not he is willing to act within two days of receiving the request.

Where the person approached responds affirmatively (within two days) then it is usually at this stage [if the Adjudicator's Contract has not already been completed] that the Parties and the Adjudicator enter into a 'bespoke' adjudicator's contract (or perhaps, at that stage, the NEC Adjudicator's Contract).

Where, however, the person so nominated either does not respond at all or responds to the effect that he or she is unable or unwilling to act, then in that circumstance the Schemes allow the *Referring Party* (alone) to request any other Adjudicator Nominating Body to select a person to act as Adjudicator [in which case the above procedure will be repeated]

It should be noted that if the Referring Party is coming to the use of an Adjudicator Nominating Body having failed to reach agreement with the Other Party upon an Adjudicator or in abandoning the Adjudicator named in the contract to attempt one of the other options, or as a result of the failure of the specified Nominating Body or Person, then so much time is likely to have elapsed after service of the original notice of intention to refer a dispute for adjudication that the seven-day timetable laid down by the legislation as an essential requirement is likely to have expired. In these circumstances, in order to comply with the essential requirements of the legislation, the Referring Party may need to consider serving a fresh Notice of Adjudication.

Making the appointment by amended NEC contract

By 'bespoke' provision in the contract

Clause 9

Option Y(UK) 2

There is no prohibition on amendment in this contract

There is no prohibition on amendment in this contract

NEC PRINCIPLES

There is no prohibition against amending any of the NEC family of contracts.

Even where, all other conditions being satisfied, the Works fall within the definition of 'construction contracts' being carried out within the United Kingdom, any amendment to the standard NEC contract will be recognised and respected under the applicable Schemes, provided that any amendment does not conflict with any of the essential requirements contained in the UK legislation.

A fertile area for amendment is in relation to the appointment of the Adjudicator. One of the difficulties in this respect (especially in relation to large projects) is the selection of an appropriate Adjudicator. If an Expert suited to the area is selected in relation to each contract then it may be necessary to appoint a large number of Adjudicators. If a single Adjudicator (other than a lawyer) is appointed to cover a number of contracts then that single Adjudicator may not have the expertise to cover every dispute which may arise.

One solution to this problem, which some Parties prefer to adopt, is to defer the appointment of the Adjudicator until the dispute has arisen and then to select an Adjudicator whose skills closely match the dispute in question. To do so, however, would require amending the NEC contracts. This will normally be done by leaving the section for naming the Adjudicator blank or striking it out and using Option Z to provide for additional conditions of contract covering the appointment of the Adjudicator.

The extent of any amendment will clearly be a matter for the Parties. Where any of the Schemes are applicable, the concern will be not so much with the particular contractual provision made but with the essential requirement that there be a timetable for the appointment of the Adjudicator and the referral of the dispute to the Adjudicator within seven days.

Potential UK human rights points

The Parties, in making amendments to their contract – and through those provisions any named Nominating Bodies or unnamed Adjudicator Nominating Bodies – should have regard to the requirements of natural justice or fairness and the principles of the human rights convention as, indeed, the case referred to below (although it pre-dates the HR Act 1996) indicates.

England and Wales

Commentary In one adjudication case – John Mowlem & Company plc *v* Hydra-Tight Ltd (6 June 2000) – a case which in fact involved the NEC Engineering and Construction Sub-contract which also used Option Z and incorporated Option Y(UK) 2, this very point came up.

In the sub-contract, the Parties did not name an Adjudicator but instead, using Option Z, provided that upon a dispute arising the Adjudicator should be nominated by the Contractor from a set of Barristers' Chambers (the intention presumably being that there could then be selected as the Adjudicator the Barrister whose experience most closely matched the dispute which had arisen).

A dispute did arise in that sub-contract, but Hydra-Tight Ltd sought to implement the applicable Scheme (the Scheme for Construction Contracts (England and Wales) Regulations) and also sought to use thereunder the services of an Adjudicator Nominating Body (first the RICS and then the ICE) to nominate an Adjudicator. Mowlem objected to that and sought to adhere to the contractual procedure for the appointment of the Adjudicator. They then sought a Declaration from the Technology and Construction Court where the matter came before His Honour Judge Toulmin.

Clause 8(1)(e) of the Parties' 'bespoke' amendment refers to membership of the set 'current at the date of the notification of the dispute'. At the outset of the case, an issue arose between the Parties as to whether this should be construed as meaning the members of the set for the time being or whether there should physically exist a piece of paper headed 'approved list of adjudicators' which should be updated from time to time as members joined and left the set of Chambers. In the opinion of His Honour Judge Toulmin, there was no difficulty in construing the list of adjudicators under clause 8.1(e) as being the members of the Chambers for the time being.

It is noteworthy, however, that His Honour Judge Toulmin went on to point out that this method enables an Adjudicator to be appointed who is free from any actual or perceived conflict of interest and would also give the Other Party an opportunity to object to a proposed Adjudicator on the grounds of actual or perceived conflict of interest.

Having concluded [on the basis of a joint submission from the Parties' representatives] that the contract was non-compliant with the HGCR Act 1996, His Honour Judge Toulmin then sought to apply the applicable Scheme (the Scheme for Construction Contracts (England and Wales) Regulations) and asked first of all whether (under para 2.1) there was a person specified in the contract to act as Adjudicator. The issue then came down to whether the set of Chambers was sufficient identification of the Adjudicator or whether the Scheme requires an individual Adjudicator to be identified in advance. His Honour Judge Toulmin concluded that the Scheme did not so require and that it was sufficient where the person specified in the contract is a member of the set of Chambers to be selected by the Contractor as Adjudicator at the time when the dispute arises.

Scotland

Although Scotland does not now have sets of Chambers and will look askance at such, the above English decision is nevertheless likely to be of persuasive authority in Scotland.

Northern Ireland

The above English decision is likely to be of persuasive value in Northern Ireland.

Procedure in relation to 'bespoke' provision in the contract

The above case is a good example of how 'bespoke' contractual provision for the appointment of an Adjudicator might be expected to operate within the applicable Scheme.

Thus, even though the contract concerned was agreed to be and was held to be non-compliant, what ought to have happened, *even under the Scheme*, was that the contractual procedure for using the person selected as the Adjudicator in the contract (in this case a set of Chambers) should have been used.

Confirming the appointment

By an Adjudicator's Contract

Clause 9	*Option Y(UK) 2*
It is envisaged that an Adjudicator's Contract will be completed	It is envisaged that an Adjudicator's Contract will be completed

NEC PRINCIPLES

By whatever means the appointment is arrived at, the Adjudicator will usually want to enter into a contract with the Parties.

The drafters of the NEC family of contracts produce an Adjudicator's Contract. They in fact produce two Forms of Agreement – one 'to be used only when the United Kingdom Housing Grants, Construction and Regeneration Act 1996 Scheme for Construction Contracts Regulations 1998 applies' and the other 'Not to be used when a United Kingdom Scheme for Construction Contracts applies'. There are Standard Conditions which apply to both.

It is envisaged by the drafters of the NEC contracts that at the time when the Parties are contracting, the name of the Adjudicator will be inserted into the contract and at that time the Parties and the named Adjudicator will also enter into the Adjudicator's Contract. However, there seems nothing to prevent the Adjudicator's Contract being entered into at a later stage.

Where the Adjudicator is appointed by some method other than by naming in the contract then different considerations may apply. The Adjudicator thereby selected when confirming a willingness to act will, usually, seek to have that Adjudicator's own 'bespoke' Adjudicator's Contract entered into. The terms of these vary but in general follow a common theme. The NEC Adjudicator's Contract states that it is capable of being used in relation to contracts which are not from the NEC family of contracts.

There is no requirement in the legislation or the Schemes for an Adjudicator's Contract to be used. However, even where the Schemes are being adopted, it is usual for an Adjudicator's Contract to be entered into. The NEC Adjudicator's Contract could be used for that purpose.

As a matter of practice, it sometimes happens that a recalcitrant Party seeks to avoid or at least delay an adjudication by refusing or delaying entering into an Adjudicator's Contract. The prevailing view appears to be that in such circumstances an Adjudicator should proceed with the adjudication in the absence of an executed Adjudicator's Contract, relying instead upon the provisions of the Scheme for protection and the recovery of fees and expenses.

Potential UK human rights points

The primary purpose of an Adjudicator's Contract is to regulate the relationship between the Parties and the Adjudicator. There are unlikely to be substantive human rights considerations arising out of these aspects.

England and Wales

There are no provisions relating to an Adjudicator's Contract.

Scotland

There are no provisions relating to an Adjudicator's Contract.

Northern Ireland

There are no provisions relating to an Adjudicator's Contract.

The referral of the dispute

Clause 9	Option Y(UK) 2
Clause 90.1	Clause 90.5
The Party submits the dispute to the Adjudicator	The notifying Party refers the dispute to the Adjudicator

NEC PRINCIPLES

The NEC family of contracts adopts what might be considered to be a two-stage process. For any claim which has arisen there is first of all notification (followed by a period of grace) and then secondly submission of the dispute.

The UK legislation also regards adjudication as a two-step process (albeit without any period of grace and reduced to a timetable of seven days). There is first the Notice of Adjudication. This initiates the process and is instrumental in the appointment of the Adjudicator. In practice, service of such a notice has been taken as an indication that the Other Party is serious and it often provokes a settlement. What the legislation does require (if the adjudication is to go ahead) is referral of the dispute to the Adjudicator within seven days of the Notice of Adjudication.

As interpreted, therefore, the Notice of Adjudication has become the determinative document – framing and interpreting the nature of the dispute – while the referral notice appears to be adopting something of a secondary role.

The relevant UK legislation (as opposed to the Schemes) does not make it an essential requirement that the referral notice should be in any particular format.

The format of the referral notice

Where Clause 9 is standing alone

Clause 9 standing alone makes no specific provision as to the form which any referral notice has to take and the drafters of the NEC family of contracts appear to be content to leave that as a matter of professional practice.

As earlier noted, the difficulty with Clause 9 standing alone, in relation to Works falling within the definition of 'construction contracts' which are being performed within the UK, is that it does not provide for the essential requirement of referral of the dispute to the Adjudicator within seven days of notification of intention to refer a dispute for adjudication.

If the view is taken that it is only necessary to imply in from the applicable Scheme that which is necessary to satisfy an essential requirement of the legislation then, because the format of the referral notice is not itself an essential requirement, it could be argued that the Parties can refer the dispute to the Adjudicator as they normally would under Clause 9.

Where, however, either the Parties have agreed between themselves that the applicable Scheme is to apply in its entirety or the view is taken that the law requires the applicable Scheme to be applied in its entirety, then consideration would have to be given to the requirements of the applicable Scheme relating to the format of the referral notice.

Where Option Y(UK) 2 has been adopted

Where Parties to an NEC contract have envisaged working within the UK on Works which fall within the definition of a 'construction contract' and have adopted Option Y(UK) 2 then it is suggested that their contract, in this respect at least, is compliant with UK legislation.

If so, then as a contract complying with the essential requirements of the legislation, nothing requires to be implied from any applicable statutory Scheme.

Option Y(UK) 2 makes no specific reference to the format which must be adopted for a referral notice. However, for the avoidance of doubt, consideration could be given to making the referral notice comply with the format suggested in the Schemes.

Potential UK human rights points

The main thrust of the human rights legislation is likely to relate to the fair and proper procedures adopted under the process of adjudication. Fair notice requires to be given and this will normally be in the Notice of Adjudication. Nevertheless, human rights considerations may arise in relation to the referral notice, its contents and timing.

England and Wales

The Scheme for Construction Contracts (England and Wales) Regulations 1998 SI No 649 provides:

Paragraph 7

(1)   Where an adjudicator has been selected in accordance with paragraphs 2, 5 or 6, the referring party shall, not later than seven days from the date of the notice of adjudication, refer the dispute in writing (the 'referral notice') to the adjudicator

(2)   A referral notice shall be accompanied by copies of, or relevant extracts from, the construction contract and such other documents as the referring party intends to rely upon.

Scotland

The Scheme for Construction Contracts (Scotland) Regulations 1998 SI No 687 provides:

Paragraph 7

(1)   Where an adjudicator has been selected in accordance with paragraphs 2, 5 or 6, the referring party shall, not later than seven days from the date of the notice of adjudication, refer the dispute in writing (the 'referral notice') to the adjudicator

(2)   A referral notice shall be accompanied by copies of, or relevant extracts from, the construction contract and such other documents as the referring party intends to rely upon.

Northern Ireland

The Scheme for Construction Contracts in Northern Ireland Regulations (Northern Ireland) 1999 Statutory Rule No 32 provides:

Paragraph 7

(1)   Where an adjudicator has been selected in accordance with paragraphs 2, 5 or 6, the referring party shall, not later than seven days from the date of the notice of adjudication, refer the dispute in writing (the 'referral notice') to the adjudicator.

(2)   A referral notice shall be accompanied by copies of, or relevant extracts from, the construction contract and such other documents as the referring party intends to rely upon.

Time limits in launching an adjudication

It is clear that UK legislation has created a very tight timetable in the time-table, running from the notice of intention to refer a dispute to adjudication, of seven days for the appointment and referral of the dispute to the Adjudicator.

Clearly, were a Notice of Adjudication to be launched on Day 1 and an approach made to the Adjudicator named in the contract only to find that that Adjudicator was indisposed and that an approach to the Nominating Body was necessary then it would be virtually impossible to comply with the time-table of seven days.

It has not yet been determined to what extent the essential requirement of appointment and referral within seven days is mandatory (such that a failure to comply with it makes any decision null and void) or directory (such that any slippage will not affect any decision made).

On the one hand, the legislation states only that the timetable have the *object* of securing the appointment and referral. On the other hand, it is within the capability of the Referring Party to remedy any defect by issuing of a fresh Notice of Adjudication. Just as the timetable for commencing an adjudication is tight, so too is the timetable for arriving at a decision. Even a slight amount of slippage in the overall timetable is likely to prejudice the Party Receiving, perhaps even to the extent of being a human rights concern. Any objection would, however, require to be taken timeously since to proceed thereafter is likely to be taken as consenting to the adjudication.

It is suggested where a Party has experienced delay in the appointment of an Adjudicator but has eventually found a suitable Adjudicator that, for the avoidance of doubt, the Party issues to that Adjudicator and the Other Party a fresh Notice of Adjudication which will effectively 're-set' the clock on the adjudication and allow the adjudication to proceed free of challenge in an unprejudiced manner.

Summary

Clause 9	*Option Y(UK) 2*
Notification	*Notification*
The Party concerned notifies the relevant person of the dispute. (some time limits apply)	The Party concerned notifies his dissatisfaction to the Project Manager. (a four week time period)
Settlement/crystallisation period a two week period	*Settlement/ crystallisation period* a four week period
Notice of intention to refer a dispute to adjudication	*Notice of intention to refer a dispute to adjudication*
	Clause 90.5

No such procedure

Either Party may give notice to the other Party at any time of his intention to refer a dispute to adjudication.

Appointment

Appointment

Unamended NEC contract

Unamended NEC contract

Contract Data:

Contract Data:

The Adjudicator is

The Adjudicator is

 Name [.....]

 Name [.....]

 Address [.....]

 Address [.....]

Amended NEC contract

Amended NEC contract

Adjudicator appointed at the time the dispute arises per procedure agreed in the contract

Adjudicator appointed at the time the dispute arises per procedure agreed in the contract

Submission or Referral

Referral

Clause 90.5

The Party submits the dispute to the Adjudicator between two and four weeks after notification of the dispute

The notifying Party refers the dispute to the Adjudicator within seven days of the notice

NEC PRINCIPLES

The procedures for the appointment and referral of the dispute to the Adjudicator which the NEC family of contracts provides for under both Clause 9 standing alone and where Option Y(UK) 2 has been adopted are summarised above.

 The basic and essential requirement (essential requirement No 2) of the relevant UK legislation, on the other hand, is simply that the contract in question shall provide a procedure which has the object of securing *both* the appointment of the Adjudicator *and* the referral of the dispute to him or her within a timetable of seven days.

 Where, therefore, the other conditions being satisfied, Works falling within the definition of 'construction contracts' are being carried out within the UK, a view will require to be taken on the compatibility of the NEC contract in question with the relevant UK legislation.

Where Clause 9 is standing alone

Leaving to one side considerations about settlement/crystallisation and when a 'dispute' has truly arisen (which we considered in Section I), the difficulty with Clause 9 standing alone is that Clause 9 does *not* provide a timetable with the object of securing the appointment of the Adjudicator and the referral of the dispute to him or her within seven days of the giving of notice of intention to refer the dispute to adjudication.

Clause 9 does not, as such, provide for a formal 'notice of adjudication' or indeed for anything formally called a 'timetable', but assuming that these are not made *vox signata* by the legislation, the difficulty with Clause 9 lies in its prohibition on submitting the dispute to the Adjudicator within the period of two weeks following notification of the dispute to the Other Party and Project Manager (as the case may be). This is clearly contradictory to the essential requirement of the UK legislation that the contract in question must provide a timetable with the object of securing the appointment of the Adjudicator and the referral of the dispute to him or her within seven days of the giving of notice of intention to refer the dispute to adjudication.

As a result, in relation to Works which fall within the definition of a 'construction contract' within the territory of the United Kingdom, an NEC Contract which contains only Clause 9 is not compliant with the legislation.

The position then is that a view requires to be taken on whether only some of the provisions of the applicable Scheme require to be imported to meet the essential requirements of the UK legislation or whether (as some first instance authority suggests (*obiter*)) the consequences of any breach of an essential requirement is that the applicable Scheme is imported wholesale.

If the view is taken, either by agreement of the Parties or by interpretation of the law, that the only implication necessary from the applicable Scheme (seen as directory) is that required to meet a missing essential requirement, then much of what might have gone before in Clause 9 could be preserved. Any notification previously given could stand and it could simply be provided – by implication – that under Clause 9 submission to the Adjudicator must be made within seven days of that notification and that this will be sufficient to comply with the essential requirements of the legislation.

If the view is taken, however, that the failure of Clause 9 is such that the applicable Scheme (seen as mandatory) requires to be implied wholesale, then whatever has gone before would require to be rejected and the Party would need to start again with a formal notice of intention to refer a dispute to adjudication in the required format, followed by the appointment of the Adjudicator and the referral of the dispute in the required format to the Adjudicator within seven days.

Where Option Y(UK) 2 has been adopted

Where Parties to an NEC Contract have foreseen themselves working within the territory of the United Kingdom on Works which fall within the definition of a 'construction contract' and have adopted into their contract Option Y(UK) 2, a view will require to be taken as to whether or not their contract is compliant with the UK legislation.

On one interpretation, the 'notice of dissatisfaction' procedure set out in Option Y(UK) 2 amounts to no more than a contractually provided for settlement/crystallisation procedure (which one authority at first instance has suggested is necessary). On another interpretation (for which authority at first instance also exists, albeit *obiter*), the 'notice of dissatisfaction' procedure set out in Option Y(UK) 2 conflicts fatally with one of the essential requirements of the UK legislation.

If the view is taken that Option Y(UK) 2 *is* compliant, then once the notice of dissatisfaction procedure has crystallised any dispute into what the Parties have contractually accepted is only then a dispute, Option Y(UK) 2 thereafter by Clause 90.5 provides for both a Notice of Adjudication and a referral notice and for service of the latter within seven days of the former and to that extent clearly complies with the applicable UK legislation.

If the view is taken, however, that Option Y(UK) 2 is *not* compliant, then a further view requires to be taken on whether only some of the provisions of the applicable Scheme require to be imported to meet the essential requirements of the UK legislation or whether (as some first instance authority suggests (*obiter*)) the consequences of any breach of an essential requirement is that the applicable Scheme is imported wholesale.

If the view is taken, either by agreement of the Parties or by interpretation of the law, that the only implication necessary from the applicable Scheme (seen as directory) is that required to meet a missing essential requirement, then much of what might have gone before in Option Y(UK) 2 could be preserved. Any notification of dissatisfaction previously given could stand and it could simply be provided – by implication – that under Option Y(UK) 2 submission to the Adjudicator must be made within seven days of that notification of dissatisfaction and that this will be sufficient to comply with the essential requirements of the legislation.

If the view is taken, however, that the failure of Option Y(UK) 2 is such that the applicable Scheme (seen as mandatory) requires to be implied wholesale, then whatever has gone before would require to be rejected and the Party would need to start again with *only* a formal notice of intention to refer a dispute to adjudication in the required format, followed by the appointment of the Adjudicator and the referral of the dispute in the required format to the Adjudicator within seven days.

Potential UK human rights points

Insofar as it is likely to impact upon adjudication, the main thrust of the human rights legislation is likely to relate to the fair and proper procedures adopted under the process of adjudication.

As such, most such complaints are likely to come from the Party Receiving and to relate to such matters as the time available to respond to and consider a submission to adjudication.

There are, therefore, unlikely to be many human rights complaints arising out of the procedures with which a Party launching an adjudication must comply in order to achieve the appointment and the referral of the dispute to the Adjudicator.

England and Wales

The essential requirement

The Scheme for Construction Contracts (England and Wales) Regulations 1998 SI No 649 provides:

Housing Grants, Construction and Regeneration Act 1996 c.53 provides:

s. 108(2) The contract shall

(b)   provide a timetable with the object of securing the appointment of the adjudicator and referral of the dispute to him within 7 days of such notice.

The provisions

Paragraph 1

(1)   Any party to a construction contract (the 'referring party') may give written notice (the 'notice of adjudication') of his intention to refer any dispute arising under the contract, to adjudication ...
(2)   The notice of adjudication shall be given to every other party to the contract.
(3)   The notice of adjudication shall set out briefly
   (a)   the nature and a brief description of the dispute and the parties involved
   (b)   details of where and when the dispute has arisen
   (c)   the nature of the redress which is sought
   (d)   the names and addresses of the parties to the contract (including, where appropriate, the addresses which the parties have specified for the giving of notices).

Paragraph 2

(1)   Following upon the giving of a notice of adjudication and subject to any agreement between the parties to the dispute as to who shall act as adjudicator
[Paragraphs 2, 5 and 6 then deal with the request for an Adjudicator]

Paragraph 3

The request referred to in paragraphs 2, 5 and 6 shall be accompanied by a copy of the notice of adjudication.

Paragraph 4

Any person requested or selected to act as adjudicator in accordance with paragraphs 2, 5 or 6 shall be a natural person acting in his personal capacity.

A person requested or selected to act as an adjudicator shall not be an employee of any of the parties to the dispute and shall declare any interest, financial or otherwise, in any matter relating to the dispute.

Paragraph 7

(1)   Where an adjudicator has been selected in accordance with paragraphs 2, 5 or 6 the referring party shall, not later than seven days from the date of the notice of adjudication, refer the dispute in writing (the 'referral notice') to the adjudicator.

(2)   A referral notice shall be accompanied by copies of, or relevant extracts from, the construction contract and such other documents as the referring party intends to rely upon.

(3)   The referring party shall, at the same time as he sends to the Adjudicator the documents referred to in paragraphs (1) and (2), send copies of those documents to every other party to the dispute.

Scotland

The essential requirement

Housing Grants, Construction and Regeneration Act 1996 c. 53 provides:

s. 108(2) The contract shall

(b)   provide a timetable with the object of securing the appointment of the adjudicator and referral of the dispute to him within 7 days of such notice.

The provisions

The Scheme for Construction Contracts (Scotland) Regulations 1998 SI No 687 provides:

Paragraph 1

(1)   Any party to a construction contract (the 'referring party') may give written notice (the 'notice of adjudication') of his intention to refer any dispute arising under the contract, to adjudication …

(2)   The notice of adjudication shall be given to every other party to the contract.

(3)   The notice of adjudication shall set out briefly

  (a) the nature and a brief description of the dispute and the parties involved

  (b) details of where and when the dispute has arisen

  (c) the nature of the redress which is sought

  (d) the names and addresses of the parties to the contract (including, where appropriate, the addresses which the parties have specified for the giving of notices).

Paragraph 2

(1)   Following upon the giving of a notice of adjudication and subject to any agreement between the parties to the dispute as to who shall act as adjudicator

[Paragraphs 2, 5 and 6 then deal with the request for an Adjudicator]

Paragraph 3

The request referred to in paragraphs 2, 5 and 6 shall be accompanied by a copy of the notice of adjudication.

Paragraph 4

Any person requested or selected to act as adjudicator in accordance with paragraphs 2, 5 or 6 shall be a natural person acting in his personal capacity.

A person requested or selected to act as an adjudicator shall not be an employee of any of the parties to the dispute and shall declare any interest, financial or otherwise, in any matter relating to the dispute.

Paragraph 7

(1)   Where an adjudicator has been selected in accordance with paragraphs 2, 5 or 6 the referring party shall, not later than seven days from the date of the notice of adjudication, refer the dispute in writing (the 'referral notice') to the adjudicator.

(2)   A referral notice shall be accompanied by copies of, or relevant extracts from, the construction contract and such other documents as the referring party intends to rely upon.

(3)   The referring party shall, at the same time as he sends to the Adjudicator the documents referred to in paragraphs (1) and (2), send copies of those documents to every other party to the dispute.

Northern Ireland

The essential requirement

The Construction Contracts (Northern Ireland) Order 1997 SI No 274 (NI) provides:

Article 7(2) The contract shall

(b)   provide a timetable with the object of securing the appointment of the adjudicator and referral of the dispute to him within 7 days of such notice.

The provisions

The Scheme for Construction Contracts in Northern Ireland Regulations (Northern Ireland) 1999 Statutory Rule 1999 No 32 provides:

Paragraph 1

(1)   Any party to a construction contract (the 'referring party') may give written notice (the 'notice of adjudication') of his intention to refer any dispute arising under the contract, to adjudication ...

(2)   The notice of adjudication shall be given to every other party to the contract.

(3)   The notice of adjudication shall set out briefly

(a) the nature and a brief description of the dispute and the parties involved
(b) details of where and when the dispute has arisen
(c) the nature of the redress which is sought
(d) the names and addresses of the parties to the contract (including, where appropriate, the addresses which the parties have specified for the giving of notices).

Paragraph 2

(1) Following upon the giving of a notice of adjudication and subject to any agreement between the parties to the dispute as to who shall act as adjudicator

[Paragraphs 2, 5 and 6 then deal with the request for an Adjudicator].

Paragraph 3

The request referred to in paragraphs 2, 5 and 6 shall be accompanied by a copy of the notice of adjudication.

Paragraph 4

Any person requested or selected to act as adjudicator in accordance with paragraphs 2, 5 or 6 shall be a natural person acting in his personal capacity. A person requested or selected to act as an adjudicator shall not be an employee of any of the parties to the dispute and shall declare any interest, financial or otherwise, in any matter relating to the dispute.

Paragraph 7

(1) Where an adjudicator has been selected in accordance with paragraphs 2, 5 or 6 the referring party shall, not later than seven days from the date of the notice of adjudication, refer the dispute in writing (the 'referral notice') to the adjudicator.
(2) A referral notice shall be accompanied by copies of, or relevant extracts from, the construction contract and such other documents as the referring party intends to rely upon.
(3) The referring party shall, at the same time as he sends to the Adjudicator the documents referred to in paragraphs (1) and (2), send copies of those documents to every other party to the dispute.

15. Initiating the adjudication

Introduction

Once the procedure for the appointment and submission of the dispute to the Adjudicator has been gone through, the Adjudicator will then seize jurisdiction over the dispute. Here again there will be an opportunity to a Party concerned to maintain an objection to that jurisdiction or to reserve their position in that respect.

If that stage is passed through, then the Adjudicator will then have regard to his or her duties and will determine the ambit of the dispute to be determined.

In this section it is therefore proposed to consider these matters under the following headings:

- Seizing the jurisdiction
- Objections to jurisdiction
- The duties of the Adjudicator
- The ambit of the dispute

Seizing the jurisdiction

Clause 9

Option Y(UK) 2

Clause 9 does not give an Adjudicator an express power to determine his or her own jurisdiction

Option Y(UK) 2 does not give an Adjudicator an express power to determine his or her own jurisdiction

NEC PRINCIPLES

Once there has been proper notification of the dispute, appointment of the Adjudicator, and referral of the dispute to the Adjudicator (and it is not yet entirely clear to what extent an Adjudicator is entitled to take those matters under review or what an Adjudicator should do where he or she finds that the proper procedures have not been followed) then the Adjudicator appointed will 'take on board' the dispute which, in legal terminology, is often known as 'seizing the jurisdiction'.

It very frequently happens in practice in adjudications, however, that immediately upon being appointed as Adjudicator, the person appointed is faced with a strenuous denial by one of the Parties that the Adjudicator has any jurisdiction to hear the dispute at all and the claim that subject matter of the dispute is one which cannot be made the subject of an adjudication.

Numerous examples of this exist and, to give but one, where the dispute relates to payments for the provision of scaffolding, the Submitting or Referring Party might argue that the provision of the scaffolding in question is included within the definition of 'construction contracts' and therefore carries an entitlement to adjudication under the HGCR Act 1996, while the Party Receiving might argue that the provision of the scaffolding in question is excluded from the definition of 'construction contracts' and that therefore there is no entitlement to adjudication under the HGCR Act 1996. What is the Adjudicator to do in these circumstances?

Where a Party puts forward a jurisdictional objection, the position in this situation appears to be a little confused in relation to the extent to which an Adjudicator may look at that issue, and this is also a situation where the approach adopted appears to vary from country to country as we consider below.

Where a Party has a jurisdictional objection then, as we shall see in the next section, it is vital that that Party (if taking part in the adjudication) maintains the jurisdictional objection clearly and consistently throughout the adjudication to prevent an *ad hoc* adjudication arising in which the Parties are deemed to have conferred jurisdiction upon the Adjudicator. Provided that this is done, however, then it seems clear that it is open to a Party contesting jurisdiction to raise the matter in Court either at their own instance (Declarator) or in defence to enforcement proceedings. Whichever view is taken, it seems clear in all territories that the Courts have the power to review a question of jurisdiction.

This is also one of those areas where the interrelationship between any contract and the applicable Scheme comes into sharp focus. Where the contract lays down clear guidelines as to the jurisdiction of the Adjudicator (as the NEC contracts do) then if the applicable Scheme is deemed to be implied piecemeal to satisfy any missing essential requirements, those jurisdictional provisions in the contract might remain. On the other hand, if the applicable Scheme is deemed to be implied wholesale, then a set of jurisdictional issues might arise which are completely different from those which the Parties have provided for in their contract.

Potential UK human rights points

It is clearly potentially an infringement of human rights were a Party to be *unable* to raise a jurisdictional objection. It may not, however, necessarily be objectionable were a Party to be unable to raise that objection at first instance (for example, before an Adjudicator in England and Wales) *provided* that a reasonable and fair avenue of appeal existed in which the question of jurisdiction could be resolved within a reasonable time. That, it could be argued, is precisely what the Courts have provided by ruling that jurisdictional issues may be raised as a defence in enforcement proceedings following immediately upon an adjudication.

England and Wales

The Scheme for Construction Contracts (England and Wales) Regulations 1998 SI No 649 provides (see also Appendix A, judgment extract 24):

Paragraph 9

(2)   An adjudicator must resign where the dispute is the same or substantially the same as one which has previously been referred for adjudication, and a decision has been taken in that adjudication.

Commentary The only express jurisdictional power which at present is given to the Adjudicator under this Scheme is that set out above.

As regards any wider power at common law on the part of an Adjudicator to rule upon his or her own jurisdiction, the position in relation to adjudication was confused but appears to have become clearer.

In England and Wales, although the principle flowing from the arbitration case of Christopher Brown *v* Oesterreichischer [1954] 1 QB 8 has been flirted with, it appears to remain the situation that in England and Wales an Adjudicator does not have the jurisdiction to determine his or her own jurisdiction – with one exception, and that is that an Adjudicator has been expressly recognised under their Scheme as having the jurisdiction to determine whether the dispute referred is the same or substantially the same as one which has previously been referred to and decided in an adjudication, because in those circumstances an Adjudicator *must* resign (see also Appendix A, judgment extracts 25 and 26).

Scotland

The Scheme for Construction Contracts (Scotland) Regulations 1998 SI No 687 provides:

Paragraph 9

(2)   An adjudicator must resign where the dispute is the same or substantially the same as one which has previously been referred for adjudication, and a decision has been taken in that adjudication.

Commentary The only express jurisdictional power which at present is given to the Adjudicator under this Scheme is that set out above.

However, as a result of the decision in the adjudication case of *Homer Burgess*, the law of Scotland appears to recognise, implied by common law, a power in the hands of an Adjudicator to determine at the outset the jurisdiction which he or she can competently seize in the adjudication (see also Appendix A, judgment extract 27).

Northern Ireland

The Scheme for Construction Contracts in Northern Ireland Regulations (Northern Ireland) 1999 Statutory Rule 1999 No 32 provides:

Paragraph 9

(2)   An adjudicator must resign where the dispute is the same or substantially the same as one which has previously been referred for adjudication, and a decision has been taken in that adjudication.

Commentary The only express jurisdictional power which at present is given to the Adjudicator under this Scheme is that set out above.

The position in Northern Ireland, where the legislation relating to adjudication has been most recently introduced, is not yet clear.

Objections to jurisdiction

Clause 9	*Option Y(UK) 2*
No express power is given to the Parties in this respect	No express power is given to the Parties in this respect

NEC PRINCIPLES

The NEC family of contracts does *not* expressly provide a procedure for the Parties to object to jurisdiction and for the Adjudicator to rule on that matter (see also Appendix A, judgment extract 28).

However, within the United Kingdom, the common law of the various territories may (although to different extents) recognise a right on the part of the Parties to raise such objections to jurisdictions. What seems to be important, also, is for any objection to jurisdiction to be maintained.

Where, therefore, Parties are (all other conditions being satisfied) using NEC contracts to carry out, within the UK, Works falling within the definition of 'construction contracts', then they should be prepared to deal with the issue of jurisdiction (upon which their contract is silent) and any objections thereto.

England and Wales

The Scheme does not give the Parties any express power to raise objections to jurisdiction.

Commentary The Party objecting to jurisdiction could apply for an injunction (although the prospects would seem unlikely there) or for a Declaration (although in practice it may not be possible to obtain this before any adjudication has run its course).

In practice in England and Wales, therefore, adjudications are at present likely to proceed in the face of any jurisdictional objections. The Party concerned is not obliged to attend the adjudication but if they decide to do so then what is important is that the Party maintains their jurisdictional objection to prevent their being taken as having consented to an *ad hoc* adjudication (see also Appendix A, judgment extracts 29–31).

Scotland

The Scheme does not give the Parties any express power to raise objections to jurisdiction.

Commentary Given that the law of Scotland appears to allow an Adjudicator to rule upon his or her own jurisdiction (see also Appendix A, judgment extract 32), any jurisdiction issues seem likely to be determined there in the first instance, with resort to the Courts thereafter where the view is taken that the Adjudicator's decision on jurisdiction was incorrect. Where the Adjudicator decides that he or she has jurisdiction and to proceed with the adjudication then interdict may be possible (although there is no recorded decision of that having been attempted so far). However, under current practice the matter seems more likely to have to await a Judicial Review.

Parties would not be obliged to attend any such adjudication in the meantime but should they do so then they would be well advised to maintain their objection throughout (see also Appendix A, judgment extract 33).

Northern Ireland

The Scheme does not give the Parties any express power to raise objections to jurisdiction.

Commentary The Party objecting to jurisdiction could apply for an injunction (although the prospects would seem unlikely there) or for a Declaration (although in practice it may not be possible to obtain this before any adjudication has run its course).

By analogy with England and Wales, it seems likely that in practice in Northern Ireland, therefore, adjudications are at present likely to proceed in the face of any jurisdictional objections. The Party concerned is not obliged to attend the adjudication but if they decide to do so then what is important is that the Party maintains their jurisdictional objection to prevent their being taken as having consented to an *ad hoc* adjudication.

The duties of the Adjudicator

The duty to act impartially

Clause 9	*Option Y(UK) 2*
Clause 92.1	Clause 90.8
The Adjudicator settles the dispute as independent adjudicator	The Adjudicator acts impartially …

NEC PRINCIPLES

The UK legislation makes it an essential requirement (essential requirement No 5) that the Adjudicator *act* impartially in carrying out his or her duties. Option Y(UK) 2 faithfully reproduces that requirement. Unusually, however, by demanding not just impartiality but independence, Clause 9 might be interpreted as going further than the applicable UK legislation requires.

It is clear that a process such as adjudication – rough, ready and intended to provide only a temporarily binding decision – is only going to be as good as the Adjudicators who operate the process of adjudication, and various commentators have also made that clear from the start.

Originally, the Government had signalled its intention of taking under its wing control over Adjudicators and over Adjudicator Nominating Bodies. As the Bill went through, however, the Government for some reason backed away from that proposal and as the Act was passed control over Adjudicators was left to self-regulation.

The Government did, however, incorporate into the legislation – making it an essential requirement – certain minimum standards which the Government expected to see observed in relation to Adjudicators. In doing so, the Government had a number of choices open to it as regards the provision made both in relation to Adjudicators and in relation to the way in which Adjudicators are required to act.

For example, it would have been open to provide that (as the Tribunal) 'The Adjudicator shall be independent and impartial' and also that the Adjudicator shall act 'independently and impartially'.

In the event, however, the Government did not go that far. No express requirement was imposed for the Adjudicator, as the Tribunal, to be anything at all. Instead, provision was restricted to the way in which the Adjudicator, as the Tribunal, is to *act*.

In relation to the way in which the Adjudicator is to act, the Government did not go so far as to require the Adjudicator to act both independently and impartially. Instead, the requirement was restricted only to that of requiring the Adjudicator to act impartially.

This was, apparently, a deliberate policy, which the Department Advisory Committee justifies on the basis that in their view it is possible (particularly for a professional person) to be impartial without being wholly independent. The example was given of the English Bar whose members might, as members of the same Chambers, appear as advocates in front of their colleagues sitting as Arbitrators or Adjudicators. While not 'independent' in the strictest sense of the word, no-one could seriously doubt that the Barristers concerned were acting impartially. There was, therefore, the Government felt, no need to add the further requirement of 'independence'. They did, however, make the need to act impartially an essential requirement. The legislation did not, however, confer an express power upon the Court to remove Adjudicators where justifiable doubt as to his or her acting impartially exists and therefore that is, presumably, a matter left to the common law of the territory in which the Adjudicator happens to be acting.

So far as the qualifications of Adjudicators are concerned, Clause 9 does not require an Adjudicator to *be* independent (and therefore the Adjudicator could be related in some way to one of the Parties) but does require the Adjudicator to settle disputes as an independent Adjudicator. Option Y(UK) 2, similarly, does not require the Adjudicator to be anything but does require the Adjudicator to act impartially.

The interrelationship between independence and impartiality, which are distinct but related concepts, is a complex and technical matter. It could be argued, however, that independence is the greater of the two and includes the latter. To that extent, it could be argued that Clause 9 complies with the essential requirement of the Act (perhaps also going some way to complying with human rights requirements) whereas Option Y(UK) 2 complies with the strict terms of the Act.

If, therefore, the view is taken that it is only necessary to imply in from the Scheme that which is necessary to comply with the essential requirements of the legislation, then it could be argued that no such implication is necessary here because the contract (whether it be using Clause 9 alone or Clause 9 with Option Y(UK) 2) already contains provision which is equivalent to, or better than, the essential requirement set out in the legislation.

If, however, either the Parties have agreed between themselves that the applicable Scheme is to apply in its entirety or the view is taken that the law requires the applicable Scheme to be applied in its entirety, then for the avoidance of doubt the provisions of the applicable Scheme as to impartiality could be treated as being implied into the contract.

Potential UK human rights points

The status of the Adjudicator is likely to become one of the major areas of debate so far as the Convention of Human Rights is concerned. Article 6(1) of the Convention, which is one of the Articles specifically incorporated into UK law by the Human Rights Act 1998 provides: 'In the determination of his civil rights and obligations ... everyone is entitled to a fair and public hearing within a reasonable time by an independent and impartial tribunal established by law.'

It is, of course, at this level, only the actions of a 'public authority' which can be declared incompatible with the Convention and 'public authority' under the HRA 1998 expressly includes Courts and tribunals and 'any person certain of whose functions are functions of a public nature'. Therefore the first question to establish would be whether or not the Adjudicator (particularly where the adjudication was obligatory under the applicable legislation, perhaps making the adjudication a tribunal established by law) was, indeed, a 'person certain of whose functions are functions of a public nature'.

Were that to be established then the subject matter of the adjudication – usually the payment of money and therefore clearly a property right or at least a civil right and obligation – would entitle the person concerned to a fair and public hearing within a reasonable time by an independent and impartial tribunal established by law.

Of particular relevance in this section is the requirement that the tribunal (i.e. the Adjudicator) be both *independent* and *impartial*. Note also, that the Adjudicator as such a tribunal would not be simply required to *act* independently and impartially but would require to *be* (and be seen to be) both independent and impartial.

Of course, even if an adjudication as they are run at the moment were, *prima facie*, incompatible with a requirement (in this case Article 6(1)) of the Convention, it would remain to be considered whether there are any defences to that breach. The decision of an Adjudicator is a provisional and temporary decision which is not (in the absence of agreement) finally determined until Arbitration (if agreed or provided for) or litigation takes place. Arbitration might suffer from the same problems as Adjudication in this respect but litigation is, beyond a paraventure, both independent and impartial. It could be argued that provided a person has eventual recourse to such an independent and impartial tribunal to finally determine their civil rights and obligations, then no breach of the Convention has taken place. On the other hand, it is not yet clear what view the European Court of Human Rights might take about allowing even a provisional interim decision to be taken by someone who can blatantly be seen not to be independent and what view they might take about having, on the decision of such a person, to hand over property rights which examples have shown may not be recoverable in the event of intervening insolvency.

Clearly, there is much to be argued as regards the application of the law relating to human rights to adjudication. In the meantime, those inclined to avoid taking the time, trouble and expense to argue the points might wish to take care to ensure that any Adjudicators appointed can be seen to be both as impartial *and* as independent as possible.

England and Wales

The essential requirement:

The HGCR Act 1996 c. 53 provides:

s. 108(2) The contract shall

(e)   impose a duty on the adjudicator to act impartially.

The provisions

The Scheme for Construction Contracts (England and Wales) Regulations 1998 SI No 649 provides:

Paragraph 12

The adjudicator shall

(a)   act impartially in carrying out his duties ...

Scotland

The essential requirement:

The HGCR Act 1996 c. 53 provides:

s. 108(2) The contract shall

(e)   impose a duty on the adjudicator to act impartially.

The provisions

The Scheme for Construction Contracts (Scotland) Regulations 1998 SI No 687 provides:

Paragraph 12

The adjudicator shall

(a)   act impartially in carrying out his duties ...

Northern Ireland

The essential requirement:

The Construction Contracts (Northern Ireland) Order 1997 SI No 274 (NI) provides:

Article 7(2) The contract shall

(e)   impose a duty on the adjudicator to act impartially.

The provisions

The Scheme for Construction Contracts in Northern Ireland Regulations (Northern Ireland) 1999 Statutory Rule 1999 No 32 provides:

Paragraph 12

The adjudicator shall

(a)   act impartially in carrying out his duties ...

The duty to act in accordance with any relevant terms of the contract

Clause 9	*Option Y(UK) 2*
No provision is made in this respect (although it is, perhaps, implied therein)	No provision is made in this respect (although it is, perhaps, implied therein)

NEC PRINCIPLES

This is perhaps a provision which really only makes sense where parts of the statutory adjudication Scheme are being overlaid over and implied into the non-complying contract in relation to Works falling within the definition of 'construction contracts' being carried out within the territories of the UK.

It could be argued it falls to be inferred from this provision that only those parts of the Scheme which have to be implied to meet an essential requirement of the legislation and that in all other respects any relevant terms of the contract will rule.

It would certainly seem reasonable to argue that the UK legislation (together with, to the extent necessary, the applicable Scheme) sets down *minimum* requirements and that if the Parties have chosen in their contract to go beyond that minimum requirement and to make other relevant provisions, then those provisions are something to which the Adjudicator will require to have regard whether the adjudication is being conducted under one of the Schemes or otherwise.

It may be that the point is also of little practical importance in that most of the essential requirements are provided for and anything else must be peripheral. Nevertheless, it emphasises the importance of Adjudicators having all of the relevant terms of the contract before them.

If the view is taken that Option Y(UK) 2 is compliant then nothing further requires to be implied into that contract and its terms will be the only relevant terms.

An NEC contract with Clause 9 standing alone is, however, clearly non-compliant. The terms of that contract will, to a greater or lesser extent, require to give way to implication from the applicable Scheme to meet the essential requirements of the legislation. What it may be important to appreciate, however, is that beyond that the terms of the NEC contract incorporating Clause 9 will remain relevant and that by this provision the Adjudicator is under a specific and express duty to observe them.

Potential UK human rights points

It is conceivable that human rights considerations will arise here where, without a relevant defence, a Party is deprived of entitlements which they have as a result of any relevant terms of their contract.

England and Wales

The Scheme for Construction Contracts (England and Wales) Regulations 1998 SI No 649 provides:

Paragraph 12

The adjudicator ...
... in carrying out his duties ... shall do so in accordance with any relevant terms of the contract ...

Scotland

The Scheme for Construction Contracts (Scotland) Regulations 1998 SI No 687 provides:

Paragraph 12

The adjudicator ...
... in carrying out his duties ... shall do so in accordance with any relevant terms of the contract ...

Northern Ireland

The Scheme for Construction Contracts in Northern Ireland Regulations (Northern Ireland) 1999 Statutory Rule 1999 No 32 provides:

Paragraph 12

The adjudicator ...
... in carrying out his duties ... shall do so in accordance with any relevant terms of the contract ...

The duty to avoid incurring unnecessary expense

Clause 9   *Option Y(UK) 2*

No provision is made in this respect   No provision is made in this respect

NEC PRINCIPLES

Many adjudication procedures presume that the Adjudicator will do no more and no less than is required to arrive at the decision and make no specific provision in this respect.

The NEC family of contracts appears to fall into that category since neither Clause 9 standing alone, nor Option Y(UK) 2 where that has been adopted, nor the Adjudicator's Contract make any specific provision in this respect.

Where, however, Works which fall within the definition of 'construction contracts' are being carried out within the territories of the United Kingdom, then various entitlements may arise under the applicable Schemes where the contract in question is non-compliant.

One of the provisions under the Schemes is an express and specific duty which is imposed upon the Adjudicator to avoid incurring unnecessary expense. This presumably allows one or other of the Parties to object were the Adjudicator to propose, say, appointing three Experts and conducting a series of visits and tests.

The extent to which an Adjudicator brought in under a contract is bound by such a provision is, as earlier noted, problematic and not yet conclusively determined. If, for example, the contract in question had accidentally omitted the essential requirement that the Adjudicator act impartially so that the contract is non-compliant, then while an implication from the applicable Scheme to satisfy the requirement of impartiality is unobjectionable, it seems a little odd if the price to pay for such an omission is also the added imposition upon the Adjudicator of a condition which exists nowhere in the contract, namely to avoid incurring unnecessary expense.

It may be that the point is of little practical importance in that most Adjudicators can be relied upon to do no more and no less than is called for in relation to the dispute in question. If the view is taken that Option Y(UK) 2 is compliant then nothing (including the specific obligation to avoid incurring unnecessary expense) requires to be implied into that contract.

An NEC contract with Clause 9 standing alone is clearly non-compliant and there, if necessary, a view will require to be taken as to whether the obligation to avoid incurring unnecessary expense does not require to be implied as it is not an essential requirement of the legislation or whether the whole scheme falls to be implied, in which case, while not under such an obligation under the original contract, the Adjudicator would then, by implication, require to avoid incurring unnecessary expense.

Potential UK human rights points

It is, perhaps, slightly unlikely that any major human rights considerations will arise in this respect, but there is a human rights principle known as 'equality of arms' and should an Adjudicator be proposing an expensive course of action which only one Party can afford, then it is conceivable that human rights considerations will arise and the applicability or otherwise of this provision will be a consideration.

England and Wales

The Scheme for Construction Contracts (England and Wales) Regulations 1998 SI No 649 provides:

Paragraph 12

The adjudicator shall

...

(b)   avoid incurring unnecessary expense.

Scotland

The Scheme for Construction Contracts (Scotland) Regulations 1998 SI No 687 provides:

The adjudicator shall

...

(b)   avoid incurring unnecessary expense.

Northern Ireland

The Scheme for Construction Contracts in Northern Ireland Regulations (Northern Ireland) 1999 Statutory Rule 1999 No 32 provides:

The adjudicator shall

...

(b)   avoid incurring unnecessary expense.

The duty to act in accordance with the applicable law of the contract

Clause 9	*Option Y(UK) 2*
Contract data	*Contract data*
1. General	1. General
The law of the contract is the law of [.....]	The law of the contract is the law of [.....]

NEC principles

This express provision is potentially a significant one (although one which would probably be implied by law in any event) at least in some respects. It is not possible to avoid the provisions of the UK legislation by providing for a different law to be the applicable law in relation to the contract because the UK legislation prevents that, but it is possible for the Parties to specify the law which is to apply to their contract (and therefore to the adjudication).

Once the adjudication has commenced, therefore, then the law which is to apply in that adjudication will, to a large extent, be regulated in accordance with the law applicable to the contract and the initiative in ascertaining the law (including, if necessary, foreign law) will extend to obtaining expert legal assistance to discover just what that applicable law is.

It is, perhaps, something of an open question as to whether or not adjudication proceedings are proceedings in relation to which the strict laws of evidence apply, but to the extent that they do (especially as regards natural justice and fairness) then those laws will be ascertained from and taken from the law applicable to the contract.

In any event, the Adjudicator must not act as an *amiable compositeur* and rewrite the contract between the Parties in a manner which seems to the Adjudicator to be the most suitable. The Adjudicator's duty is to decide the dispute in accordance with the legal rights and duties which the Parties have and those are ascertained from the law which the Parties have provided is to be applicable to their contract.

While not affecting the application of the legislation covering adjudication in relation to Works falling within the definition of 'construction contracts' within the territory of the UK, the choice of the law applicable to the contract might nevertheless have an effect upon the enforceability of any decision which the Adjudicator arrives at.

Regardless, therefore, of whether or not the contract containing Clause 9 or Option Y(UK) 2 is or is not compliant with the relevant UK legislation, Parties can rest content that the law which should be applied in any adjudication should be the law which they have chosen as applicable to their contract and this provision expressly confirms that.

Potential UK human rights points

It is conceivable that human rights considerations will arise in this area.

England and Wales

The legislation

Housing Grants, Construction and Regeneration Act 1996 c. 53 provides

s. 104(7)

This Part applies whether or not the law of England and Wales ... is otherwise the applicable law in relation to the contract.

The provisions

The Scheme for Construction Contracts (England and Wales) Regulations 1998 SI No 649 provides:

Paragraph 12

The adjudicator shall

> reach his decision in accordance with the applicable law in relation to the contract.

Scotland

The legislation

Housing Grants, Construction and Regeneration Act 1996 c. 53 provides:

s. 104(7)

This Part applies whether or not the law of England and Wales ... is otherwise the applicable law in relation to the contract.

The provisions

The Scheme for Construction Contracts (Scotland) Regulations 1998 SI No 687 provides:

Paragraph 12

The adjudicator shall

> reach his decision in accordance with the applicable law in relation to the contract.

Northern Ireland

The legislation

Construction Contracts (Northern Ireland) Order 1997 provides:

Article 3(7)

This order applies whether or not the law of Northern Ireland is otherwise the applicable law in relation to the contract.

The provisions

The Scheme for Construction Contract in Northern Ireland

Paragraph 12

The adjudicator shall

> reach his decision in accordance with the applicable law in relation to the contract.

The ambit of the dispute

Clause 9

Option Y(UK) 2

There is no specific provision covering this aspect (but see the reference in the Guidance Notes mentioned below)

There is no specific provision covering this aspect (but see the reference in the Guidance Notes mentioned below)

NEC PRINCIPLES

Having seized jurisdiction and determined his or her duties, the Adjudicator will then normally turn to a consideration of the ambit of the dispute upon which the Adjudicator is to arrive at a decision.

As it has developed, the nature of the dispute referred to, and under consideration by, the Adjudicator has assumed increasing importance in the process of adjudication.

As might be expected from a process intended to be short, sharp, and to produce a temporarily binding decision in relation to a current dispute, there is a natural inclination to concentrate upon single dispute being referred, decided upon and passed on, and a disinclination to allow the adjudication be bogged down by allowing the nature of the dispute under consideration to be extended. In the reported cases to date the Courts have been strongly supportive of such an approach.

As a result of this approach, cross-claims, set-offs and abatements are discouraged and it is expected that a Party with such claims will issue their own Notice of Adjudication and launch their own adjudication. Were adjudications relating to any claims and cross-claims to be raised in close proximity to each other then any results could, if appropriate, soon be adjusted in outcome by being netted off against each other.

Some contracts adopt a firm approach in this respect and do not permit the combination of disputes in adjudications (except perhaps in closely defined exceptions). Such contracts normally say so expressly. However, Clause 9 – with or without Option Y(UK) 2 – does not make express provision in this respect, although it is expressly stated in the Guidance Notes (although not permitted to be used in interpretation) that 'The Parties are not permitted to widen a dispute referred to the Adjudicator beyond that notified under Clause 90.1.' The manner in which it is closely provided as an evident exception that Main contract and Sub-contract disputes (only) may be combined in an adjudication also suggests that (with the exception stated) the overall approach of the NEC family of contracts is to confine adjudications to the individual disputes referred.

The Schemes, however, provide otherwise and make extensive provision for adjusting the ambit of the dispute between the parties. In the first place, the Schemes give the Adjudicator (alone) a wide power to take into account matters under the contract which he considers are necessarily connected with the dispute. In the second place, the Schemes allow the Adjudicator to take into account any other matters which the Parties to the dispute agree should be within the scope of the adjudication. A specific power is also given under the Schemes to allow (with the consent of the Parties) a number of disputes under way to be combined under one adjudication and one Adjudicator (with the other Adjudicators, suitably remunerated, resigning and the time for the decision being extended).

Careful consideration should be given to such requests because multi-party and multi-issue adjudications can quickly become complex and unwieldy and at odds with the objective of adjudication, which is the provision of a simple and quick procedure for providing the parties with a temporarily binding decision. On the other hand, the possibility of achieving a common result for all the disputes will clearly be a consideration, as will the savings in time and expense by attending only one as opposed to several adjudications.

This is, however, another area where the potential conflict between any contract and the applicable Scheme comes into sharp focus. If the view is taken that it is only necessary to imply from the Scheme into the contract that which is necessary to satisfy the essential requirements set out in the legislation, then since the ability to combine disputes is not an essential requirement it could be argued that the implication of these parts of the Schemes should not be permitted. On another interpretation, since the Schemes provide that in carrying out his or her duties the Adjudicator shall do so 'in accordance with any relevant terms of the contract', then where the contract (expressly or by implication) prohibits the combination of disputes, that is a provision which should be respected by the Adjudicator in the face of any attempt to combine disputes or take into consideration matters not originally referred.

If, however, either the Parties have agreed between themselves that the applicable Scheme is to apply in its entirety or the view is taken that the law requires the applicable Scheme to be applied in its entirety, then the result would be that the referral might no longer be determinative. This would mean that – although not within the contemplation (or even expressly prohibited) of the Parties when contracting – it would be open to the Parties to agree to combine disputes and to the Adjudicator to take into account any other matters which, in the view of the Adjudicator alone, are necessarily connected with the dispute.

Clearly, as applies throughout adjudication, the agreement of all Parties involved will cure any difficulties in this area no matter what the contract says (although any such alteration of the contract should obviously be recorded in writing). Any difficulties in this area are likely to arise where one Party wishes the adjudication restricted to the dispute referred while the other Party and/or the Adjudicator wish to extend the adjudication to cover matters not originally referred. It is suggested that care should be exercised in this area where it is clear from the contract that such extensions are prohibited.

Cross-claims

In general, the approach which appears to be being adopted is that it is *a* dispute which should be referred to adjudication. Cross-claims and abatements are to be discouraged and, where necessary, should form their own adjudication which could run side-by-side with the adjudication already under way, theoretically producing much the same situation when the results of the two adjudications become known at the end of the day (see also Appendix A, judgment extracts 34–36).

Potential UK human rights points

The general approach of human rights legislation is to concentrate upon the fairness of overall procedures, leaving incidental details of procedure to be resolved under domestic law. This aspect is, therefore, unlikely to feature large under human rights legislation, although if the civil rights and obligations of a Party were extended and decided in an adjudication of which that Party was unaware or did not consent to, then such a matter could conceivably stray into the area of human rights.

England and Wales

(see also Appendix A, judgment extract3 37–39)

Specific power to the parties to combine disputes

Paragraph 8

(1)   The adjudicator may, with the consent of all parties to those disputes, adjudicate at the same time on more than one dispute under the same contract.

(2)   The adjudicator may, with the consent of all the parties to those disputes, adjudicate at the same time on related disputes under different contracts, whether or not one or more of those parties is a party to those disputes.

The consequences under the Scheme of agreeing to combine disputes

Paragraph 8

(3)   All the parties in paragraphs (1) and (2) respectively may agree to extend the period within which the adjudicator may reach a decision in relation to all or any of these disputes.

[Paragraph 19(1) The adjudicator shall reach his decision not later than

   …

   (c)   such period exceeding twenty eight days after the referral notice as the parties to the dispute may, after the giving of notice, agree]

(4)   Where an adjudicator ceases to act because a dispute is to be adjudicated on by another person in terms of this paragraph, that adjudicator's fees and expenses shall be determined in accordance with paragraph 25.

[Paragraph 25. The adjudicator shall be entitled to the payment of such reasonable amount as he may determine by way of fees and expenses reasonably incurred by him. The parties shall be jointly and severally liable for any sums which remain outstanding following the making of any determination on how the payments shall be apportioned]

The general power

Paragraph 20

The Adjudicator shall determine the matters in dispute. He may take into account any other matters which the parties to the dispute agree should be within the scope of the adjudication or which are matters under the contract which he considers are necessarily connected with the dispute ...

Scheme for Construction Contracts (England and Wales) Regulations 1998 SI No 649

Scotland

Specific power to the parties to combine disputes

Paragraph 8

(1)   The adjudicator may, with the consent of all parties to those disputes, adjudicate at the same time on more than one dispute under the same contract.

(2)   The adjudicator may, with the consent of all the parties to those disputes, adjudicate at the same time on related disputes under different contracts, whether or not one or more of those parties is a party to those disputes.

The consequences under the Scheme of agreeing to combine disputes

Paragraph 8

(3)   All the parties in paragraphs (1) and (2) respectively may agree to extend the period within which the adjudicator may reach a decision in relation to all or any of these disputes.

[Paragraph 19(1) The adjudicator shall reach his decision not later than-

...

(c)   such period exceeding twenty eight days after the referral notice as the parties to the dispute may, after the giving of notice, agree]

(4)   Where an adjudicator ceases to act because a dispute is to be adjudicated on by another person in terms of this paragraph, that adjudicator's fees and expenses shall be determined in accordance with paragraph 25.

[Paragraph 25. The adjudicator shall be entitled to the payment of such reasonable amount as he may determine by way of fees and expenses reasonably incurred by him. The parties shall be jointly and severally liable for any sums which remain outstanding following the making of any determination on how the payments shall be apportioned]

The general power

Paragraph 20

The Adjudicator shall determine the matters in dispute. He may take into account any other matters which the parties to the dispute agree should be within the scope of the adjudication or which are matters under the contract which he considers are necessarily connected with the dispute ...

Scheme for Construction Contracts (Scotland) Regulations
1998 SI No 687

Northern Ireland

Specific power to the parties to combine disputes

Paragraph 8

(1)   The adjudicator may, with the consent of all parties to those disputes, adjudicate at the same time on more than one dispute under the same contract.

(2)   The adjudicator may, with the consent of all the parties to those disputes, adjudicate at the same time on related disputes under different contracts, whether or not one or more of those parties is a party to those disputes.

The consequences under the Scheme of agreeing to combine disputes

Paragraph 8

(3)   All the parties in paragraphs (1) and (2) respectively may agree to extend the period within which the adjudicator may reach a decision in relation to all or any of these disputes.

[Paragraph 19(1) The adjudicator shall reach his decision not later than

...

  (c)   such period exceeding twenty eight days after the referral notice as the parties to the dispute may, after the giving of notice, agree]

(4)   Where an adjudicator ceases to act because a dispute is to be adjudicated on by another person in terms of this paragraph, that adjudicator's fees and expenses shall be determined in accordance with paragraph 25.

[Paragraph 25. The adjudicator shall be entitled to the payment of such reasonable amount as he may determine by way of fees and expenses reasonably incurred by him. The parties shall be jointly and severally liable for any sums which remain outstanding following the making of any determination on how the payments shall be apportioned]

The general power

Paragraph 20

The Adjudicator shall determine the matters in dispute. He may take into account any other matters which the parties to the dispute agree should be within the scope of the adjudication or which are matters under the contract which he considers are necessarily connected with the dispute ...

The Scheme for Construction Contracts in Northern Ireland Regulations (Northern Ireland) 1999 Statutory Rule 1999 No 32.

Main Contracts and Sub-contracts

Clause 9	*Option Y(UK) 2*
Main contract	*Main contract*
If a matter disputed under or in connection with a subcontract is also a matter disputed under or in connection with this contract, the Contractor may submit the subcontract dispute to the Adjudicator at the same time dispute as the main contract submission.	If a matter disputed under or in connection with a subcontract is also a matter disputed under or in connection with this contract, the Contractor may submit the subcontract dispute to the Adjudicator at the same time as the main contract submission.
The Adjudicator then settles the two disputes together and references to the Parties for purposes of the dispute are interpreted as including the Subcontractor	The Adjudicator then gives his decision on the two disputes together and references to the Parties for the purposes of the dispute are interpreted as including the Subcontractor
Subcontract	*Subcontract*

NEC PRINCIPLES

Whatever view is taken and provision made in relation to the combination of disputes generally, the position in relation to disputes under Main Contracts and Sub-contracts are normally regarded as a special case in the construction industry in that what happens in one very often impacts on what happens in another.

As the Guidance Notes point out, where a dispute arises which affects work which has also been sub-contracted, then the dispute might affect not only the Employer and the Contractor but also the Contractor and the Subcontractor. As the Guidance Notes observe, this saves time and expense and prevents a dispute being dealt with by different Adjudicators who may make different decisions.

Special provision is often made therefore to cover the Main Contract and Sub-contract situation and this is also to be found in both Clause 9 and when Option Y(UK) 2 is adopted, although this is, however, possible only where the relevant provisions are in the respective contracts.

If, therefore, such provision is in fact there in both the Main Contract and the Sub-contract, then applying the principle provided for in the Schemes that in carrying out his or her duties the Adjudicator shall do so 'in accordance with any relevant terms of the contract', those provisions would allow the Adjudicator under the contract to combine disputes under the Main Contract and Sub-contract.

If, however, those provisions are *not* provided for and the view is taken that it is only necessary to imply into the contract that from the Scheme which is necessary to comply with the essential requirements set down by the legislation then, since the combining of Main Contracts and Sub-contracts is not an essential requirement of the legislation, there would on that view in fact be no power for the Adjudicator to combine Main Contract and Sub-contract disputes.

Where either the parties have agreed between themselves that the applicable Scheme is to apply in its entirety or the view is taken that the law requires the applicable Scheme to be applied in its entirety, then clearly under either (with the consent of the Parties) the general power or the specific power – and with the same consequences flowing therefrom explained in the preceding section – would be there for the Adjudicator to combine Main Contracts and Sub-contracts.

Potential UK human rights points

While conceivable, it is unlikely that any major human rights issues will arise in this area.

England and Wales

Specific power to the parties to combine disputes

Paragraph 8

(1)   The adjudicator may, with the consent of all parties to those disputes, adjudicate at the same time on more than one dispute under the same contract.

(2)   The adjudicator may, with the consent of all the parties to those disputes, adjudicate at the same time on related disputes under different contracts, whether or not one or more of those parties is a party to those disputes.

The general power

Paragraph 20

The Adjudicator shall determine the matters in dispute. He may take into account any other matters which the parties to the dispute agree should be within the scope of the adjudication or which are matters under the contract which he considers are necessarily connected with the dispute ...

> Scheme for Construction Contracts (England and Wales)
> Regulations 1998 SI No 649

Scotland

Specific power to the parties to combine disputes

Paragraph 8

(1)   The adjudicator may, with the consent of all parties to those disputes, adjudicate at the same time on more than one dispute under the same contract.

(2)   The adjudicator may, with the consent of all the parties to those disputes, adjudicate at the same time on related disputes under different contracts, whether or not one or more of those parties is a party to those disputes.

The general power

Paragraph 20

The Adjudicator shall determine the matters in dispute. He may take into account any other matters which the parties to the dispute agree should be within the scope of the adjudication or which are matters under the contract which he considers are necessarily connected with the dispute ...

> Scheme for Construction Contracts (Scotland)
> Regulations 1998 SI No 687

Northern Ireland

Specific power to the parties to combine disputes

Paragraph 8

(1)   The adjudicator may, with the consent of all parties to those disputes, adjudicate at the same time on more than one dispute under the same contract.

(2)   The adjudicator may, with the consent of all the parties to those disputes, adjudicate at the same time on related disputes under different contracts, whether or not one or more of those parties is a party to those disputes.

The general power

Paragraph 20

The Adjudicator shall determine the matters in dispute. He may take into account any other matters which the parties to the dispute agree should be within the scope of the adjudication or which are matters under the contract which he considers are necessarily connected with the dispute ...

The Scheme for Construction Contracts in Northern Ireland Regulations (Northern Ireland) 1999 Statutory Rule 1999 No 32

16. The conduct of the adjudication

Introduction

The procedure which the Adjudicator decides should be followed can vary, with some of the smaller adjudications becoming document-only where an early decision is arrived at and with some of the larger adjudications extending to testing and site visits where the decision takes longer to arrive at, but most adjudications follow the same essential pattern. This might be described as follows:

- The essentials of an Adjudication
  - Putting the case for the Submitting Party
  - Putting the case for the Responding Party
  - Adjustment of the cases
- The function of the Adjudicator
- The approach of the Adjudicator
- Specific powers available to the Adjudicator
- Fairness in the adjudication
- Co-operation by the Parties

The essentials of an adjudication

Putting the case for the Submitting Party

Clause 9

The initial document will have been the notification of the dispute to the Project Manager (and, where applicable, the other Party). That will then be followed by the submission of the dispute to the Adjudicator.

The Party submitting the dispute to the Adjudicator includes with his submission information to be considered by the Adjudicator.

Option Y(UK) 2

The initial document will have been the notice of dissatisfaction to the Project Manager and the Other Party.That will then be followed by both a notice of intention to refer a dispute to adjudication and then a referral to the Adjudicator.

The Party referring the dispute to the Adjudicator includes with his submission information to be considered by the Adjudicator.

NEC PRINCIPLES

It is clearly important that the Adjudicator has sufficient information to determine the dispute. In order to commence the adjudication and focus upon exactly what the dispute is, most adjudication procedures require the initiating Party to provide details of the dispute and in the interests of speed usually also require that these details of the dispute are provided at the same time as the notice calling for the adjudication.

The NEC adjudication procedures are no exception in this respect. Both Clause 9 and Option Y(UK) 2 require the Party submitting or referring the dispute to the Adjudicator to include with his submission information to be considered by the Adjudicator.

Neither contract goes into any further detail as to the contents of such information. The Explanatory Notes do offer a little more guidance by noting that it is important that the Adjudicator has all the relevant information to enable him or her to put themselves in the position of the Project Manager or Supervisor when the action was taken or not taken as the case may be, and that information therefore has to be as full as is appropriate to the dispute.

The Schemes, however, do go into some detail in relation to the information to be supplied both in relation to the Notice of Adjudication and the referral notice. Here again, it is difficult to know whether these provisions are mandatory or directory and much is likely to turn on the view taken.

If the view is taken that such provisions are directory only, and the view is also taken that it is only necessary to imply in from the applicable Scheme into the contract that which is provided by the legislation to be an essential requirement, then it could be argued that Clause 9 is, in fact, perfectly compliant as it stands. There is no legislative requirement to use the words 'notice of adjudication' and, therefore, where a Party sends a letter submitting a dispute to the Adjudicator and including therewith information to be considered by the Adjudicator, it could be argued that the directory requirements have been complied with. The same applies to Option Y(UK) 2 where that had been adopted.

Where, however, the view is taken that these requirements are mandatory, and either the Parties have agreed or taken the view that only the applicable Scheme will apply in its entirety, then clearly the provisions of the Scheme relating to both the Notice of Adjudication and the referral notice should be fully complied with. The consequences where this has not been done have yet to be tested.

Even where not strictly obliged to do so, Parties submitting information in an adjudication may, to avoid unnecessary difficulties, wish to volunteer to follow as closely as possible the formats of the Scheme and this could be commended to those using NEC contracts in relation to Works within the United Kingdom which might be interpreted as 'construction contracts'.

Potential UK human rights points

Clearly the Party Responding must be given fair notice of the case which they have to meet. Domestic adjudication decisions have highlighted the importance to be attached to the definition of the dispute in the original notice of adjudication. Human rights considerations are also likely (particularly given the short time period for the whole process) to focus upon the extent to which full and fair notice of the dispute to be adjudicated upon has been given in the notification.

In relation to the conduct of an adjudication, so far as human rights issues are concerned the cases of Elaney Contracts Ltd *v* The Vestry, 30 August 2000 and Austin Hall Building Ltd *v* Buckland Securities Ltd, 11 April 2001, have decided, at First Instance, that the European Convention of Human Rights does not apply to an adjudication. That position may, however, be distinguished or overturned on an appeal. It should be noted further that the principles to be found in the Human Rights Convention are often the same as the principles to be found in domestic UK law under the Rules of Natural Justice, and a number of cases have declared that these Rules do apply to adjudications.

England and Wales

The Scheme for Construction Contracts (England and Wales) Regulations 1998 SI No 649 provides:

Paragraph 1(3)

The Notice of Adjudication shall set out briefly-

    (a) the nature and a brief description of the dispute and the parties involved
    (b) details of where and when the dispute has arisen
    (c) the nature of the redress which is sought
    (d) the names and addresses of the parties to the contract (including, where appropriate, the addresses which the parties have specified for the giving of notices).

Paragraph 7

(2)   A Referral Notice shall be accompanied by copies of, or relevant extracts from, the construction contract and such other documents as the Referring Party intends to rely upon.

Scotland

The Scheme for Construction Contracts (Scotland) Regulations 1998 SI No 687 provides:

Paragraph 1(3)

The Notice of Adjudication shall set out briefly-

    (a) the nature and a brief description of the dispute and the parties involved
    (b) details of where and when the dispute has arisen
    (c) the nature of the redress which is sought
    (d) the names and addresses of the parties to the contract (including, where appropriate, the addresses which the parties have specified for the giving of notices).

Paragraph 7

(2)   A Referral Notice shall be accompanied by copies of, or relevant extracts from, the construction contract and such other documents as the Referring Party intends to rely upon.

Northern Ireland

The Scheme for Construction Contracts in Northern Ireland Regulations (Northern Ireland) 1999 Statutory Rule 1999 No 32 provides:

Paragraph 1(3)

The Notice of Adjudication shall set out briefly-

(a) the nature and a brief description of the dispute and the parties involved
(b) details of where and when the dispute has arisen
(c) the nature of the redress which is sought
(d) the names and addresses of the parties to the contract (including, where appropriate, the addresses which the parties have specified for the giving of notices).

Paragraph 7

(2)   A Referral Notice shall be accompanied by copies of, or relevant extracts from, the construction contract and such other documents as the Referring Party intends to rely upon.

Putting the case for the Party Responding

Clause 9	*Option Y(UK) 2*
Clause 91.1	Clause 90.6
Any further information from a Party to be considered by the Adjudicator is provided within four weeks from the submission.	Any further information from a Party to be considered by the Adjudicator is provided within fourteen days of referral
The four week period in this clause may be extended if requested by the Adjudicator in view of the nature of the dispute and agreed by the Parties	

NEC PRINCIPLES

Adjudication has been described as deciding judicially in a contest between amateurs and that description is, perhaps, particularly apt when considering the essentials of an adjudication.

Some consider an adjudication to be simply the referral of a dispute by the Submitting Party to the Adjudicator for a decision. It is certainly the case that in the interests of speed most adjudication procedures provide for the Submitting Party to submit their case along with the notice calling for an adjudication. That does not, however, by any stretch of the imagination mean that the Party who receives that notice calling for an adjudication and its associated case is precluded from responding. As a matter of principle (encompassing human rights, natural justice and fairness) the Party in receipt is entitled to make an equally full case to the Adjudicator before calling upon the Adjudicator to balance and decide, judicially, their amateur contest.

As a matter of practice, once seized of the jurisdiction, many Adjudicators prefer to take control of the proceedings and to issue Directions as to when any response from the Responding Party has to be received by. More worryingly, some Adjudicators are attempting to limit the length of any response by issuing Directions such that the response be restricted to no more than seven pages of A4.

In principle, however, the Party in receipt does not require to wait for Directions before submitting a response. Indeed, given the very tight limits involved in adjudication generally such a Party might be better advised to begin preparing their response as soon as they receive the Notice of Adjudication and then putting in the response as soon as it is ready. The Schemes expressly require the Adjudicator to consider such a response.

Clause 9 standing alone

An NEC contract with Clause 9 standing alone imposes no restrictions, other than time, on any response by the Party Receiving. Although such a contract is non-compliant, nor do the Schemes impose any restrictions, other than the ultimate time for the decision, on any response by the Party Receiving.

In principle, therefore, a Party Receiving could deliver their response at any time, although if complying with the contract itself such a Party would face a time limit (possibly extendible) of four weeks from the date of the submission with which they should comply.

Of course, the Adjudicator could intervene with a Direction relating to the format of any response and/or the time limit for any response and the Party Receiving would be well advised to respect such a Direction.

Option Y(UK) 2

An NEC contract incorporating Option Y(UK) 2 imposes no restrictions, other than time, on any response by the Party Receiving. Such a contract could be argued to be compliant and therefore determinative of the matter. Even where considered applicable, nor do the Schemes impose any restrictions, other than the ultimate time for the decision, on any response by the Party Receiving.

In principle, therefore, a Party Receiving could deliver their response at any time, although if complying with a contract containing Option Y(UK) 2 itself such a Party would face a time limit (possibly extendible) of fourteen days from the date of the referral with which they should comply.

Of course, the Adjudicator could intervene with a Direction relating to the format of any response and/or the time limit for any response and the Party Receiving would be well advised to respect such a Direction.

Generally

Of course, where the Parties agree that the applicable Scheme applies in its entirety or take the view that the law requires the applicable Scheme to apply in its entirety, then in theory (where the Adjudicator issues no Directions) these contractual terms (with their time limits) fall away and instead there is implied into the contract the terms of the applicable Scheme which imposes no time limit at all (other then the time for the decision itself) on any response.

It could be also be argued, of course, that this would conflict with the obligation of the Adjudicator to carry out his duties in accordance with any relevant terms of the contract, which in this case might be interpreted as a time limit of four weeks and fourteen days respectively on any response.

On the other hand, it could be argued that since a response by the Party Receiving is not an essential requirement of the UK legislation nothing requires to be implied into the contract and that the existing contractual terms with their time limit of four weeks and fourteen days respectively should be allowed to rule. In other words, in the absence of any Direction from the Adjudicator the Party Receiving should be allowed virtually up to the time when the Adjudicator issues his or her decision.

Potential UK human rights points

This area is likely to be a major area of contention in relation to human rights.

Adjudication generally has been criticised for the practice (more difficult where an NEC contract is involved) of a Submitting Party taking months to carefully fashion a case which is then sprung upon the other side as an 'ambush' in which the Party requiring to answer the case is given only 14 days by the Adjudicator to do so. In these circumstances, a failure to give the Party Responding an adequate, and perhaps even equal, time to respond could well be interpreted as a breach of human rights.

The process of adjudication itself is likely to come under sustained human rights scrutiny. If adjudication itself (and its 28-day limit) survives human rights scrutiny (perhaps because of the availability of the avenue of appeal to final determination) then a Direction by the Adjudicator to respond within fourteen days will, in context, also probably survive a human rights scrutiny.

However, a failure to give the Other Party an opportunity to respond at all, a failure to give the Other Party a reasonable opportunity to respond (and fourteen days could, perhaps, be viewed as an absolute minimum) and the imposition of unreasonable restrictions (e.g. not more than fourteen pages) all carry the potential to be regarded as abuses of human rights.

Of even more concern is the practice of issuing a Direction limiting the response of the Party Receiving. Unless the case for the Submitting Party is of the same length it is potentially an abuse of human rights to deny 'equality of arms' and to seek to restrict the Party Receiving in this manner.

In relation to the conduct of an adjudication, so far as human rights issues are concerned the cases of Elaney Contracts Ltd v The Vestry, 30 August 2000 and Austin Hall Building Ltd v Buckland Securities Ltd, 11 April 2001, have decided, at First Instance, that the European Convention of Human Rights does not apply to an adjudication. That position may, however, be distinguished or overturned on an appeal. It should be noted further that the principles to be found in the Human Rights Convention are often the same as the principles to be found in domestic UK law under the Rules of Natural Justice, and a number of cases have declared that these Rules do apply to adjudications.

England and Wales

The Scheme for Construction Contracts (England and Wales) Regulations 1998 SI No 649 provides:

Paragraph 17

The adjudicator shall consider any relevant information submitted to him by any of the parties to the dispute ...

Scotland

The Scheme for Construction Contracts (Scotland) Regulations 1998 SI No 687 provides:

Paragraph 17

The adjudicator shall consider any relevant information submitted to him by any of the parties to the dispute ...

Northern Ireland

The Scheme for Construction Contracts in Northern Ireland Regulations (Northern Ireland) 1999 Statutory Rule 1999 No 32 (NI) provides:

Paragraph 17

The adjudicator shall consider any relevant information submitted to him by any of the parties to the dispute ...

Adjustment of the cases

Clause 9	*Option Y(UK) 2*
Clause 91.1	Clause 90.6
Any further information from a Party to be considered by the Adjudicator is provided within four weeks from the submission.	Any further information from a Party to be considered by the Adjudicator is provided within fourteen days of referral.
The four week period in this clause may be extended if requested by the Adjudicator in view of the nature of the dispute and agreed by the Parties.	

NEC PRINCIPLES

Once the Submitting Party has submitted their case, the Party Receiving normally likes to make a response. Once the Party Responding have submitted their response, the Submitting Party often likes to make a reply. Although the scope for altering the basic nature of the dispute has been judicially interpreted as being limited, both Parties often wish to adjust their cases.

As a matter of practice, once seized of the jurisdiction, many Adjudicators prefer to take control of the proceedings and to issue Directions as to when any adjustment has to be received by. More worryingly, some Adjudicators are attempting to limit the length of any response by issuing Directions such that any adjustment be restricted to no more than, say, three pages of A4.

In principle, however, unless made the subject of such a Direction at the outset, the Parties do not require to wait for Directions before adjusting. Indeed, given the very tight limits involved in adjudication generally the Parties might well be advised to adjust as soon as they feel that it is necessary to do so. The Schemes expressly require the Adjudicator to consider such an adjustment.

Clause 9 standing alone

An NEC contract with Clause 9 standing alone imposes no restrictions, other than time, on any adjustments by either Party who can, therefore (in the absence of Directions), adjust as often as they like within the time allowed. Although such a contract is non-compliant, nor do the Schemes impose any restrictions, other than the ultimate time for the decision, on any adjustments.

In principle, therefore, either Party could deliver adjustments at any time, although if complying with the contract itself such a Party would face a time limit (possibly extendible) of four weeks from the date of the submission with which they should comply.

Of course, the Adjudicator could intervene with a Direction relating to the format of any adjustments and/or the time limit for any adjustment and the Party Receiving would be well advised to respect such a Direction.

Option Y(UK) 2

An NEC contract incorporating Option Y(UK) 2 imposes no restrictions, other than time, on any adjustments by the Parties. Such a contract could be argued to be compliant and therefore determinative of the matter. Even where considered applicable, nor do the Schemes impose any restrictions, other than the ultimate time for the decision, on adjustments by the Parties.

In principle, therefore, a Party could deliver their adjustments at any time, although if complying with a contract containing Option Y(UK) 2 itself such a Party would face a time limit (possibly extendible) of fourteen days from the date of the referral with which they should comply.

Of course, the Adjudicator could intervene with a Direction relating to the format of any adjustment and/or the time limit for any adjustment and the Party Receiving would be well advised to respect such a Direction.

Generally

Of course, where the Parties agree that the applicable Scheme applies in its entirety or take the view that the law requires the applicable Scheme to apply in its entirety, then in theory (where the Adjudicator issues no Directions) these contractual terms (with their time limits) fall away and instead there is implied into the contract the terms of the applicable Scheme which imposes no time limit at all (other then the time for the decision itself) on any adjustment.

It could be also be argued, of course, that this would conflict with the obligation of the Adjudicator to carry out his duties in accordance with any relevant terms of the contract which in this case might be interpreted as a time limit of four weeks and fourteen days respectively on any adjustments.

On the other hand, it could be argued that since adjustment by the Parties is not an essential requirement of the UK legislation nothing requires to be implied into the contract and that the existing contractual terms with their time limit of four weeks and fourteen days respectively should be allowed to rule. In other words that, in the absence of Directions from the Adjudicator, that the Parties should be allowed to adjust their cases virtually up to the point in time at which the Adjudicator issues his or her decision.

In relation to the conduct of an adjudication, so far as human rights issues are concerned the cases of Elaney Contracts Ltd *v* The Vestry, 30 August 2000 and Austin Hall Building Ltd *v* Buckland Securities Ltd, 11 April 2001, have decided, at First Instance, that the European Convention of Human Rights does not apply to an adjudication. That position may, however, be distinguished or overturned on an appeal. It should be noted further that the principles to be found in the Human Rights Convention are often the same as the principles to be found in domestic UK law under the Rules of Natural Justice, and a number of cases have declared that these Rules do apply to adjudications.

Potential UK human rights points

This area is also likely to be a major area of contention in relation to human rights.

The denial of an opportunity to put their case fully and properly is likely to be regarded as a *prima facie* breach of human rights, especially where the denial relates to one Party only.

Of even more concern is the practice of issuing a Direction limiting the format of any adjustments. Unless the case for the Submitting Party is of the same length it is potentially an abuse of human rights to deny 'equality of arms' and to seek to restrict the Party Receiving in this manner.

England and Wales

The Scheme for Construction Contracts (England and Wales) Regulations 1998 SI No 649 provides:

Paragraph 17

The adjudicator shall consider any relevant information submitted to him by any of the parties to the dispute ...

Scotland

The Scheme for Construction Contracts (Scotland) Regulations 1998 SI No 687 provides:

Paragraph 17

The adjudicator shall consider any relevant information submitted to him by any of the parties to the dispute ...

Northern Ireland

The Scheme for Construction Contracts in Northern Ireland Regulations (Northern Ireland) 1999 Statutory Rule 1999 No 32 (NI) provides:

Paragraph 17

The adjudicator shall consider any relevant information submitted to him by any of the parties to the dispute ...

Further procedure in the adjudication

The function of the Adjudicator

Clause 9

Option Y(UK) 2

There is no specific provision covering this aspect

There is no specific provision covering this aspect

NEC PRINCIPLES

The essentials of an adjudication – the case for the Submitting Party, the case for the Party Responding and any adjustment to those cases – is something which is provided for in the adjudication procedures themselves. Thereafter, as a general principle, Adjudicators are normally given express powers to determine their own case management.

Unusually, however, neither Clause 9, Option Y(UK) 2, nor the Guidance Notes make any reference to this aspect at all.

The result would appear to be that under the NEC family of contracts, the powers which an Adjudicator has (including the power to determine the specific procedures which the adjudication will follow) will (in the same way as the duties which an Adjudicator has to observe the principles of natural justice) depend upon the laws of either the law of the contract or the law of the territories in which the Works are being carried out.

The Schemes, however – perhaps for the avoidance of doubt – expressly provide that the Adjudicator 'shall decide on the procedure to be followed in the adjudication' and (presumably without prejudice to that *eusdem generis* provision) detail a number of specific powers which the Adjudicator is given. We consider the general power here and the specific power next.

It is not thought that there is likely to be much conflict in this area in that the specific powers given under the Schemes are the sort of sensible powers which might be expected to be seen in an adjudication and which are therefore capable of being implied as powers held by an Adjudicator. However, to inspect the site or carry out tests, the consent of one or other of the Parties may be required, which one would not expect to be withheld but which, if withheld, could conceivably give rise to difficulties since the contracts do not impose an express obligation upon the Parties to so comply or make any provision for what is to happen should the Parties fail to do so.

If the view is taken that it is only necessary to imply in from the Scheme into the contract that which is necessary to satisfy the essential requirements set out in the legislation then, since it could be argued that the implication of the specific powers set out in the Schemes are in fact necessary to allow an Adjudicator to come to the 'decision' which itself *is* an essential requirement, it may be permissible – should an argument arise on the point – to imply those specific powers into the contract.

If, however, either the Parties have agreed between themselves that the applicable Scheme is to apply in its entirety or the view is taken that the law requires the applicable Scheme to be applied in its entirety, then both the specific and the general powers are there.

Potential UK human rights points

The general approach of human rights legislation is to concentrate upon the fairness of overall procedures. Where, therefore, the Adjudicator is settling the 'case management' or is the 'master of the procedure' then it is essential that the Adjudicator sets procedures which are in line with the standards currently emanating from the Court of Human Rights as a failure to do so could clearly result in a breach of human rights. For example, were an Adjudicator to determine the language to be used in the adjudication but to have no regard to the needs and concerns of those Parties who are not familiar with that language, then that could clearly be regarded as a breach of human rights. The specific powers are considered next.

England and Wales

The scheme for Construction Contracts (England and Wales) Regulations 1998 SI No 649 provides:

Paragraph 13

The adjudicator ... shall decide on the procedure to be followed in the adjudication ...

Scotland

The Scheme for Construction Contracts (Scotland) Regulations 1998 SI No 687 provides:

Paragraph 13

The adjudicator ... shall decide on the procedure to be followed in the adjudication ...

Northern Ireland

The Scheme for Construction Contracts in Northern Ireland Regulations (Northern Ireland) 1999 Statutory Rule 1999 No 32 provides:

Paragraph 13

The adjudicator ... shall decide on the procedure to be followed in the adjudication ...

The approach of the Adjudicator

The right to take the initiative in ascertaining the facts and the law

Clause 9	*Option Y(UK) 2*
Primary level	*Primary level*
Clause 9 makes no provision in this respect	Clause 90.8 provides: The Adjudicator may take the initiative in ascertaining the facts and the law
Secondary level	*Secondary level*
Clause 92.1 provides that the Adjudicator settles the dispute as independent adjudicator and not as arbitrator	Under Option Y(UK) 2 Clause 92.1 provides that the Adjudicator gives his decision on the dispute as independent adjudicator and not as arbitrator

NEC PRINCIPLES

It is an essential requirement of the UK legislation (essential requirement No 6) that the construction contract should give the Adjudicator the right to take the initiative in ascertaining the facts and the law.

It is probably this principle (alongside the fact that adjudication is a temporary decision not capable of founding estoppel whereas Arbitration is a final decision capable of founding estoppel) which as much as anything distinguishes Arbitration from adjudication. Arbitration can be regarded as a voluntary adversarial process in which the Parties make their respective submissions on fact and law upon which the Arbitrator then sits in judgment. Adjudication, on the other hand, does not confine the Adjudicator to any submissions made but permits the Adjudicator to adopt an inquisitorial role and to take the initiative in ascertaining the facts and the law.

At a primary level, such a provision removes the element of doubt. It could be argued that, by analogy with Arbitration, an Adjudicator has an implied power to obtain legal advice, although it could also be argued (especially as regards paying for such advice) that unless the contract confers an express power of delegation then the person appointed under the contract has no authority to delegate. This provision – made an essential requirement – removes that element of doubt by effectively allowing the Adjudicator to take the initiative (and delegate) in ascertaining the law. Equally, as a rough and ready decision intended to speedily provide a temporarily binding decision, such a process cannot be allowed to be handicapped by a Party refusing or delaying to make a submission so that if, in order to arrive at the necessary decision, the Adjudicator needs to ascertain a fact then rather than wait for the Parties, this provision – made an essential requirement – removes that element of doubt by effectively allowing the Adjudicator to take the initiative (and delegate) in ascertaining the facts also. By the same token, if the Adjudicator selected happens to be a lawyer (and therefore already familiar with the law), then this provision removes that element of doubt by effectively allowing the Adjudicator to take the initiative (and delegate to an appointed Expert) in ascertaining the facts. It can also be pointed out that this essential requirement takes an Adjudicator out of the adversarial frame and into the inquisitorial frame. An Adjudicator is not expected to be merely judge and decide upon whatever the Parties have (or have not) submitted in an adversarial contest. Instead, it could be said that an Adjudicator is expected to use his or her knowledge and skill to ascertain just what law and facts are necessary to arrive at the most appropriate decision at that point in time and then, if necessary, to go out and get those facts and law and then (all within the required time limit) issue the appropriate decision.

At a secondary level, however, provisions such as these might be taken to have an even deeper effect. In an adversarial process – including, to some extent, Arbitration – the decision-maker giving reasons generally records the evidence and submissions made and then issues the decision with the reasons for that decision. Where that decision-maker can be shown to have made a mistake and to have misunderstood the facts or submissions or to have misapplied the law, then the decision taken may be challenged and a Court will correct those errors. Where, however, the decision-maker is appointed as an Expert then the Parties will be taken to have agreed to be bound by the decision of that Expert – right or wrong – and in general the Court will *not* interfere so as to correct any such errors and substitute the decision of the Court for that of the Expert. This may be what the drafters of the NEC family of contracts are trying to achieve by the above provisions and it may also be what the drafters of the Scheme are trying to achieve by their provisions. To some extent, in their reported decision on adjudication to date, the Courts have supported the drafters in that objective.

Whatever the underlying intention, the legislation makes it an essential requirement that the contract shall *enable* (note, this is not an *obligation* on the part of an Adjudicator to do so on every occasion, just an entitlement whenever the Adjudicator deems it necessary) the Adjudicator to take the initiative in ascertaining the facts and the law.

Clause 9 standing alone

It has to be admitted that Clause 9 standing alone does not comply with that essential requirement.

Option Y(UK) 2

It is clear that Option Y(UK) 2 does comply with this requirement.

Problems in this area are likely to arise only where the Adjudicator has taken some initiative in arriving at the decision to which a Party objects. Even if the view is taken that it is only necessary to imply in from the Scheme that which is necessary to comply with the essential requirements of the legislation, then as an essential requirement the part of the applicable Scheme providing for this will, for work carried out to construction contracts within the territories of the UK, need to be held to be implied into a contract containing Clause 9 only.

Clearly, such implication will not be required where Option Y(UK) 2 has been adopted for the essential provision will then be there. Nor will such implication be necessary where either the Parties have agreed between themselves that the applicable Scheme is to apply in its entirety or the view is taken that the law requires the applicable Scheme to be applied in its entirety, since the necessary provision (note, restricted to that which is 'necessary to determine the dispute') will then be there under the applicable Scheme.

Potential UK human rights points

It is highly unlikely that giving the Adjudicator the initiative to ascertain the facts and the law is, of itself, likely to be regarded as a contravention of the Human Rights Convention. Such a provision really does little more than create an inquisitorial system, a system which Europe has long found unobjectionable. Where human rights aspects may creep in, however, and where Adjudicators must take care, is the manner in which the power to take the initiative to ascertain the facts and the law is exercised.

In certain circumstances, it might be regarded as unacceptable, under human rights law (Article 6) and even under domestic law, for an Adjudicator to ascertain and apply the facts and the law in an unfair manner. For example, an Adjudicator who is holding a hearing and who first ascertains some facts and then shares those facts with only one of the Parties might be subject to some criticism and perhaps further proceedings. The entitlement to ascertain the facts and law must be exercised with care and fairness.

England and Wales

The essential requirement:

The HGCR Act 1996 c. 53 provides:

s. 108(2) The contract shall

...

> (f) enable the adjudicator to take the initiative in ascertaining the facts and the law.

The provisions

The Scheme for Construction Contracts (England and Wales) Regulations 1998 SI No 649 provides:

Paragraph 13

The adjudicator may take the initiative in ascertaining the facts and the law necessary to determine the dispute.

Scotland

The essential requirement:

The HGCR Act 1996 c. 53 provides:

s. 108(2) The contract shall

…
> (f) enable the adjudicator to take the initiative in ascertaining the facts and the law.

The provisions

The Scheme for Construction Contracts (Scotland) Regulations 1998 SI No 687 provides:

Paragraph 13

The adjudicator may take the initiative in ascertaining the facts and the law necessary to determine the dispute ...

Northern Ireland

The essential requirement:

The Construction Contracts (Northern Ireland) Order 1997 SI No 274 (NI) provides:

Article 7(2) The contract shall

…
> (f) enable the adjudicator to take the initiative in ascertaining the facts and the law.

The provisions

The Scheme for Construction Contracts in Northern Ireland Regulations (Northern Ireland) 1999 Statutory Rule 1999 No 32 provides:

Paragraph 13

The adjudicator may take the initiative in ascertaining the facts and the law necessary to determine the dispute ...

Specific powers available to the Adjudicator

Clause 9   *Option Y(UK) 2*

There is no specific provision in this   There is no specific provision in this
respect (although it may be implied)   respect (although it may be implied)

NEC PRINCIPLES

Having received the case for the Submitting Party and the case for the Party Responding (together with any adjustments) the Adjudicator will often be in a position to bring his expertise to bear on the dispute and to arrive at a decision on a documents-only basis.

In more complex disputes, however, the Adjudicator, from his experience, may feel it necessary to go further.

Clause 9 standing alone

Clause 9 gives the Adjudicator no specific powers. Such powers may, however, be implied under the law of the contract or the law of the territory to enable the Adjudicator to perform his function. In relation to NEC contracts in particular, which are founded upon a policy of co-operation, there should be no objection from the Parties to any reasonable step which the Adjudicator wishes to take in the course of arriving at the decision.

Option Y(UK) 2

Option Y(UK) 2 gives the Adjudicator no specific powers. Such powers may, however, be implied under the law of the contract or the law of the territory to enable the Adjudicator to perform his function. In relation to NEC contracts in particular, which are founded upon a policy of co-operation, there should be no objection from the Parties to any reasonable step which the Adjudicator wishes to take in the course of arriving at the decision.

Generally

Where the Works concerned fall within the definition of 'construction contracts' being carried out within the territories of the UK then, again, much depends upon the interpretation adopted.

If it is agreed that, in any event, specific powers such as these fall to be implied under the law of the contract or the law of the territory then there will not be an issue.

If the Parties are agreed that the applicable Scheme is to apply in its entirety or take the view that the law requires that, then by implication those specific powers contained in the Scheme will be implied from the applicable Scheme into the contract and the adjudication in question.

On the other hand, since these specific powers are not essential requirements of the legislation, it could be argued that they should not be implied into the contract and their exercise could be resisted. The purported specific power to limit the length of written documents or oral representations may be of particular concern.

Potential UK human rights points

The existence of these specific powers are unlikely, of themselves, to raise human rights issues. However, the purported exercise of such specific powers either against the will of a Party or outwith the knowledge of a Party could give rise to human rights issues. The power to restrict representation might also be contentious unless applied equally to both sides. The purported specific power to limit the length of written documents or oral representations may be contentious.

England and Wales

The Scheme for Construction Contracts (England and Wales) Regulations 1998 SI 649 provides:

Paragraph 13

... In particular [the Adjudicator] may-

(a) request any party to the contract to supply him with such documents as he may reasonably require, including, if he so directs, any written statement from any party to the contract supporting or supplementing the referral notice and any other documents given under paragraph 7(2)

(b) decide the language or languages to be used in the adjudication and whether a translation of any document is to be provided and if so by whom

(c) meet and question any of the parties to the contract and their representatives

(d) subject to obtaining any necessary consent from a third party or parties, make such site visits and inspections as he considers appropriate, whether accompanied by the parties or not

(e) subject to obtaining any necessary consent from a third party or parties, carry out any tests or experiments

(f) obtain and consider such representations and submissions as he requires, and, provided he has notified the parties of his intention, appoint experts, assessors or legal advisers

(g) give directions as to the timetable for the adjudication, any deadlines, or limits as to the length of written documents or oral representations to be complied with, and

(h) issue other directions relating to the conduct of the adjudication.

Paragraph 16

(1) Subject to any agreement between the parties to the contrary, and to the terms of paragraph (2) below, any party to the dispute may be assisted by, or represented by, such advisers or representatives (whether legally qualified or not) as he considers appropriate.

(2)   Where the adjudicator is considering oral evidence or representations, a party to the dispute may not be represented by more than one person, unless the adjudicator gives directions to the contrary.

Scotland

The Scheme for Construction Contracts (Scotland) Regulations 1998 SI No 687 provides:

Paragraph 13

... In particular [the Adjudicator] may-

(a)   request any party to the contract to supply him with such documents as he may reasonably require, including, if he so directs, any written statement from any party to the contract supporting or supplementing the referral notice and any other documents given under paragraph 7(2)

(b)   decide the language or languages to be used in the adjudication and whether a translation of any document is to be provided and if so by whom

(c)   meet and question any of the parties to the contract and their representatives

(d)   subject to obtaining any necessary consent from a third party or parties, make such site visits and inspections as he considers appropriate, whether accompanied by the parties or not

(e)   subject to obtaining any necessary consent from a third party or parties, carry out any tests or experiments

(f)   obtain and consider such representations and submissions as he requires, and, provided he has notified the parties of his intention, appoint experts, assessors or legal advisers

(g)   give directions as to the timetable for the adjudication, any deadlines, or limits as to the length of written documents or oral representations to be complied with, and

(h)   issue other directions relating to the conduct of the adjudication.

Paragraph 16

(1)   Subject to any agreement between the parties to the contrary, and to the terms of paragraph (2) below, any party to the dispute may be assisted by, or represented by, such advisers or representatives (whether legally qualified or not) as he considers appropriate.

(2)   Where the adjudicator is considering oral evidence or representations, a party to the dispute may not be represented by more than one person, unless the adjudicator gives directions to the contrary.

Northern Ireland

The Scheme for Construction Contracts in Northern Ireland Regulations (Northern Ireland) 1999 Statutory Rule No 32 (NI) provides:

Paragraph 13

... In particular [the Adjudicator] may-

(a) request any party to the contract to supply him with such documents as he may reasonably require, including, if he so directs, any written statement from any party to the contract supporting or supplementing the referral notice and any other documents given under paragraph 7(2)

(b) decide the language or languages to be used in the adjudication and whether a translation of any document is to be provided and if so by whom

(c) meet and question any of the parties to the contract and their representatives

(d) subject to obtaining any necessary consent from a third party or parties, make such site visits and inspections as he considers appropriate, whether accompanied by the parties or not

(e) subject to obtaining any necessary consent from a third party or parties, carry out any tests or experiments

(f) obtain and consider such representations and submissions as he requires, and, provided he has notified the parties of his intention, appoint experts, assessors or legal advisers

(g) give directions as to the timetable for the adjudication, any deadlines, or limits as to the length of written documents or oral representations to be complied with, and

(h) issue other directions relating to the conduct of the adjudication.

Paragraph 16

(1) Subject to any agreement between the parties to the contrary, and to the terms of paragraph (2) below, any party to the dispute may be assisted by, or represented by, such advisers or representatives (whether legally qualified or not) as he considers appropriate.

(2) Where the adjudicator is considering oral evidence or representations, a party to the dispute may not be represented by more than one person, unless the adjudicator gives directions to the contrary.

Fairness in the adjudication

Clause 9

There is no specific provision in this respect (although it may be implied)

Option Y(UK) 2

There is no specific provision in this respect (although it may be implied)

NEC PRINCIPLES

The principle that an adjudication should be fair is of wide application and is likely to be applied as a matter of law from outwith the contract. That law might come from the European Convention of Human Rights applied through the Human Rights Act 1998; the principles of natural justice or of fairness coming from the law of the territory in which the adjudication is taking place or the law of the contract under which the adjudication is taking place.

Clause 9 standing alone

Clause 9 standing alone makes no specific provision in this respect.

Option Y(UK) 2

Option Y(UK) 2 makes no specific provision in this respect.

Potential UK human rights points

This is likely to be the main battle-ground in relation to the application of human rights principles to adjudication. Article 6 of the European Convention on Human Rights, now incorporated into UK legislation by the Human Rights Act 1996 provides, in relation to civil rights, that 'everyone is entitled to a *fair* and public hearing within a reasonable time by an independent and impartial tribunal established by law.'

The concept of 'fairness' incorporated therein has been the subject of a number of decisions at European level. It can be compared to the concept of 'natural justice' which exists within the UK domestic law.

There are, however, a number of unanswered questions in relation to the application of these principles, not least the extent to which they must be observed in every adjudication or whether it will be sufficient for any deficiencies to be corrected on review. This is likely to be a major area of litigation over the next few years.

This is something to which Parties and Adjudicators are likely to have to pay close regard in the future. Various aspects of the Human Rights Act are reserved for superior Courts and it is likely that the application of the European Convention on Human Rights will be considered by the Court of Appeal at some stage. In the meantime, however, regard will require to be had to the decisions at first instance referred to below.

England and Wales

The Scheme for Construction Contracts (England and Wales) Regulations 1998 SI 649 provides:

Paragraph 17

The Adjudicator ... shall make available to [the Parties] any information to be taken into account in reaching his decision.

Commentary Apart from acting impartially (something which UK natural justice would be likely to have demanded in any case but something which human rights principles has upgraded to independence) there is really only one such principle set out in the above Scheme. This is an unsurprising principle, for if an Adjudicator is selected for his or her expertise and brings that expertise to bear in taking the initiative to arrive at a decision then natural justice (and human rights) demands that the Adjudicator should share that information with the Parties and invite their comments before utilising that information to arrive at the decision. This provision merely provides for that expressly in England and Wales.

There have, however, been a number of adjudication cases in England and Wales touching upon these issues.

The first of these is Discain Project Services Ltd *v* Opecprime Development Ltd. In that case, an adjudication took place but questions arose as to, *inter alia*, conversations which the Adjudicator had had with only one of the Parties. In defence to enforcement proceedings the matter came before His Honour Judge Bowsher in the Technology and Construction Court. His Honour Judge Bowsher indicated first of all that because of the speed with which things are being done, one can find in many adjudications a breach of the rules of natural justice if one looks hard enough, but that a Court should not be astute to upset a decision of an Adjudicator on the grounds of procedural error. However, His Honour Judge Bowsher also indicated that where an Adjudicator did not comply with the rules of natural justice (such as by creating a very serious risk of bias) such that compliance with those rules of natural justice might have produced a different decision on the part of the Adjudicator, then a Court might decline to enforce that decision (as the Court in fact did in this case). His Honour Judge Bowsher added that while he had been writing about the rules of natural justice (and before the HRA came into force) the same principles would apply in relation to human rights when that legislation was in force (as it now is w.e.f 2 October 2000).

The second of these decisions is that of Elanay Contracts Ltd *v* The Vestry. Here, the Adjudicator applied to the Referring Party for an extension of time to produce his decision (the maximum permitted extension being fourteen days) but was granted an extension of only seven days. Objection to enforcement proceedings was taken on the basis of Article 6 and the matter came before His Honour Judge Havery in the Technology and Construction Court. There does not appear, from the report of the decision, to have been a great deal of argument and citation before the Court but nevertheless, at first instance, His Honour Judge Havery said:

> In my judgment, Article 6 of the European Convention on Human Rights does not apply to an adjudicator's award or to proceedings before an adjudicator and that is because, although they are the decision or determination of a question of civil rights, they are not in any sense a final determination. When I say that, I am not talking about first instance or appeals, but merely that the determination is itself provisional in the sense that the matter can be re-opened.

(See also Appendix A, judgment extracts 40 and 41.)

Scotland

The Scheme for Construction Contracts (Scotland) Regulations 1998 SI No 687 provides:

Paragraph 17

The Adjudicator ... shall make available to [the Parties] any information to be taken into account in reaching his decision.

Commentary Apart from acting impartially (something which UK natural justice would be likely to have demanded in any case but something which human rights principles has upgraded to independence) there is really only one such principle set out in the above Scheme. This is an unsurprising principle, for if an Adjudicator is selected for his or her expertise and brings that expertise to bear in taking the initiative to arrive at a decision, then natural justice (and human rights) demands that the Adjudicator should share that information with the Parties and invite their comments before utilising that information to arrive at the decision. This provision merely provides for that expressly in Scotland.

The above English cases are likely to be regarded as persuasive in Scotland.

Northern Ireland

The Scheme for Construction Contracts in Northern Ireland Regulations (Northern Ireland) 1999 Statutory Rule No 32 (NI) provides:

Paragraph 17

The Adjudicator ... shall make available to [the Parties] any information to be taken into account in reaching his decision.

Commentary Apart from acting impartially (something which UK natural justice would be likely to have demanded in any case but something which human rights principles has upgraded to independence) there is really only one such principle set out in the above Scheme. This is an unsurprising principle, for if an Adjudicator is selected for his or her expertise and brings that expertise to bear in taking the initiative to arrive at a decision, then natural justice (and human rights) demands that the Adjudicator should share that information with the Parties and invite their comments before utilising that information to arrive at the decision. This provision merely provides for that expressly in Northern Ireland.

The above English cases are likely to be regarded as persuasive in Northern Ireland.

Co-operation by the parties

Clause 9   *Option Y(UK) 2*

There is no specific provision in this respect

There is no specific provision in this respect

NEC PRINCIPLES

Once the basic case and the basic response (if any) are to hand then the Adjudicator will be in a much better position to ascertain the true nature of the dispute and decide what, by way of case management, is likely to be needed to take the initiative and arrive at a fair and proper decision. Here, the co-operation of the Parties will be important in ensuring that the information necessary to a proper decision is ingathered.

Under NEC contracts, both under Clause 9 and Option Y(UK) 2, the co-operation of the Parties is to be expected since that is the foundation upon which the NEC contracts have been built. In the event, however, of the Adjudicator encountering a recalcitrant and non-co-operative Party, then it might well be the case that under the law of the territory in which the adjudication is taking place or the law which applies to the contract under which the adjudication is taking place, there might be implied by law a right on the part of the Adjudicator to give such weight as the Adjudicator considers appropriate to any evidence produced or not produced by the non-co-operative Party.

For the avoidance of doubt, however, the Schemes arm the Adjudicator with a specific power in this respect.

Again, much will depend upon the interpretation adopted as to whether such a specific power requires to be implied into the contract in question and, if so, whether it is competent to do so from the applicable Scheme.

Potential UK human rights points

Adjudicators will require to exercise care in this area.

England and Wales

The Scheme for Construction Contracts (England and Wales) Regulations 1998 SI No 649 provides:

Paragraph 14

The parties shall comply with any request or direction of the adjudicator in relation to the adjudication.

Paragraph 15

If, without showing sufficient cause, a party fails to comply with any request, direction or timetable of the adjudicator made in accordance with his powers, fails to produce any document or written statement requested by the adjudicator, or in any other way fails to comply with a requirement under these provisions relating to the adjudication, the adjudicator may-

(a) continue the adjudication in the absence of that party or of the document or written statement requested,
(b) draw such inferences from that failure to comply as circumstances may, in the adjudicator's opinion, be justified, and
(c) make a decision on the basis of the information before him attaching such weight as he thinks fit to any evidence submitted to him outside any period he may have requested or directed.

Scotland

The Scheme for Construction Contracts (Scotland) Regulations 1998 SI No 687 provides:

Paragraph 14

The parties shall comply with any request or direction of the adjudicator in relation to the adjudication.

Paragraph 15

If, without showing sufficient cause, a party fails to comply with any request, direction or timetable of the adjudicator made in accordance with his powers, fails to produce any document or written statement requested by the adjudicator, or in any other way fails to comply with a requirement under these provisions relating to the adjudication, the adjudicator may-

(a) continue the adjudication in the absence of that party or of the document or written statement requested,
(b) draw such inferences from that failure to comply as circumstances may, in the adjudicator's opinion, be justified, and
(c) make a decision on the basis of the information before him attaching such weight as he thinks fit to any evidence submitted to him outside any period he may have requested or directed.

Northern Ireland

The Scheme for Construction Contracts in Northern Ireland Regulations (Northern Ireland) 1999 Statutory Rule 1999 No 32 (NI) provides:

Paragraph 14

The parties shall comply with any request or direction of the adjudicator in relation to the adjudication.

Paragraph 15

If, without showing sufficient cause, a party fails to comply with any request, direction or timetable of the adjudicator made in accordance with his powers, fails to produce any document or written statement requested by the adjudicator, or in any other way fails to comply with a requirement under these provisions relating to the adjudication, the adjudicator may

(a) continue the adjudication in the absence of that party or of the document or written statement requested,
(b) draw such inferences from that failure to comply as circumstances may, in the adjudicator's opinion, be justified, and
(c) make a decision on the basis of the information before him attaching such weight as he thinks fit to any evidence submitted to him outside any period he may have requested or directed.

Terminating the adjudication

Revoking the adjudication

Clause 9

There is no specific provision covering this aspect although there is some provision in the NEC Adjudicator's Contract

Option Y(UK) 2

There is no specific provision covering this aspect although there is some provision in the NEC Adjudicator's Contract

NEC PRINCIPLES

It follows from the principle of adjudication being contractual that the Parties should be able, by their agreement, to withdraw from an adjudication and bring the process to a premature end without the need for a decision.

Even at a basic level, an adjudication involves participants in a substantial amount of (perhaps irrecoverable) time, effort and cost. It is also capable of resulting in the loss of a certain amount of goodwill. For these and other reasons, the adjudication of a dispute is something which most Parties attempt to avoid if possible.

One of the benefits of the two-week period of grace between notification of the dispute and submission of the dispute which is provided for in Clause 9 and the seven-day period between service of the Notice of Adjudication and service of the Referral Notice which is provided for in Option Y(UK) 2 and the Schemes is that they allow a Party who had failed to appreciate the seriousness of the situation and who had not realised that what was in their mind a 'difference' had, in the minds of the Other Party, grown into a 'dispute' to take corrective action to resolve the dispute and avoid an adjudication.

By the same token, when considered submissions have been made by one Party and a considered response made by the Other Party (and sometimes with a few 'signals' picked up from the approach to the dispute of the Adjudicator) a certain realisation sinks in and the dispute can (retaining the goodwill) be amicably resolved without the need for a full adjudication. While getting an adjudication started is a relatively simple exercise, bringing an adjudication which has started to an early conclusion may not, however, be so simple, unless the Parties are in agreement in that respect.

It is only sensible, therefore, to allow the Parties to withdraw from an adjudication by revoking the appointment of the Adjudicator and bringing an adjudication to a premature end. As earlier noted, this is almost certainly an implied power on the part of the Parties, but it is usual for express provision to be made for the 'tying up of loose ends' in relation to what has, after all, been the running of a formal adjudication. Unusually, however, neither Clause 9, Option Y(UK) 2, nor the Guidance Notes make any reference to this aspect at all.

One of the reasons for that, of course, is that with the NEC family of contracts being so dependent upon a spirit of co-operation, the bringing of an adjudication to a premature end should present no difficulties in that respect (particularly given the NEC attitude to costs).

The Schemes, however – perhaps for the avoidance of doubt – do make express provision for revoking the appointment of an Adjudicator and bringing an adjudication to a premature end.

For the avoidance of doubt, however, (and in a provision which may turn out to be of significant effect, on which see below) the Schemes make specific provision allowing for the Parties to revoke the appointment of an Adjudicator. This can arise either where there is default/misconduct or in other circumstances.

Revocation for default or misconduct

Where the Parties are agreed that there has been misconduct on the part of the Adjudicator or that the Adjudicator has been in default (and this is likely to be primarily where the Adjudicator has failed to issue his or her decision within the 28 days or other agreed extended period) then the Schemes provide that the Parties can together agree to revoke the appointment of the Adjudicator. There is no specific requirement for this to be in writing, although it would clearly be desirable for the Parties so to do.

It would be open (and perhaps even likely) for the Adjudicator to challenge such a revocation in Court and therefore the Parties would require to be reasonably clear as to their grounds. However, where an Adjudicator is clearly in default then the Schemes expressly leave it open to the Parties to dispose of that Adjudicator (without cost) by revoking his or her appointment and then, if so desired, starting another adjudication.

Fees

Where the Parties together revoke the appointment of an Adjudicator on this ground then the Scheme provides that the Parties shall not be liable to pay the Adjudicator's fees and expenses. This sanction is clearly an added incentive for an Adjudicator to produce the decision in time, for a failure to do so – a default – may result in the Adjudicator losing any entitlement to any fees or expenses.

Any fees paid to the Adjudicator in advance to launch the adjudication (a common provision in Adjudication Contracts) would theoretically be recoverable in these circumstances.

Revocation in other circumstances

After an adjudication has commenced and papers have been formally exchanged with perhaps some form of preliminary meeting then the real issues in any dispute tend to come more into focus. Where this happens to one Party only then there may be little which that one Party can do about the progress of an adjudication. Where, however – perhaps to preserve goodwill – the Parties themselves *together* agree upon some other way forward and neither Party any longer requires or desires the formal award of an Adjudicator, then under the Schemes it is possible for the Parties to revoke the appointment of the Adjudicator at any time. There is no specific requirement for this to be in writing, although it would clearly be desirable for the Parties so to do.

Fees

Where the Parties together revoke the appointment of an Adjudicator on this ground then the Scheme provides firstly, that the Adjudicator shall be entitled to the payment of such reasonable amount as he may determine by way of fees and expenses incurred by him and secondly, that following upon the making by the Adjudicator of any determination on how the payment shall be apportioned, the Parties shall be jointly and severally liable for any sum which remains outstanding (which means that the Adjudicator could recover all sums due from one Party leaving it to that Party to recover any balance due from the other Party). This provision is clearly there to protect the fees and expenses of a duly appointed Adjudicator where the Parties decide to terminate an adjudication early by revoking the appointment of the Adjudicator.

Should a question arise as to the level of an Adjudicator's fees and expenses, then no formal method of resolving that question has been provided. Presumably, an unpaid Adjudicator would sue for his or her outstanding fees and expenses on the strength of this provision (para 11). Were the Party or Parties to defend that action then a Court would undoubtedly be influenced by the discretion given to the Adjudicator by this provision. Were the Court to be satisfied that an issue arose, however, then there are various taxation procedures available to assist the Court.

If the view is taken that it is only necessary to imply from the Scheme into the contract that which is necessary to satisfy the essential requirements set out in the legislation then, since this is not an essential requirement of the legislation, the provisions of the Scheme in that respect should not be implied and everything will depend upon the agreement of the Parties. This may, in fact, be a particular cause for concern since, if the Parties have come to specific agreement in their contract as to costs, it could be argued that the Adjudicator should observe these contractual provisions as to costs and/or expenses and that where no essential requirement is involved the completely different approach to costs and/or expenses contained in the Scheme should not be implied into the contract.

If, however, either the Parties have agreed between themselves that the applicable Scheme is to apply in its entirety or the view is taken that the law requires the applicable Scheme to be applied in its entirety, then both the provisions for the revocation of the appointment of the Adjudicator and the consequences flowing therefrom are there.

Potential UK human rights points

It is unlikely that any human rights points will arise in this area, although it is conceivable that difficult questions could arise in relation to attempts to revoke the appointment of an Adjudicator on the grounds of misconduct.

England and Wales

The Scheme for Construction Contracts (England and Wales) Regulations 1998 SI No 649 provides:

Paragraph 11

(1)   The parties to a dispute may at any time agree to revoke the appointment of the adjudicator. The adjudicator shall be entitled to the payment of such reasonable amount as he may determine by way of fees and expenses incurred by him. The parties shall be jointly and severally liable for any sum which remains outstanding following the making of any determination on how the payment shall be apportioned.

(2)   Where the revocation of the appointment of the adjudicator is due to the default or misconduct of the adjudicator, the parties shall not be liable to pay the adjudicator's fees and expenses.

Scotland

The Scheme for Construction Contracts (Scotland) Regulations 1998 SI No 687 provides:

Paragraph 11

(1)   The parties to a dispute may at any time agree to revoke the appointment of the adjudicator. The adjudicator shall be entitled to the payment of such reasonable amount as he may determine by way of fees and expenses incurred by him. The parties shall be jointly and severally liable for any sum which remains outstanding following the making of any determination on how the payment shall be apportioned.

(2)   Where the revocation of the appointment of the adjudicator is due to the default or misconduct of the adjudicator, the parties shall not be liable to pay the adjudicator's fees and expenses.

Northern Ireland

The Scheme for Construction Contracts in Northern Ireland Regulations (Northern Ireland) 1999 Statutory Rule 1999 No 32 provides:

Paragraph 11

(1)   The parties to a dispute may at any time agree to revoke the appointment of the adjudicator. The adjudicator shall be entitled to the payment of such reasonable amount as he may determine by way of fees and expenses incurred by him. The parties shall be jointly and severally liable for any sum which remains outstanding following the making of any determination on how the payment shall be apportioned.

(2)   Where the revocation of the appointment of the adjudicator is due to the default or misconduct of the adjudicator, the parties shall not be liable to pay the adjudicator's fees and expenses.

The resignation of the Adjudicator

Clause 9	*Option Y(UK) 2*
If the Adjudicator resigns … the Parties choose a new adjudicator jointly. If the Parties have not chosen a new adjudicator jointly within four weeks of the Adjudicator resigning … a Party may ask the person stated in the Contract Data to choose a new adjudicator and the Parties accept his choice. The new adjudicator is appointed as Adjudicator under the NEC Adjudicator's Contract. He has power to settle disputes that were currently submitted to his predecessor but had not been settled at the time when his predecessor resigned ... The date of his appointment is the submission of these disputes to him as Adjudicator	If the Adjudicator resigns ... the parties choose a new adjudicator jointly. If the Parties have not chosen a new adjudicator jointly within four weeks of the Adjudicator resigning … a Party may ask the person stated in the Contract Data to choose a new adjudicator and the Parties accept his choice. The new adjudicator is appointed as Adjudicator under the NEC Adjudicator's Contract. He has power to decide on disputes that were currently submitted to his predecessor but had not been settled at the time when his predecessor resigned ... The date of his appointment is the submission of these disputes to him as Adjudicator
Contract Data	*Contract Data*

Clause 5.2 of the Adjudicator's Contract provides:

The Adjudicator may, by notifying the Parties, terminate his appointment if
- he considers that he cannot act because of a conflict of interest
- he is unable to act as Adjudicator, or
- he has not been paid an amount due within five weeks of the date by which payment should have been made.

NEC PRINCIPLES

It is only sensible to make provision for the resignation of an Adjudicator as there are a large number of potential reasons (including an inability to come to a decision within the stipulated time or even at all) why an Adjudicator might wish to resign.

Both Clause 9 and Option Y(UK) 2 make provision in this respect. The Parties are allowed to jointly choose a new Adjudicator. If the Parties cannot agree then the person stated in the Contract Data as the person to choose a new Adjudicator may be asked by a Party to choose a new Adjudicator and the Parties are contractually bound to accept his choice. There would appear to be something of a lacuna if the Parties are unable to agree and, *per incuriam*, the Parties have not completed that part of the Contract Data with the name of a nominator.

These contracts state that 'The new adjudicator is appointed as Adjudicator under the NEC Adjudicator's Contract' and that could be interpreted as meaning that even where the Parties have not entered into and signed an Adjudicator's Contract, by their signature to these contracts the terms of the Adjudicator's Contract will be implied into this contract.

The new Adjudicator is expressly given the power to settle disputes that were currently submitted to his predecessor but had not been settled at the time when his predecessor resigned. The date of his appointment is stipulated to be the date of submission of these disputes to him and, although the contracts do not expressly say so, the time for his decision is presumably (with perhaps an extension if requested by the Adjudicator in view of the nature of the dispute and agreed by the Parties) four weeks thereafter.

It should be noted that the Adjudicator's Contract (if entered into by the Parties) makes additional provision as regards the resignation of the Adjudicator. Under that contract an Adjudicator is permitted to resign where the Adjudicator considers that he or she cannot act because of a conflict of interest; is unable to act as Adjudicator (a remarkably open-ended provision), or has not been paid an amount due within five weeks of the date by which payment should have been made (the Adjudicator's Contract making provision for the Adjudicator's fee to be invoiced and paid by instalments).

Presumably, resignation may take place *at any time*. No provision is made for the involvement or consent of the Parties. There is a requirement for the Adjudicator to notify the Parties but no requirement for this to be in writing, although it would clearly be more prudent to do so.

The question of any liability on the part of an Adjudicator in respect of resignation will, however, be less complex since the Adjudicator's Contract makes specific provision as to risks (on which see below).

The Schemes also make provision for the resignation of an Adjudicator. Compulsory resignation (where the dispute is the same or substantially the same as one which has previously been referred to adjudication, and a decision has been taken in that adjudication) has been dealt with previously, but the Scheme also gives an Adjudicator the power to resign at any time on giving notice in writing to the Parties to the dispute.

Where an Adjudicator does so, the Schemes allow the Referring Party to serve a fresh Notice of Adjudication and effectively go through the whole process again of selecting an Adjudicator and referring the dispute to that Adjudicator.

The Schemes also provide that the Parties, if requested by the new Adjudicator and insofar as it is reasonably practicable for them to do so, to supply the new Adjudicator with copies of all documents which they had made available to the previous Adjudicator.

The Scheme also provides that where a dispute varies significantly from the dispute referred to the Adjudicator in the Referral Notice and for that reason he or she is not competent to decide it, the Adjudicator shall be entitled to the payment of such reasonable amount as he may determine by way of fees and expenses reasonably incurred by him. The Parties shall be jointly and severally liable for any sum which remains outstanding following the making of any determination on how the payment shall be apportioned.

The consequences of a resignation

The consequences of the resignation of an Adjudicator can, perhaps, be looked at in two stages – removing the old Adjudicator (with all the consequences which flow from that) and appointing the new Adjudicator (with all the consequences which flow from that).

Removing the old Adjudicator

Where an Adjudicator resigns, the removal of that old Adjudicator is likely to be determined primarily by the Adjudicator's Contract. Some Adjudicators have their own Adjudicator's Contract which they prefer the Parties to sign and which may make provision for such eventualities. The drafters of the NEC contract clearly envisage, however, the NEC Adjudicator's Contract being used.

That Adjudicator's Contract permits an Adjudicator to invoice his or her fee in instalments and to resign if that fee is not paid. No further provision is made and an Adjudicator would presumably require to sue all Parties in a Court of law for the outstanding balance which has caused the resignation.

The Scheme appears to envisage (leaving to one side the provisions of any Adjudicator's Contract separately entered into) that when the Adjudicator ceases to act through resignation then so his or her entitlement to a fee ceases, with one exception – a specific saving is made for an entitlement to a fee on the part of an Adjudicator where a dispute varies significantly from the dispute referred to him or her in the referral notice and for that reason he or she is not competent to decide the dispute.

No matter what view is taken of the applicability of the Scheme to the contract, this is probably a situation where the Adjudicator's Contract (if there is one) will sit above both the contract and the Scheme and will regulate what is to happen in the event of the Adjudicator's resignation. Essentially, if the Adjudicator has not made provision in his or her contract for payment upon resignation, then the Adjudicator may not have an entitlement to any such payment. Beyond that, having expressly provided in their contract to cover the circumstances of the resignation of the Adjudicator, it is difficult to see why the provisions of the Scheme relating to resignation should require to be implied. Where the Parties have agreed or taken the view that the applicable Scheme must be implied in its entirety, however, then by doing so they must be taken to have agreed the entitlement to the payment, jointly and severally, of the amount of the Adjudicator's reasonable fees and expenses outstanding following upon determination in the circumstances where a dispute varies significantly from the dispute referred and for that reason the Adjudicator has not felt competent to decide the dispute and has resigned.

Clearly, Parties can be considerably inconvenienced where a Notice of Adjudication and Referral Notice have been issued and considerable time, effort and expense invested in pursuing or defending the adjudication, the Adjudicator suddenly issues a notice of resignation at the eleventh hour. Fees may have to be paid and further expenditure incurred in appointing a new Adjudicator and re-referring the dispute to the new Adjudicator.

Some parties may feel inclined to seek to recover all or some of some of the expenditure incurred from the Adjudicator who has resigned but much will depend upon the terms of the contract involved. However, the provision (if there is one) providing for the immunity of the Adjudicator may be wide enough to cover that situation.

Appointing a replacement Adjudicator

Having got rid of the old Adjudicator, the pressing need – in order to arrive at a decision – then becomes that of getting a new Adjudicator in place.

Here, there may be essentially no real conflict between the Scheme and the contract in that the Scheme allows a new Adjudicator to be appointed by, *inter alia*, the agreement of the Parties or the provisions of the contract. Here, both Clause 9 and Option Y(UK) 2 allow the Parties to agree a replacement Adjudicator, failing which the Contract Data under which both Clause 9 and Option Y(UK) 2 are intended to operate allow for (and bind the Parties to) the inclusion in the Contract Data of the identity of a person who will nominate the replacement Adjudicator in the event of the resignation of an Adjudicator. In most instances, those contractual provisions are likely to be enough to achieve the appointment of a replacement Adjudicator and no implication from the applicable Scheme will be necessary.

It is only where agreement between the Parties as to a replacement Adjudicator and that part of the Contract Data has, *per incuriam*, not been completed that difficulties may arise. Here, for 'construction contracts' in the UK it may well become necessary to imply into the contract certain provisions from the Scheme in order to achieve the appointment of a replacement Adjudicator and get the process back on line towards a decision. The Schemes allow the entire Adjudicator selection process (including where necessary the use of an Adjudicator Nominating Body) to be used for the appointment of a replacement Adjudicator and also make some provision for what Parties must do to assist that replacement Adjudicator.

Potential UK human rights points

The resignation of an Adjudicator and the appointment of a replacement Adjudicator is a potential minefield if the requirement for the Adjudicator to be both independent and impartial is recognised but the potential circumstances are so infinite that each case would require to be looked at in its own circumstances.

England and Wales

The Scheme for Construction Contracts (England and Wales) Regulations 1998 SI 649 provides:

s. 108

Paragraph 9

(1)   An adjudicator may resign at any time on giving notice in writing to the parties to the dispute.

(2)   ...

(3)   Where an adjudicator ceases to act under paragraph 9(1)-

  (a)   the referring party may serve a fresh notice under paragraph 1 and shall request an adjudicator to act in accordance with paragraphs 2 to 7; and

  (b)   if requested by the new adjudicator and insofar as it is reasonably practicable, the parties shall supply him with copies of all documents which they had made available to the previous adjudicator

(4)   Where an adjudicator resigns ... where a dispute varies significantly from the dispute referred to him in the referral notice and for that reason he is not competent to decide it, the adjudicator shall be entitled to the payment of such reasonable amount as he may determine by way of fees and expenses reasonably incurred by him. The parties shall be jointly and severally liable for any sum which remains outstanding following the making of any determination on how the payment shall be apportioned.

Scotland

The Scheme for Construction Contracts (Scotland) Regulations 1998 SI No 687 provides:

Paragraph 9

(1)   An adjudicator may resign at any time on giving notice in writing to the parties to the dispute.

(2)   ...

(3)   Where an adjudicator ceases to act under paragraph 9(1)-

  (a)   the referring party may serve a fresh notice under paragraph 1 and shall request an adjudicator to act in accordance with paragraphs 2 to 7; and

  (b)   if requested by the new adjudicator and insofar as it is reasonably practicable, the parties shall supply him with copies of all documents which they had made available to the previous adjudicator

(4) Where an adjudicator resigns in the circumstances ... where a dispute varies significantly from the dispute referred to him in the referral notice and for that reason he is not competent to decide it, the adjudicator shall be entitled to the payment of such reasonable amount as he may determine by way of fees and expenses reasonably incurred by him. The parties shall be jointly and severally liable for any sum which remains outstanding following the making of any determination on how the payment shall be apportioned.

Northern Ireland

The Scheme for Construction Contracts in Northern Ireland Regulations (Northern Ireland) 1999 Statutory Rule 1999 No 32 provides:

Paragraph 9

(1)   An adjudicator may resign at any time on giving notice in writing to the parties to the dispute.
(2)   ...
(3)   Where an adjudicator ceases to act under paragraph 9(1)-
  (a) the referring party may serve a fresh notice under paragraph 1 and shall request an adjudicator to act in accordance with paragraphs 2 to 7; and
  (b) if requested by the new adjudicator and insofar as it is reasonably practicable, the parties shall supply him with copies of all documents which they had made available to the previous adjudicator
(4)   Where an adjudicator resigns in the circumstances ... where a dispute varies significantly from the dispute referred to him in the referral notice and for that reason he is not competent to decide it, the adjudicator shall be entitled to the payment of such reasonable amount as he may determine by way of fees and expenses reasonably incurred by him. The parties shall be jointly and severally liable for any sum which remains outstanding following the making of any determination on how the payment shall be apportioned.

Other matters relating to the adjudication

Immunity on the part of the Adjudicator and his agents and employees

Clause 9	*Option Y(UK) 2*
	Clause 90.12
No provision is made	The Adjudicator is not liable for anything done or omitted in the discharge or purported discharge of his function as adjudicator unless the act or omission is in bad faith and any employee or agent of the Adjudicator is similarly protected from liability.

The NEC Adjudicator's Contract provides:

4.   Risks

4.1   The Adjudicator, his employees and agents, are not liable to the Parties for an action or failure to take action in an adjudication unless the action or failure to take action is in bad faith.

4.2   The Parties indemnify the Adjudicator, his employees and agents, against claims, compensation and costs arising out of the Adjudicator's decision unless his decision was made in bad faith.

NEC PRINCIPLES

It is an essential requirement in the legislation (essential requirement No 8) – probably to ensure a reasonable supply of Adjudicators – that the immunity of not only the Adjudicator, but also his agents and employees, is provided for.

The NEC Adjudicator's Contract does provide that but the provision requires to be in the construction contract itself. Option Y(UK) 2 provides that but it has to be accepted that Clause 9 standing alone does not. Where, therefore, a 'construction contract' is being executed in the territories of the United Kingdom, the provisions of the applicable Scheme relating to immunity will require to be implied into that contract.

Potential UK human rights points

There are unlikely to be human rights points arising in this area.

England and Wales

The essential requirement

The HGCR Act 1996 c. 53 provides:

s. 108

(4)   The contract shall also provide that the adjudicator is not liable for anything done or omitted in the discharge or purported discharge of his functions as adjudicator unless the act or omission is in bad faith, and that any employee or agent of the adjudicator is similarly protected from liability.

The provision of the Scheme

The Scheme for Construction Contracts (England and Wales) Regulations 1998 SI No 649 provides:

Paragraph 25

The adjudicator shall not be liable for anything done or omitted in the discharge or purported discharge of his functions as adjudicator unless the act or omission is in bad faith, and any employee or agent of the adjudicator shall be similarly protected from liability.

Scotland

The essential requirement

The Housing Grants, Construction and Regeneration Act 1996 c. 53 provides:

s. 108

(4)   The contract shall also provide that the adjudicator is not liable for anything done or omitted in the discharge or purported discharge of his functions as adjudicator unless the act or omission is in bad faith, and that any employee or agent of the adjudicator is similarly protected from liability.

The provision of the Scheme

The Scheme for Construction Contracts (Scotland) Regulations 1998 SI No 687 provides:

Paragraph 25

The adjudicator shall not be liable for anything done or omitted in the discharge or purported discharge of his functions as adjudicator unless the act or omission is in bad faith, and any employee or agent of the adjudicator shall be similarly protected from liability.

Northern Ireland

The essential requirement

The Construction Contracts (Northern Ireland) Order 1997 SI No 274 (NI) provides:

s. 108

(4)   The contract shall also provide that the adjudicator is not liable for anything done or omitted in the discharge or purported discharge of his functions as adjudicator unless the act or omission is in bad faith, and that any employee or agent of the adjudicator is similarly protected from liability.

The provision of the Scheme

The Scheme for Construction Contracts in Northern Ireland Regulations (Northern Ireland) 1999 Statutory Rule 1999 No 32 provides:

Paragraph 25

The adjudicator shall not be liable for anything done or omitted in the discharge or purported discharge of his functions as adjudicator unless the act or omission is in bad faith, and any employee or agent of the adjudicator shall be similarly protected from liability.

Confidentiality on the part of the Adjudicator and Parties

Clause 9   *Option Y(UK) 2*

No provision is made in this respect   No provision is made in this respect

The Adjudicator's Contract provides:

2. Adjudication

2.3 The Parties and the Adjudicator keep the Adjudicator's decision and information provided for an adjudication as confidential to those who have a proper interest in them.

NEC PRINCIPLES

It is clearly desirable that the proceedings of an adjudication remain confidential in the first instance (although that confidentiality may be lost by law if the matter proceeds to litigation).

Potential UK human rights points

There are unlikely to be any human rights points arising in this area.

England and Wales

The Scheme for Construction Contracts (England and Wales) Regulations 1998 SI No 649 provides:

Paragraph 18

The adjudicator and any party to the dispute shall not disclose to any other person any information or document provided to him in connection with the adjudication which the party supplying it has indicated is to be treated as confidential, except to the extent that it is necessary for the purposes of, or in connection with, the adjudication.

Scotland

The Scheme for Construction Contracts (Scotland) Regulations 1998 SI No 687 provides:

Paragraph 18

The adjudicator and any party to the dispute shall not disclose to any other person any information or document provided to him in connection with the adjudication which the party supplying it has indicated is to be treated as confidential, except to the extent that it is necessary for the purposes of, or in connection with, the adjudication.

Northern Ireland

The Scheme for Construction Contracts in Northern Ireland Regulations (Northern Ireland) 1999 Statutory Rule 1999 No 32 provides:

Paragraph 18

The adjudicator and any party to the dispute shall not disclose to any other person any information or document provided to him in connection with the adjudication which the party supplying it has indicated is to be treated as confidential, except to the extent that it is necessary for the purposes of, or in connection with, the adjudication.

Retention of the papers by the adjudicator

Clause 9   *Option Y(UK) 2*

No provision is made in this respect   No provision is made in this respect

The Adjudicator's Contract provides:

2.   Adjudication
2.4   The Adjudicator keeps documents provided to him by the Parties until termination.

NEC PRINCIPLES

The Adjudicator's Contract provides that the Adjudicator shall keep the documents provided to him by the Parties until termination. Presumably, since the Adjudicator's Contract also provides that unless previously terminated, the Adjudicator's appointment terminates on the date stated in the Contract Data, that means until the contract as a whole is terminated. There is no comparable provision in the Schemes. Presumably, even under the Schemes, where the adjudication is running under the Adjudicator's Contract then this contractual provision should be observed.

Potential UK human rights points

There are unlikely to be any human rights points arising in this area.

England and Wales

No provision is made in this respect.

Scotland

No provision is made in this respect.

Northern Ireland

No provision is made in this respect.

17. The decision of the Adjudicator

Introduction

The decision of the Adjudicator is, of course, the aim of the exercise. It is proposed to consider that here in relation to the following:

- The (basic) time for the decision
- Late decisions
- Extending the time for the decision
  - The Adjudicator's decision
  - Making the decision peremptory
  - The award
  - Interest
  - Costs
  - Adjudicator's fees and expenses
  - Other matters
  - Reasons
  - Correcting the decision

The (basic) time for the decision

Clause 9

Clause 91.1

The Adjudicator notifies his decision within four weeks of the end of the period for providing information

Option Y(UK) 2

Clause 90.9

The Adjudicator reaches a decision within twenty eight days of referral

NEC PRINCIPLES

In order to provide a procedure which would *speedily* arrive at a temporarily binding decision there is clearly required to be a time limit set upon the process and the time limit selected – twenty-eight days – was made a basic essential requirement (essential requirement No 3) in the legislation.

In this respect, Clause 9, with its open-ended provision of four weeks, is clearly non-compliant whereas Option Y(UK) 2 has amended the situation in order to become compliant.

It is suggested, therefore, that Option Y(UK) 2 is compliant but where – in relation to a 'construction contract' in the territories of the United Kingdom – Clause 9 is being used alone, then it will at least be necessary to imply into that contract those parts of the applicable Scheme which impose the essential requirement that the Adjudicator arrive at a decision within a basic period, and where it is considered that the applicable Scheme is to be applied wholesale, that will also be a requirement.

The Schemes follow the essential requirement by imposing a basic time limit for the decision of the Adjudicator within twenty-eight days of referral, although allowance is also made for the extension of this period which we consider next.

Potential UK human rights points

The period of time allowed for an adjudication is also likely to become one of the major areas of debate so far as the Convention of Human Rights is concerned. Article 6(1) of the Convention, which is one of the Articles specifically incorporated into UK law by the Human Rights Act 1998, provides: 'In the determination of his civil rights and obligations ... everyone is entitled to a fair and public hearing within a reasonable time by an independent and impartial tribunal established by law.'

It could be argued that for a hearing to be 'fair' an adequate amount of time must be allowed for the hearing and that the period of twenty-eight days is inadequate in that respect. However, it is also necessary to consider the extent to which any difficulties in that respect can be resolved in any 'final determination' (such as Arbitration or litigation).

In relation to the conduct of an adjudication, so far as human rights issues are concerned the cases of Elaney Contracts Ltd *v* The Vestry, 30 August 2000, and Austin Hall Building Ltd *v* Buckland Securities Ltd, 11 April 2001, have decided, at First Instance, that the European Convention of Human Rights does not apply to an adjudication. That position may, however, be distinguished or overturned on an appeal. It should be noted further that the principles to be found in the Human Rights Convention are often the same as the principles to be found in domestic UK law under the Rules of Natural Justice and a number of cases have declared that these Rules do apply to adjudications.

England and Wales

The essential requirement:

The HGCR Act 1996 c. 53 provides:

s. 108(2) The contract shall

... (c) require the adjudicator to reach a decision within 28 days of referral ...

The provisions

The Scheme for Construction Contracts (England and Wales) Regulations 1998 SI No 649 provides:

Paragraph 19

(1)   The adjudicator shall reach his decision not later than-
    (a) twenty eight days after the date of the referral notice ...

Commentary

In an *extempore* decision, the case of Elanay Contracts Ltd *v* The Vestry has already decided, at first instance, that Article 6 of the European Convention on Human Rights does not apply to adjudication in this respect, although the matter may be re-visited in other cases or on appeal.

Scotland

The essential requirement:

The HGCR Act 1996 c. 53 provides:

s. 108(2) The contract shall

...

  (c) require the adjudicator to reach a decision within 28 days of referral ...

The provisions

The Scheme for Construction Contracts (Scotland) Regulations 1998 SI No 687 provides:

Paragraph 19

(1)   The adjudicator shall reach his decision not later than-
  (a) twenty eight days after the date of the referral notice ...

Commentary The English case referred to above is likely to be of persuasive value in Scotland.

Northern Ireland

The essential requirement:

The Construction Contracts (Northern Ireland) Order 1997 SI No 274 (NI) provides:

Article 7(2) The contract shall

...

  (c) require the adjudicator to reach a decision within 28 days of referral
    ...

The provisions

Paragraph 19

(1)   The adjudicator shall reach his decision not later than-
  (a) twenty eight days after the date of the referral notice ...

Commentary The English case referred to above is likely to be of persuasive value in Northern Ireland.

Late decisions

Clause 9	*Option Y(UK) 2*
Clause 91.1	Clause 90.9
The Adjudicator notifies his decision within four weeks of the end of the period for providing information.	The Adjudicator reaches a decision within twenty eight days of referral or such longer period as is agreed by the Parties after the dispute has been referred. The Adjudicator may extend the period of twenty eight days by up to fourteen days with the consent of the notifying Party.
There is no provision for this time to be extended	There is no provision for this time to be extended

NEC PRINCIPLES

It is clear that basic time limit (twenty-eight days) for Adjudicator's decisions which, in relation to 'construction contracts' the UK legislation sets down as the period within which the Adjudicator is to issue his or her decision, is a tight time limit.

In practice, it appears that in many cases the Adjudicator has to try to secure the consent of the Parties to an extension of the time for the decision. Even then, however, complexities or pressure of business or inadvertence, may result in that decision not being produced on time.

With these practical difficulties in mind, some adjudication procedures make express provision allowing the Parties to agree to accept the Adjudicator's decision issued late. The NEC conditions in this respect (and there is no difference here between a contract containing Clause 9 standing alone and a contract which has adopted Option Y(UK) 2) make no provision allowing the decision of the Adjudicator to be received late. Perhaps surprisingly, nor do the Schemes contain any express provision aimed at allowing late decisions.

Accordingly, no matter upon what basis the adjudication is being run, in these circumstances there is no express provision allowing the decision of the Adjudicator to be received late (although, of course, *all* of the Parties together could agree to treat a decision which was late and invalid as a valid decision although it would be wise to have any such agreement reduced to writing).

Where the Parties stand upon their entitlements the failure on the part of the Adjudicator (which presumably disentitles him or her to their fees and expenses) to reach a decision in time is an end of the adjudication so far as both the NEC contracts and the applicable Schemes are concerned.

Thereafter, however, (as we shall see later) the paths diverge. Under the NEC family of contracts, there is no provision for another adjudication and resort (if any) must be had to the tribunal. Under the Schemes, however, (and, for the first time, at the option of either Party) another adjudication may be commenced.

Potential UK human rights points

The fact that decisions are not allowed to be received late is unlikely to raise any major human right points.

England and Wales

No provision is made for the decision of the Adjudicator to be received late.

Scotland

No provision is made for the decision of the Adjudicator to be received late.

Northern Ireland

No provision is made for the decision of the Adjudicator to be received late.

Extending the time for the decision

Clause 9	*Option Y(UK) 2*
Clause 91.1	Clause 90.9
The Adjudicator notifies his decision within four weeks of the end of the period for providing information [the period for providing information is 'within four weeks from the submission']	The Adjudicator reaches a decision within twenty eight days of referral or such longer period as is agreed by the Parties after the dispute has been referred.
The four week periods in this clause may be extended if requested by the Adjudicator in view of the nature of the dispute and agreed by the Parties	The Adjudicator may extend the period of twenty eight days by up to fourteen days with the consent of the notifying Party.

NEC PRINCIPLES

There will be occasions where the basic time limit set down for a decision will require to be extended but, in order to prevent abuse of the extension procedure and provide a procedure which would *speedily* arrive at a temporarily binding decision, a sensible procedure will seek to control the circumstances in which extensions are allowed. These have, therefore, also been made a basic essential requirement (essential requirement No 4) in the legislation.

By virtue of the fact that the basic time limit set down for the decision by Clause 9 is non-compliant, its extension periods are by definition, also non-compliant. Option Y(UK) 2 has, however, amended the situation in order to become compliant.

It is suggested, therefore, that Option Y(UK) 2 is compliant but where – in relation to a 'construction contract' in the territories of the United

Kingdom – Clause 9 is being used alone, then it will be necessary to imply into that contract at least those parts of the applicable Scheme (essential requirements) which control any extension of the basic period within which the Adjudicator must arrive at a decision. Where the view is taken that the Scheme requires to be implied wholesale then the same periods will apply.

The Schemes follow the essential requirement by allowing the Adjudicator, with the consent of the Party by whom the dispute was referred, to extend the period of 28 days by up to fourteen days and allow all the Parties, after the dispute has been referred, to extend the period of 28 days by such longer period as is agreed by the Parties.

Potential UK human rights points

As earlier noted, the period of time allowed for an adjudication is also likely to become one of the major areas of debate so far as the Convention of Human Rights is concerned in that it could be argued that for a hearing to be 'fair' an adequate amount of time must be allowed for the hearing and that the period of twenty-eight days is inadequate in that respect.

Accordingly, where a Party refuses to agree any extension then they may be inviting a human rights challenge, whereas where a Party agrees a reasonable extension then they may be forestalling a human rights challenge in this respect.

England and Wales

The essential requirement:

The HGCR Act 1996 c. 53 provides:

s. 108(2) The contract shall

…

(c)   require the adjudicator to reach a decision within 28 days of referral or such longer period as is agreed by the parties after the dispute has been referred.

(d)   allow the adjudicator to extend the period of 28 days by up to 14 days, with the consent of the party by whom the dispute was referred.

The provisions

The Scheme for Construction Contracts (England and Wales) Regulations 1998 SI No 649 provides:

Paragraph 19

(1)   The adjudicator shall reach his decision not later than-
   (a)   twenty eight days after the date of the referral notice ..., or
   (b)   forty two days after the date of the referral notice if the referring party so consents, or
   (c)   such period exceeding twenty eight days after the referral notice as the parties to the dispute may, after the giving of that notice, agree.

Scotland

The essential requirement:

The HGCR Act 1996 c. 53 provides:

s. 108(2) The contract shall

...

    (c) require the adjudicator to reach a decision within 28 days of referral or such longer period as is agreed by the parties after the dispute has been referred.

    (d) allow the adjudicator to extend the period of 28 days by up to 14 days, with the consent of the party by whom the dispute was referred.

The provisions

The Scheme for Construction Contracts (Scotland) Regulations 1998 SI No 687 provides:

Paragraph 19

(1)   The adjudicator shall reach his decision not later than-

    (a) twenty eight days after the date of the referral notice ..., or

    (b) forty two days after the date of the referral notice if the referring party so consents, or

    (c) such period exceeding twenty eight days after the referral notice as the parties to the dispute may, after the giving of that notice, agree.

Northern Ireland

The essential requirement:

The Construction Contracts (Northern Ireland) Order 1997 SI No 274 (NI) provides:

Article 7(2) The contract shall-

...

    (c) require the adjudicator to reach a decision within 28 days of referral or such longer period as is agreed by the parties after the dispute has been referred.

    (d) allow the adjudicator to extend the period of 28 days by up to 14 days, with the consent of the party by whom the dispute was referred.

The provisions

The Scheme for Construction Contracts in Northern Ireland Regulations (Northern Ireland) 1999 Statutory Rule 1999 No 32 provides:

Paragraph 19

(1)   The adjudicator shall reach his decision not later than-

    (a) twenty eight days after the date of the referral notice ..., or

(b) forty two days after the date of the referral notice if the referring party so consents, or

(c) such period exceeding twenty eight days after the referral notice as the parties to the dispute may, after the giving of that notice, agree.

The Adjudicator's decision

Clause 9

Option Y(UK) 2

Clause 90.2

Clause 90.9

The Adjudicator settles the dispute by notifying the Parties and the Project Manager of his decision together with his reasons within the time allowed by this contract

The Adjudicator reaches a decision ...

Clause 90.10

The Adjudicator provides his reasons to the Parties and to the Project Manager with his decision

NEC PRINCIPLES

No details are provided in either Clause 9 or Option Y(UK) 2 as to how a decision and its associated reasons are to be drafted.

The Schemes are similarly laconic, making some provision for individual items but in general providing simply that 'The adjudicator shall decide the matters in dispute'. However, individual provisions in the Schemes, precedent and practice have added much to the way in which an Adjudicator arrives at his or her decision where, the other conditions being satisfied, Works falling within the definition of 'construction contracts' are being undertaken within the UK.

In these circumstances, an adjudication decision may resemble the following:

* Making the award peremptory
* The award
* Interest
* Costs
* Adjudicator's fees and expenses
* Other matters
* Reasons

It is proposed to consider each of these items below.

Potential UK human rights points

A number of human rights considerations such as the extent to which a Party has an entitlement to proper reasons, could arise in this area.

England and Wales

The Scheme for Construction Contracts (England and Wales) Regulations 1998 SI No 649 provides:

Paragraph 20

The adjudicator shall decide the matters in dispute.

Scotland

The Scheme for Construction Contracts (Scotland) Regulations 1998 SI No 687 provides:

Paragraph 20

The adjudicator shall decide the matters in dispute.

Northern Ireland

The Scheme for Construction Contracts in Northern Ireland Regulations (Northern Ireland) 1999 Statutory Rule 1999 No 32 provides:

Paragraph 20

(see also Appendix A, judgment extracts 42 and 43)

Making the decision peremptory

Clause 9   *Option Y(UK) 2*

No provision is made in this respect   No provision is made in this respect

NEC PRINCIPLES

It is clearly in line with the stated desire of having the decision of the Adjudicator treated as temporarily binding pending any competent review of the decision that some procedure should be available for the temporary enforcement of such decisions which the parties have contractually agreed are to be binding.

Neither Clause 9 nor Option Y(UK) 2 make any provision in that respect. The Schemes do, however, make extensive provision in that respect and one such provision is the power which the Schemes give to the Adjudicator to order the Parties to comply peremptorily with his or her decision.

Again, such a provision causes difficulties of interpretation and application.

If Option Y(UK) 2 is regarded as being compliant with the essential requirements of the UK legislation then nothing further – and in particular no power to the Adjudicator to issue his or her decisions peremptorily – requires to be implied into such a contract or any adjudication running under it.

Even accepting that Clause 9 standing alone is non-compliant, it could be argued that there only requires to be implied from the applicable Scheme into such a contract that which is necessary to meet the essential requirements of the UK legislation and that a power on the part of an Adjudicator to issue decisions peremptorily – not being an essential requirement of the UK legislation – does not fall into that category and does not require to be implied.

Where the Parties agree that the applicable Scheme is to apply in its entirety or take the view that the law requires the applicable Scheme to apply in its entirety, then they should do so in the knowledge that, although there is no such provision in their contract, by doing so they are giving the Adjudicator the power to issue his or her decision peremptorily (with all that that implies in terms of enforcement – on which see Section III).

A peremptory Order is an Order which carries sanctions with a failure to comply with it. The Schemes allow an Adjudicator, if he or she thinks fit, to order any of the Parties to comply peremptorily with the decision or any part of it.

There has been some *dicta* in England and Wales, however, to suggest that Adjudicators should exercise some restraint in making their decisions peremptory, should not do so without giving the Parties an opportunity to comment specifically upon the proposal to make the decision peremptory, and that even where a decision has been made peremptory, the Courts will not automatically enforce it as such.

Potential UK human rights points

This area carries the potential to be a minefield in relation to human rights considerations. The very suggestion that in proceedings such as these an Adjudicator should have the power to issue peremptory decisions without the Parties having contractually agreed to confer such a power upon the Adjudicator might itself be regarded as a breach of human rights. Certainly, to make such a decision peremptory without giving the Parties an opportunity to comment upon that point is likely to be regarded as a breach of human rights.

England and Wales

The Scheme for Construction Contracts (England and Wales) Regulations 1998 SI No 649 provides:

Paragraph 23

(1) In his decision, the adjudicator may, if he thinks fit, order any of the parties to comply peremptorily with his decision or any part of it.

Commentary At an early stage in adjudication, it became the practice in England and Wales for Adjudicators to mark their decisions as peremptory almost as a matter of course. His Honour Judge Dyson has suggested, however, that Adjudicators should not do so, in particular should not do so without giving the Parties an opportunity to comment, and that even where

Adjudicators mark a decision as to be complied with peremptorily, the Courts will not necessarily give effect to that.

Scotland

The Scheme for Construction Contracts (Scotland) Regulations 1998 SI No 687 provides:

Paragraph 23

(1)   In his decision, the adjudicator may, if he thinks fit, order any of the parties to comply peremptorily with his decision or any part of it.

Commentary Making decisions as to be complied with peremptorily does not feature large in Scotland and there do not appear to have been any cases in this area so far. As a matter of practice, any English decisions are unlikely to be treated as being of persuasive value in this respect.

Northern Ireland

The Scheme for Construction Contracts in Northern Ireland Regulations (Northern Ireland) 1999 Statutory Rule 1999 No 32 provides:

Paragraph 23

(1)   In his decision, the adjudicator may, if he thinks fit, order any of the parties to comply peremptorily with his decision or any part of it.

Commentary It is too early for any practice to have been identified in Northern Ireland.

The award

Clause 9	*Option Y(UK) 2*
No specific provision is made as regards the form which the award is to take.	No specific provision is made as regards the form which the award is to take.

The Adjudicator's Contract makes no specific provision in this respect.

NEC PRINCIPLES

Just as virtually any dispute can be made the subject of an adjudication so virtually every dispute can be made the subject of an award. It is possible to seek an award which obliges a Party to perform an act or cease performing an act but in practice most disputes are couched in terms in which the remedy sought is expressed monetarily so that the award sought is also in those terms (and easier to enforce).

One would not expect to see any provision in the Adjudicator's Contract as to the type of award which an Adjudicator may make. Any such provision would require to come from the contract itself. Neither Clause 9 alone nor

Clause 9 with Option Y(UK) 2 make any specific provision in that respect, nor do the Schemes. It is, therefore, largely left as a matter of practice.

It is probably accurate to say, therefore, that in these circumstances there is no limit on what may be referred to an Adjudicator for a decision and what an Adjudicator might award in that respect.

In theory, therefore, a Referring Party could refer the workmanship of a wall to the Adjudicator and ask the Adjudicator for a decision declaring that the wall was defective. In theory, a Referring Party could ask an Adjudicator to make an award ordering that a wall be rebuilt. Awards such as these are, however, of limited use and most adjudications have in practice arrived at the situation where some sort of enforceable money award is being sought.

Potential UK human rights points

An award is likely to cover a property right, and any failure in the procedural process by which those property rights are being removed is likely to result in a challenge based on the Human Rights Convention.

England and Wales

No specific provision is made as to the form of an award.

Scotland

No specific provision is made as to the form of an award.

Northern Ireland

No specific provision is made as to the form of an award.

Interest

Clause 51.3 provides:

If an amount due is corrected in a later certificate ... following a decision of the Adjudicator interest on the correcting amount is paid. Interest is assessed from the date when the incorrect amount was certified until the date when the correcting amount is certified and is included in the assessment which includes the correcting amount.

Clause 9	*Option Y(UK) 2*
By implication, interest could be awarded under this clause where Clause 51.3 applies	By implication, interest could be awarded under this clause where Clause 51.3 applies

The Adjudicator's Contract makes no specific provision in this respect.

NEC PRINCIPLES

A power on the part of the Adjudicator to add interest to any sum awarded must come from the contract and without such a provision in the contract there is probably no power on the part of the Adjudicator to add an award of interest to any award made.

Clause 9 and Option Y(UK) 2 do give a power to award interest but *only*, it seems, in the restricted circumstances where there are Certificates.

The Schemes do allow the Adjudicator to award interest but the provisions are a little difficult to interpret. It is not entirely clear whether the Adjudicator is being given a general power to award interest which is 'capped' by any provision in the contract as to interest or whether it is only where the contract provides for interest that the Adjudicator is given the discretion to make an award of interest.

Potential UK human rights points

Interest is a property right and a civil right and human rights considerations are as likely to arise in this respect as in any other.

England and Wales

The Scheme for Construction Contracts (England and Wales) Regulations 1998 SI No 649 provides:

Paragraph 20

In particular [the Adjudicator] may

...

(c) having regard to any term of the contract relating to the payment of interest decide the circumstances in which, and the rates at which, and the periods for which, simple or compound rates of interest shall be paid.

Commentary It is not entirely clear whether the Adjudicator is being given a general power to award interest which is 'capped' by any provision in the contract as to interest or whether it is only where the contract provides for interest that the Adjudicator is given the discretion to make an award of interest.

Scotland

The Scheme for Construction Contracts (Scotland) Regulations 1998 SI No 687 provides:

Paragraph 20

In particular [the Adjudicator] may

...

(c) having regard to any term of the contract relating to the payment of interest decide the circumstances in which, and the rates at which, and the periods for which, simple or compound rates of interest shall be paid.

Commentary It is not entirely clear whether the Adjudicator is being given a general power to award interest which is 'capped' by any provision in the contract as to interest or whether it is only where the contract provides for interest that the Adjudicator is given the discretion to make an award of interest.

Northern Ireland

The Scheme for Construction Contracts in Northern Ireland Regulations (Northern Ireland) 1999 Statutory Rule 1999 No 32 provides:

Paragraph 20

In particular [the Adjudicator] may

...

(c)   having regard to any term of the contract relating to the payment of interest decide the circumstances in which, and the rates at which, and the periods for which, simple or compound rates of interest shall be paid.

Commentary It is not entirely clear whether the Adjudicator is being given a general power to award interest which is 'capped' by any provision in the contract as to interest or whether it is only where the contract provides for interest that the Adjudicator is given the discretion to make an award of interest.

Costs

Clause 9	*Option Y(UK) 2*
No specific provision is made in this respect	No specific provision is made in this respect

The Adjudicator's Contract makes no specific provision in this respect.

NEC PRINCIPLES

In theory, there is no power anywhere – not in the contracts, the Adjudicator's Contract, the legislation or the Scheme – for an Adjudicator to award costs.

In theory, therefore, if there is no power in the applicable Scheme to award costs and the contract involved is silent on costs then there should be no award of costs by the Adjudicator.

Nevertheless, by precedent, an implied power on the part of an Adjudicator to award costs has been recognised in certain circumstances.

If, therefore, the Parties wish to put costs at issue or wish to avoid costs being put at issue then Parties will need to exercise some care in their conduct.

Potential UK human rights points

Costs are rarely regarded as being fundamental and the prospect for this area being the subject of a human rights challenge is remote.

England and Wales

No provision for costs is made.

Scotland

No provision for costs is made.

Northern Ireland

No provision for costs is made (see also Appendix A, judgment extracts 44 and 45).

Adjudicator's fees and expenses

Clause 9

No specific provision is made in this respect

Option Y(UK) 2

No specific provision is made in this respect

The Adjudicator's Contract provides:

Clause 3.1

Unless otherwise agreed, the Parties pay the Adjudicator his fee and Expenses in equal shares ...

Clause 3.2

After each decision on a dispute has been communicated to the Parties and after termination the Adjudicator invoices each Party for that Party's share of his fees and expenses.

NEC PRINCIPLES

In theory, this matter falls to be resolved by the Adjudicator's Contract (if there is one). In practice, 'bespoke' Adjudicator's Contracts will demand that either the Parties jointly or the Referring Party alone make at least a substantial payment on account of the Adjudicator's fees and expenses, so that when issuing the decision all that remains is any re-allocation (usually in line with success) determined. Under 'bespoke' contracts some Adjudicators will not release their decision until all of their fees and expenses have been paid by at least one Party (possibly re-allocated later).

The NEC Adjudicator's Contract, however, envisages (in the absence of any other agreement) the equal sharing of Adjudicator's Fees and Expenses. There will never, therefore, (in the absence of any other agreement by the Parties) be any question of the Adjudicator allocating his fees and expenses. It appears to be envisaged under the NEC Adjudicator's Contract that there will be no requirement for fees and expenses 'up-front' in that it is only after each decision on a dispute has been communicated to the Parties that the Adjudicator invoices each Party for his share. The power of resignation for non-payment of the Adjudicator's Account for more than five weeks would therefore appear to relate not to the current dispute but to any future disputes.

Neither Clause 9 nor Option Y(UK) 2 make any specific provision about an entitlement to, or the allocation of, Adjudicator's fees and expenses. In the absence of an Adjudicator's Contract an Adjudicator may be hard pressed to recover any fees, save on a common law *quantum meruit* basis.

This is, however, an area where the Contract and the applicable Scheme may come into conflict in that the latter gives the Adjudicator the power to determine and allocate his or her fees and expenses while the former does not.

Where the Parties have either agreed or taken the view that the Scheme (only) is to apply in its entirety then clearly there will be no difficulty, as the power on the part of the Adjudicator to determine and allocate his or her fees and expenses is expressly there in the Scheme and the Parties will be taken to have agreed to that. The Schemes differ slightly as between England and Wales, Northern Ireland and Scotland. Somewhat worryingly, the determination and allocation of fees is a matter which appears to have been left entirely to the discretion of the Adjudicator with no avenue of appeal (unless practice can forge one).

The difficulty arises where the Contract and the applicable Scheme are being read side-by-side. Given that the fees and expenses of the Adjudicator are not an essential requirement of the legislation, there would appear to be no requirement to imply such a power from the Scheme into a contract (and all the more so where the Adjudicator is obliged to apply the contract) where the Parties have specifically provided that (in the absence of any agreement) the fees and expenses of the Adjudicator shall be shared equally.

Potential UK human rights points

Fees and expenses are rarely regarded as being fundamental and the prospect for this area being the subject of a human rights challenge is remote.

England and Wales

The Scheme for Construction Contracts (England and Wales) Regulations 1998 SI No 649 provides:

Paragraph 25

The adjudicator shall be entitled to the payment of such reasonable amount as he may determine by way of fees and expenses reasonably incurred by him. The parties shall be jointly and severally liable for any sum which remains outstanding following the making of any determination on how the payment shall be apportioned.

Scotland

The Scheme for Construction Contracts (Scotland) Regulations 1998 SI No 687 provides:

Paragraph 25

(1)   The adjudicator shall be entitled to the payment of such reasonable amount as he may determine by way of fees and expenses incurred by him and the parties shall be jointly and severally liable to pay that amount to the adjudicator.

(2)   Without prejudice to the right of the adjudicator to effect recovery from any party in accordance with sub-paragraph (1) the adjudicator may by direction determine the apportionment between the parties of liability for his fees and expenses.Note that this is an area where the adjudication procedures in Scotland differ from the rest of the UK.

The significance of this provision appears to be that the Parties in Scotland are to be jointly and severally liable for the Adjudicator's fees and expenses irrespective of any allocation of these fees and expenses by the Adjudicator in his decision. In practice, that would allow an Adjudicator to recover all of his or her fees and expenses from one Party leaving it to that Party to thereafter recover from the other Party and allocation set out in the decision.

Note also the quaint note by Chris Dancaster that he considers it unethical for an Adjudicator to exercise a lien of his or her Decision until the Adjudicator's fees and expenses have been paid in fall.

Northern Ireland

The Scheme for Construction Contracts in Northern Ireland Regulations (Northern Ireland) 1999 Statutory Rule 1999 No 32 provides:

Paragraph 25

The adjudicator shall be entitled to the payment of such reasonable amount as he may determine by way of fees and expenses reasonably incurred by him. The parties shall be jointly and severally liable for any sum which remains outstanding following the making of any determination on how the payment shall be apportioned.

Other matters

Clause 9	*Option Y(UK) 2*
No specific provision is made in this respect	No specific provision is made in this respect

NEC principles

In theory, an Adjudicator should be able to include in the decision any other matter which the Parties have referred to him. Neither Clause 9 nor the Adjudicator's Contract nor the Schemes make any specific provision (either of an inclusionary or exclusionary nature) regarding any other matters which an Adjudicator may or may not include in the overall decision.

Potential UK human rights points

It is unlikely that any human rights considerations will arise in this respect.

England and Wales

No specific provision is made in this respect.

Scotland

No specific provision is made in this respect.

Northern Ireland

No specific provision is made in this respect.

Reasons

Clause 9	*Option Y(UK) 2*
Clause 90.2	Clause 90.10
The Adjudicator settles the decision by notifying the Parties and the Project Manager of his decision *together with his reasons*	The Adjudicator provides his reasons to the Parties and to the Project Manager with his decision

NEC PRINCIPLES

The NEC family of contracts, whether under Clause 9 or Option Y(UK) 2, clearly envisages that reasons will be provided automatically by the Adjudicator in every adjudication. The Schemes, on the other hand, provide that the Adjudicator shall provide reasons for his decision only 'if requested by one of the parties to the dispute'. The resultant position is, therefore, a little uncertain.

Where the Contract is being combined with the Scheme and the Adjudicator is carrying out his duties 'in accordance with any relevant terms of the contract' it could be argued that – even where not specifically requested to do so by one of the Parties to the dispute – an Adjudicator should always provide reasons as envisaged by the Contract.

Where, however, either the Parties have agreed that the applicable Scheme only will apply in its entirety or the view is taken that the law requires the Scheme only to be applied in its entirety, then for the avoidance of doubt a Party wishing reasons should specifically request reasons from the Adjudicator (ideally at the outset of the adjudication).

Potential UK human rights points

The actual decision provided by the Adjudicator is, of course, the most important part of the process and as well as providing one of the focus points for any human rights challenge, a defective decision could itself conceivably give rise to human rights issues.

England and Wales

The Scheme for Construction Contracts (England and Wales) Regulations 1998 SI No 649 provides:

Paragraph 22

If requested by one of the parties to the dispute, the adjudicator shall provide reasons for his decision.

Scotland

The Scheme for Construction Contracts (Scotland) Regulations 1998 SI No 687 provides:

Paragraph 22

If requested by one of the parties to the dispute, the adjudicator shall provide reasons for his decision.

Northern Ireland

The Scheme for Construction Contracts in Northern Ireland Regulations (Northern Ireland) 1999 Statutory Rule 1999 No 32 provides:

Paragraph 22

If requested by one of the parties to the dispute, the adjudicator shall provide reasons for his decision.

Correcting the decision

Clause 9   *Option Y(UK) 2*

No provision is made in this respect   No provision is made in this respect

NEC PRINCIPLES

It is only sensible, particularly in proceedings of this sort, to allow the Adjudicator to correct any minor (as opposed to major) slips. Some adjudication procedures make express provision for this.

Neither Clause 9 nor the Adjudicator's Contract make any provision for the correction of mistakes by the Adjudicator, nor is there express provision in any of the applicable Schemes. It is possible, however, that a 'slip rule' may be implied from either the law applicable to the contract or the law of the territory in which the adjudication is taking place.

Potential UK human rights points

This is unlikely to be an area of real contention in relation to human rights considerations.

England and Wales

No express provision is made in this respect (see also Appendix A, judgment extracts 45 and 46).

Scotland

No express provision is made in this respect.

Northern Ireland

No express provision is made in this respect.

Section III

What may follow the process of adjudication

Introduction

Following upon the process of adjudication one of two things are likely to happen within the time limit set down for the adjudication (the basic 28-day period plus any extensions) – either the Adjudicator will fail to issue a decision or the Adjudicator will issue a decision.

It is open to a Party to an NEC contract to express dissatisfaction with either of these events and to thereafter (where suitable provision has been made) to seek to have the dispute final determined by the tribunal. Under the applicable Scheme the Party may seek to have the dispute finally determined by agreement, by Arbitration (if provided for or agreed) or by litigation.

However, pending that final determination (if applicable) under both the NEC family of contracts and the applicable Schemes, the decision of the Adjudicator must in the interim be treated as binding.

Of course, simply providing that a decision is to be treated as binding in the interim may not automatically have that effect in practice and resort must sometimes be had to enforcement proceedings. Sometimes it may also be necessary for any objections to jurisdiction carried forward to be raised in defence to enforcement proceedings.

Lastly, it remains to consider the means available for final determination of the dispute by review in the tribunal.

We will consider these as follows:

- Dissatisfaction with the Adjudicator failing to reach a decision
- Dissatisfaction with the decision of the Adjudicator
- The status of the Adjudicator's decision
- Interim enforcement of the decision of the Adjudicator
  - Contractual provision for enforcement procedures
  - Court procedure for summary enforcement
- Objections to jurisdiction in defence to enforcement proceedings
- Final determination
  - The procedure of the tribunal

- The agreement of the parties
- Arbitration
- Litigation

18. Matters relating to the decision of the Adjudicator

Dissatisfaction with the Adjudicator failing to reach a decision

Clause 9

Option Y(UK) 2

Clause 93.1

Clause 93.1

If after the Adjudicator fails to [notify his decision] within the time provided by this contract, a Party is dissatisfied, that Party notifies the other Party of his intention to refer the matter which he disputes to the tribunal

If after the Adjudicator fails to [notify his decision] within the time provided by this contract, a Party is dissatisfied, that Party notifies the other Party of his intention to refer the matter which he disputes to the tribunal

NEC principles

It is clearly desirable to have some provision in contractually-provided dispute resolution procedures to cater for the situation where the Adjudicator fails to reach his or her decision within the time limit set down in the contract.

The adoption of Option Y(UK) 2 does not change the situation in that respect and, therefore, under that Option or under Clause 9 standing alone the position under Clause 93 is the same – a Party dissatisfied with the failure of the Adjudicator to timeously notify the Parties of the decision may (provided the various other conditions for so doing are met) refer the dispute to the tribunal specified in the contract for a decision.

Time limit for the decision

The time limit for the decision of the Adjudicator and the consequences flowing therefrom is an issue which will require to be addressed by the Parties in relation to 'construction contracts' being executed within the UK.

Where Clause 9 is standing alone is clearly non-compliant with an essential requirement of the legislation in that respect. Clause 91.1 provides a time limit for the decision of the Adjudicator as follows: 'The Adjudicator notifies his decision within four weeks of the end of the period for providing information'. The period for providing information is four weeks from the date of the submission of the dispute to the Adjudicator, although both the four-week period for providing information and the four-week period for the decision of the Adjudicator may be extended in certain restricted circumstances, namely where requested by the Adjudicator on the ground only that it is in view of the nature of the dispute and that any extension requires to be agreed by all the Parties.

Where Option Y(UK) 2 has been adopted, then it is suggested that it is, in this respect, compliant with the essential requirements of the UK legislation in that it provides (Clause 90.9) 'The Adjudicator reaches a decision within twenty eight days of referral or such longer period as is agreed by the Parties after the dispute has been referred. The Adjudicator may extend the period of twenty eight days by up to fourteen days with the consent of the notifying Party'.

Where, all other conditions being satisfied, the Works being carried out within the UK fall within the definition of 'construction contracts' then since the time limits for the decision (and any extensions) are essential requirements of the UK legislation either the contract will require to comply (as Option Y(UK) 2 does in this respect) or, at the very least sufficient of the applicable Scheme will require to be implied into the contract in question to meet the essential requirements of the UK legislation (as will be the case where Clause 9 is standing alone). Thereafter, a view will require to be taken as to the consequences which are to follow a failure on the part of the Adjudicator to issue a decision in time.

If the Parties have agreed that the applicable Scheme is to apply in its entirety or the Parties have taken the view that the law requires the applicable Scheme to apply in its entirety then two possible interpretations would appear to result – either regard is had to the terms of the applicable contract (which in this case provides for the matter to go to the tribunal) or regard is had to the terms of the applicable Scheme (in which case the matter may go to another Adjudicator).

If the view is taken that only those parts of the applicable Scheme necessary to satisfy the essential requirements of the legislation are to be implied into the contract then the time limits which the NEC contract (in Clause 9) provides for the decision of the Adjudicator would fall out to be replaced by implication with those provisions of the applicable Scheme which match the essential time requirements of the applicable UK legislation but, that having been done, thereafter the provisions of the contract – providing for the matter to then be considered by the tribunal – would rule. This is particularly relevant in the case of an NEC contract incorporating Option Y(UK) 2 for if its notice of dissatisfaction procedure is regarded as merely settlement/crystallisation of the dispute so that such a contract is compliant with the UK legislation then under that contract the provisions as to disputes going to the tribunal on the failure of the Adjudicator to reach a decision must rule.

Failure to reach a decision

Where the view is taken that the provisions of the contract are to rule

Where the essential time limit (either the basic time limit or any extended time limit) of the applicable UK legislation has not been complied with then under the contract the resulting position would be as follows:

Under Option Y(UK) 2 or Clause 9 standing alone, the position is this: Clause 93.1 provides: 'If after the Adjudicator fails [to notify his decision] within the time provided by this contract, a Party is dissatisfied, that Party notifies the other Party of his intention to refer the matter which he disputes to the *tribunal*'.

Clause 93.1 goes on, in this respect, to provide: 'It [the dispute] is not referable to the tribunal unless the dissatisfied Party notifies his intention within four weeks of the time provided by this contract for this notification if the Adjudicator fails to notify his decision within that time.'

Clause 93.1 further provides that 'The tribunal proceedings are not started before Completion of the whole of the works or earlier termination.'

Accordingly, the above two-stage process would apply and if followed would result in the matter going to the tribunal in the event of the failure of the Adjudicator to timeously notify the decision.

Where the view is taken that the provisions of the Scheme are to rule

The Schemes simply state that where the Adjudicator fails, *for any reason*, to reach his or her decision ... then that appears to be an end of the matter. That Adjudicator would appear to be *functus*, not having performed his or her task (and therefore not entitled to any fee or expenses or obliged to repay any payments already made). Any *prima facie* claim against an Adjudicator for any waste of time and money in this respect might be precluded by the immunity clause.

All that has gone before in the previous adjudication will be as nothing (although the Schemes have express provision to copy it to the new Adjudicator) but the Parties – and for the first time the option is given not just to the Referring Party but to *any of the Parties to the dispute* – are expressly given the option of starting again. It appears to be a terrible waste to lose the results of a hard-fought 28-day adjudication simply because, *per incuriam*, the decision was issued one day late, but should one or more of the Parties stand upon their entitlements then that would appear to be the position.

Under the Schemes, the position is that *any* of the Parties can serve a fresh Notice of Adjudication, go through the loop to have another Adjudicator appointed, and then (hopefully) obtain a decision on the dispute from the new Adjudicator.

Potential UK human rights points

If the approach by the Courts to human rights concerns in relation to adjudication centres around any 'final determination' then the route to that final determination will be of importance and in that respect this is, potentially, an area of serious concern in relation to human rights although the point does not seem to have been taken so far.

England and Wales

The Scheme for Construction Contracts (England and Wales) Regulations 1998 SI No 649 provides:

Paragraph 7

(1)   Where an adjudicator has been selected in accordance with paragraphs 2, 5 or 6, the referring party shall, not later than seven days from the date of the notice of adjudication, refer the dispute in writing (the 'referral notice') to the adjudicator.

Paragraph 19

(1)   The adjudicator shall reach his decision not later than-
  (a) twenty eight days after the date of the referral notice mentioned in paragraph 7(1), or
  (b) forty two days after the date of the referral notice if the referring party so consents, or
  (c) such period exceeding twenty eight days after the referral notice as the parties to the dispute may, after the giving of that notice, agree.

(2)   Where the adjudicator fails, for whatever reason, to reach his decision in accordance with paragraph (1)
  (a) any of the parties to the dispute may serve a fresh notice under paragraph 1 and shall request an adjudicator to act in accordance with paragraphs 2 to 7; and
  (b) if requested by the new adjudicator and insofar as reasonably practicable, the parties shall supply him with copies of all documents which they had made available to the previous adjudicator.

Scotland

The Scheme for Construction Contracts (Scotland) Regulations 1998 SI No 687 provides:

Paragraph 7

(1)   Where an adjudicator has been selected in accordance with paragraphs 2, 5 or 6, the referring party shall, not later than seven days from the date of the notice of adjudication, refer the dispute in writing (the 'referral notice') to the adjudicator.

Paragraph 19

(1)   The adjudicator shall reach his decision not later than-
  (a) twenty eight days after the date of the referral notice mentioned in paragraph 7(1), or
  (b) forty two days after the date of the referral notice if the referring party so consents, or
  (c) such period exceeding twenty eight days after the referral notice as the parties to the dispute may, after the giving of that notice, agree.

(2)   Where the adjudicator fails, for whatever reason, to reach his decision in accordance with paragraph (1)

(a) any of the parties to the dispute may serve a fresh notice under paragraph 1 and shall request an adjudicator to act in accordance with paragraphs 2 to 7; and

(b) if requested by the new adjudicator and insofar as reasonably practicable, the parties shall supply him with copies of all documents which they had made available to the previous adjudicator.

Northern Ireland

The Scheme for Construction Contracts in Northern Ireland Regulations (Northern Ireland) 1999 Statutory Rule 1999 No 32 provides:

Paragraph 7

(1) Where an adjudicator has been selected in accordance with paragraphs 2, 5 or 6, the referring party shall, not later than seven days from the date of the notice of adjudication, refer the dispute in writing (the 'referral notice') to the adjudicator.

Paragraph 19

(1) The adjudicator shall reach his decision not later than-
  (a) twenty eight days after the date of the referral notice mentioned in paragraph 7(1), or
  (b) forty two days after the date of the referral notice if the referring party so consents, or
  (c) such period exceeding twenty eight days after the referral notice as the parties to the dispute may, after the giving of that notice, agree.

(2) Where the adjudicator fails, for whatever reason, to reach his decision in accordance with paragraph (1)
  (a) any of the parties to the dispute may serve a fresh notice under paragraph 1 and shall request an adjudicator to act in accordance with paragraphs 2 to 7; and
  (b) if requested by the new adjudicator and insofar as reasonably practicable, the parties shall supply him with copies of all documents which they had made available to the previous adjudicator.

Dissatisfaction with the decision of the Adjudicator

Clause 9	*Option Y(UK) 2*
Clause 93.1	Clause 93.1
If after the Adjudicator notifies his decision, a Party is dissatisfied, that Party notifies the other Party of his intention to refer the matter which he disputes to the tribunal	If after the Adjudicator notifies his decision, a Party is dissatisfied, that Party notifies the other Party of his intention to refer the matter which he disputes to the tribunal

NEC PRINCIPLES

Where, in a contractually provided dispute resolution procedure, adjudication is provided as an intermediate means of resolving disputes, it is clearly desirable to have some provision in that contractually provided dispute resolution procedure for the final determination of that dispute.

It is noteworthy, however, that there is no avenue for final determination *automatically* provided in the NEC family of contracts. There is provision for such a procedure (the *tribunal*) but it appears to depend upon the Parties inserting in the Contract Data section relating to the tribunal information determining just what the tribunal is to be.

Assuming that such provision for the constitution of a tribunal is made then the adoption of Option Y(UK) 2 does not change the situation in that respect and therefore under that Option or under Clause 9 standing alone the position under Clause 93 is the same – a Party dissatisfied with the decision of the Adjudicator may (provided the various other conditions for so doing are met) refer the dispute to the tribunal specified in the contract for a final decision.

Where Clause 9 is standing alone then final determination of the dispute will be by means of the tribunal inserted in the Contract Data.

Where Option Y(UK) 2 has been adopted, then final determination of the dispute will be by means of the tribunal inserted in the Contract Data.

Where, all other conditions being satisfied, the Works being carried out within the UK fall within the definition of 'construction contracts' then – while concentrating upon making the decision of the Adjudicator binding in the interim – the UK legislation appears (as an essential requirement) to envisage final determination being by means of 'arbitration (if the contract provides for arbitration or the parties otherwise agree to arbitration) or by agreement'. Strictly speaking, therefore, a view will require to be taken as to the consequences which are to follow dissatisfaction with the decision of the Adjudicator.

If the Parties have agreed that the applicable Scheme is to apply in its entirety or the Parties have taken the view that the law requires the applicable Scheme to apply in its entirety then logically irrespective of the provisions of their contract as to the '*tribunal*', their dispute can only be determined by one of three means – by Arbitration (but only if the contract provides for Arbitration or the Parties otherwise agree to Arbitration), by litigation or by agreement.

If the view is taken that even where applying the applicable Scheme wholesale regard must still be had to the contract or, alternatively, if the view is taken that only those parts of the applicable Scheme necessary to satisfy the essential requirements of the legislation (although this is, unfortunately, expressed as an essential requirement) are to be implied into the contract, then it could be argued that the provisions of the contract – providing for the matter to then be considered by the tribunal – should rule. This is particularly relevant in the case of an NEC contract incorporating Option Y(UK) 2, for if its notice of dissatisfaction procedure is regarded as merely settlement/crystallisation of the dispute so that such a contract is compliant with the UK legislation, then under that contract the provisions as to disputes going to the tribunal on dissatisfaction with the decision of the Adjudicator must rule.

Clearly, no contract will arise where the NEC contract provides for 'arbitration' as the *tribunal* since that will then match the requirements of the applicable legislation and the Scheme.

Dissatisfaction with the decision

Where the view is taken that the provisions of the contract are to rule

Under Option Y(UK) 2 or Clause 9 standing alone, the position is this: Clause 93.1 provides: 'If after the Adjudicator [notifies his decision], a Party is dissatisfied, that Party notifies the other Party of his intention to refer the matter which he disputes to the *tribunal*'.

Clause 93.1 goes on, in this respect, to provide: 'It [the dispute] is not referable to the tribunal unless the dissatisfied Party notifies his intention within four weeks of notification of the Adjudicator's decision.'

Clause 93.1 further provides that 'The tribunal proceedings are not started before Completion of the whole of the works or earlier termination.'

Accordingly, the above two-stage process would apply and if followed would result in the matter going to the tribunal in the event of dissatisfaction with the decision of the Adjudicator. Furthermore, whatever form of dispute resolution which the Parties have inserted as the *tribunal* – for example, Expert Determination, DRB, mini-arb or the like – will be the means used to arrive at the final determination of the dispute.

Where the view is taken that the provisions of the Scheme are to rule

The Schemes simply state that '... the dispute is finally determined by legal proceedings, by arbitration (if the contract provides for arbitration or the parties otherwise agree to arbitration) or by agreement between the parties.'

No difficulty will arise where the NEC contract provides for 'arbitration' as the tribunal because that will then match the Scheme. Otherwise (unless an extended interpretation is given to the word 'agreement' any other dispute resolution procedure provided for as the tribunal will fall away leaving only (in the absence of agreement between the parties)) litigation as the means of final determination of the dispute.

Potential UK human rights points

If the approach by the Courts to human rights concerns in relation to adjudication centres around any 'final determination' then the route to that final determination will be of importance and in that respect this is, potentially, an area of serious concern in relation to human rights although the point does not seem to have been taken so far.

England and Wales

The essential requirement

The HGCR Act 1996 c. 53 provides:

s. 108

(3)   The contract shall provide that the decision of the adjudicator is binding until the dispute is finally determined by legal proceedings, by arbitration (if the contract provides for arbitration or the parties otherwise agree to arbitration) or by agreement.

The provision of the Scheme

The Scheme for Construction Contracts (England and Wales) Regulations 1998 SI No 649 provides:

Paragraph 23

(2)   The decision of the adjudicator shall be binding on the parties, and they shall comply with it until the dispute is finally determined by legal proceedings, by arbitration (if the contract provides for arbitration or the parties otherwise agree to arbitration) or by agreement between the parties.

Scotland

The essential requirement

The HGCR Act 1996 c. 53 provides:

s. 108

(3)   The contract shall provide that the decision of the adjudicator is binding until the dispute is finally determined by legal proceedings, by arbitration (if the contract provides for arbitration or the parties otherwise agree to arbitration) or by agreement.

The provision of the Scheme

The Scheme for Construction Contracts (Scotland) Regulations 1998 SI No 687 provides:

Paragraph 23

(2)   The decision of the adjudicator shall be binding on the parties, and they shall comply with it until the dispute is finally determined by legal proceedings, by arbitration (if the contract provides for arbitration or the parties otherwise agree to arbitration) or by agreement between the parties.

Northern Ireland

The essential requirement

The Construction Contracts (Northern Ireland) Order 1997 SI No 274 (NI) provides:

Article 7

(3)   The contract shall provide that the decision of the adjudicator is binding until the dispute is finally determined by legal proceedings, by arbitration (if the contract provides for arbitration or the parties otherwise agree to arbitration) or by agreement.

The provision of the Scheme

The Scheme for Construction Contracts in Northern Ireland Regulations (Northern Ireland) 1999 Statutory Rule 1999 No 32 provides:

Paragraph 23

(2)   The decision of the adjudicator shall be binding on the parties, and they shall comply with it until the dispute is finally determined by legal proceedings, by arbitration (if the contract provides for arbitration or the parties otherwise agree to arbitration) or by agreement between the parties.

The status of the Adjudicator's decision

Clause 9	*Option Y(UK) 2*
Clause 90.2	Clause 90.11
The decision is final and binding unless and until revised by the tribunal	The decision of the Adjudicator is binding until the dispute is finally determined by the tribunal or by agreement

The Adjudicator's Contract

No provision is made in this respect.

NEC PRINCIPLES

It is an essential requirement (essential requirement no 7) of the UK legislation – indeed, it may be considered as essential to the very concept of adjudication – that the decision of the Adjudicator should be treated by the Parties as binding until such time as the whole matter is (if necessary) finally determined in the manner provided for.

Both Clause 9 and Option Y(UK) 2 specifically provide for this and therefore there should be no need to imply anything into the contracts in that respect. It is, perhaps, noteworthy that while Clause 9 provides that the decision of the Adjudicator is both final and binding, Option Y(UK) 2 provides simply that the decision of the Adjudicator is binding. Where, however, the

Parties have agreed to take the view that the applicable Scheme should apply in its entirety, then equivalent provisions are to be found there.

The temporary binding nature of the decision of the Adjudicator

The NEC family of contracts and the applicable Schemes are, therefore, agreed that a decision of an Adjudicator is to be treated by the Parties as temporarily binding pending the final resolution (if any) of the dispute.

The finally binding nature of the decision of the Adjudicator

It is, of course (as the Schemes expressly provide), open to the Parties to decide to accept the decision of the Adjudicator as finally determinative of the dispute between them – indeed, so far as can be ascertained that appears to be happening in practice in the majority of cases.

Where one or other of the Parties are dissatisfied with the decision of the Adjudicator, however, then it may be open to that Party to seek to have the decision of the Adjudicator reviewed and finally determined. The legislation providing for adjudication has concentrated upon providing for the process of adjudication itself and is not greatly concerned with what is to happen thereafter, although it does mention Arbitration and litigation.

The extent to which, in the face of that legislation (and its essential requirement), the Parties are entitled to insist upon some other form of dispute resolution which the parties have provided for in their contract as the tribunal is problematic. Normally, resort to litigation as a final avenue of appeal cannot be denied to Parties, but one of the circumstances in which it may be is in fact where the Parties contractually agree that a decision shall be final which – in the absence of provision for a tribunal – is exactly what Clause 9 does.

Potential UK human rights points

The interrelationship between the procedure provided for any final determination and the interim adjudication procedures are likely to be a major battle-ground in the field of human rights. On one view, provided the procedure for final determination complies with the Convention of Human Rights and any problems can be corrected there, then the interim procedure will not be made the subject of close human rights scrutiny. On another view, no one should be deprived – even temporarily – of their (perhaps irrecoverable) property rights by a procedure which is unfair, and therefore adjudication procedures should be compliant with human rights.

England and Wales

The essential requirement

The HGCR Act 1996 c. 53 provides:

s. 108

(3)   The contract shall provide that the decision of the adjudicator is binding until the dispute is finally determined by legal proceedings, by arbitration (if the contract provides for arbitration or the parties otherwise agree to arbitration) or by agreement.

The provision of the Scheme

The Scheme for Construction Contracts (England and Wales) Regulations 1998 SI No 649 provides:

Paragraph 23

(2)   The decision of the adjudicator shall be binding on the parties, and they shall comply with it until the dispute is finally determined by legal proceedings, by arbitration (if the contract provides for arbitration or the parties otherwise agree to arbitration) or by agreement between the parties.

The essential requirement

The HGCR Act 1996 c. 53 provides:

s. 108

(3)   The contract shall provide that the decision of the adjudicator is binding until the dispute is finally determined by legal proceedings, by arbitration (if the contract provides for arbitration or the parties otherwise agree to arbitration) or by agreement.

The provision of the Scheme

The Scheme for Construction Contracts (Scotland) Regulations 1998 Sl No 687 provides:

Paragraph 23

(2)   The decision of the adjudicator shall be binding on the parties, and they shall comply with it until the dispute is finally determined by legal proceedings, by arbitration (if the contract provides for arbitration or the parties otherwise agree to arbitration) or by agreement between the parties.

Northern Ireland

The essential requirement

The Construction Contracts (Northern Ireland) Order 1997 SI No 74 (NI) provides:

Article 7

(3)   The contract shall provide that the decision of the adjudicator is binding until the dispute is finally determined by legal proceedings, by arbitration (if the contract provides for arbitration or the parties otherwise agree to arbitration) or by agreement.

The provision of the Scheme

The Scheme for Construction Contracts in Northern Ireland Regulations (Northern Ireland) 1999 Statutory Rule No. 32 provides:

Paragraph 23

(2)   The decision of the adjudicator shall be binding on the parties, and they shall comply with it until the dispute is finally determined by legal proceedings, by arbitration (if the contract provides for arbitration between the parties or the parties otherwise agree to arbitration) or by agreement between the parties.

Interim enforcement of the decision of the Adjudicator

Introduction

Conscious of the need to ensure that the decisions of Adjudicators are in fact treated as binding by the Parties, provision within the United Kingdom has been made both for enforcement under the applicable Schemes and for enforcement by law generally.

It is also possible to raise any objections to jurisdiction as a defence to these proceedings and that we consider in the next section. It is proposed to consider in this section both of the methods of enforcing the decisions of the Adjudicator.

*   'Contractual' provision for enforcement
*   Court procedure for summary enforcement

'Contractual' provision for enforcement

Clause 9   *Option Y(UK) 2*

No provision is made in this respect   No provision is made in this respect

NEC PRINCIPLES

Where it is agreed that a procedure should be supplied for the proper and expeditious resolution of disputes then it may not be regarded as entirely out of line with that approach were some procedures to be introduced which would ensure that the procedure did in effect work by providing a means for its proper and expeditious compliance.

This does exist in other procedures. For example, in relation to the procedure of Arbitration in England and Wales such a procedure exists and the Arbitration Act 1996 carries the power of the tribunal to make peremptory orders in cases of default by the Parties (s. 41) and also makes provision for the enforcement of the tribunal's peremptory orders by the Courts (s. 42).

The NEC family of contracts makes no provision in that respect. However, the applicable Schemes do confer upon the Adjudicator the power to issue his or her decision (or any part of it) peremptorily and in the case of England and Wales also make provision for the enforcement of the Adjudicator's peremptory orders by the Courts.

On a literal interpretation of the provision, however, since it provides 'unless otherwise agreed by the parties' it would appear open to the Parties to amend their NEC contract to provide that the Court may not make an order requiring a Party to comply with a peremptory order made by the tribunal.

In Scotland, provision is made for the use of the Books of Council and Session and the applicable Scheme seeks to impose a duty upon a Party to subscribe the decision of the Adjudicator before a witness so as to allow that procedure to be implemented.

Again, however, such provisions cause difficulties of interpretation and application.

If Option Y(UK) 2 is regarded as being compliant with the essential requirements of the UK legislation then nothing further – and in particular no power to the Adjudicator to issue his or her decisions peremptorily – requires to be implied into such a contract or any adjudication running under it.

Even accepting that Clause 9 standing alone is non-compliant, it could be argued that there only requires to be implied from the applicable Scheme into such a contract that which is necessary to meet the essential requirements of the UK legislation and that a power on the part of an Adjudicator to issue decisions peremptorily – not being an essential requirement of the UK legislation – does not fall into that category and does not require to be implied.

Where the Parties agree that the applicable Scheme is to apply in its entirety or take the view that the law requires the applicable Scheme to apply in its entirety then they should do so in the knowledge that, although there is no such provision in their contract, by doing so they are not only giving the Adjudicator the power to issue his or her decision peremptorily, but are also accepting that any such decision issued peremptorily by the Adjudicator may be summarily enforced by, as the case may be, the Courts or through the Books of Council and Session.

Potential UK human rights points

Human rights considerations are likely to arise (especially where allied with other concerns) in relation to the extent to which sanctions can be imposed upon a Party for failure to comply with an Order made peremptory by someone to whom the Parties have not contractually given the power to make decision peremptorily.

Clearly, however, where the Parties have contractually agreed to either the Court procedure in England and Wales or the Books of Council and Session procedure of Scotland then such considerations will not arise.

England and Wales

The Scheme for Construction Contracts (England and Wales) Regulations 1998 SI No 649 provides:

Paragraph 24

Section 42 of the Arbitration Act 1996 shall apply to this Scheme subject to the following modifications-

(a)   in subsection (2) for the word 'tribunal' wherever it appears there shall be substituted the word 'adjudicator'.

(b)   in subparagraph (b) of subsection (2) for the words 'arbitral proceedings' there shall be substituted the word 'adjudication'.

(c)   subparagraph (c) of subsection (2) shall be deleted, and

(d)   subsection (3) shall be deleted.

In effect, therefore, this provision as applied to adjudication will read as follows:

42.

(1)   Unless otherwise agreed by the parties, the court may make an order requiring a party to comply with a peremptory order made by the [Adjudicator]

(2)   An application for an order under this section may be made
(a)   by the Adjudicator (upon notice to the parties)
(b)   by a party to the adjudication with the permission of the Adjudicator (and upon notice to the other parties), or
(c)   ... [deleted] ...

(3)   ... [deleted] ...

(4)   No order shall be made under this section unless the court is satisfied that the person to whom the tribunal's order was directed has failed to comply with it within the time prescribed in the order or, if no time was prescribed, within a reasonable time.

(5)   The leave of the court is required for any appeal from a decision of the court under this section.

Commentary In the early stages of adjudication Adjudicators seemed to make it a practice to direct virtually automatically that their decisions be complied with peremptorily. There has been some judicial observation, however, that it is inappropriate to do so automatically and that it should only be done so after consideration and after the Parties have had an opportunity to make representation on that point. Furthermore, it has been suggested that although an Adjudicator may declare their decision peremptory, the Courts retain a discretion in the matter and will not automatically treat it as such.

Enforcement of Adjudicator's decisions in England and Wales
See Appendix A, judgment extracts 48–67.

Scotland
The Scheme for Construction Contracts (Scotland) Regulations 1998 SI No 687 provides:

Paragraph 24

> Where a party or the adjudicator wishes to register the decision for execution in the Books of Council and Session, any other party shall, on being requested to do so, forthwith consent to such registration by subscribing the decision before a witness.

Commentary This is a valuable procedure which has worked well in Scotland over a large number of years. There is, however, no reported instance of this being used in adjudication. The practical difficulty (although there are ways round this) is that the all Parties must at some stage consent by signature to registration.

Theoretically, since they are directed by legislation to do so in the above circumstances, a Party might be in contempt of Court by refusing a direct order of the Court to do so (in which case the Clerk of Court may be ordered to sign in his stead). There have been informal hints, however, that the preference is for these procedures not to be used. There are, however, alternative means of getting to the same end result.

Enforcement of Adjudicator's decisions in Scotland
See Appendix A, judgment extracts 68–78.

Northern Ireland
The Scheme for Construction Contracts in Northern Ireland Regulations (Northern Ireland) 1999 provides:

Paragraph 24

Section 42 of the Arbitration Act 1996 shall apply to this Scheme subject to the following modifications-

(a)   in subsection (2) for the word 'tribunal' wherever it appears there shall be substituted the word 'adjudicator'.

(b)   in subparagraph (b) of subsection (2) for the words 'arbitral proceedings' there shall be substituted the word 'adjudication'.

(c)   subparagraph (c) of subsection (2) shall be deleted, and
(d)   subsection (3) shall be deleted.

In effect, therefore, this provision as applied to adjudication will read as follows:

42.

(1)   Unless otherwise agreed by the parties, the court may make an order requiring a party to comply with a peremptory order made by the [Adjudicator]
(2)   An application for an order under this section may be made
  (a) by the Adjudicator (upon notice to the parties)
  (b) by a party to the adjudication with the permission of the Adjudicator (and upon notice to the other parties), or
  (c) ... [deleted] ...
(3)   ... [deleted] ...
(4)   No order shall be made under this section unless the court is satisfied that the person to whom the tribunal's order was directed has failed to comply with it within the time prescribed in the order or, if no time was prescribed, within a reasonable time.
(5)   The leave of the court is required for any appeal from a decision of the court under this section.

Commentary It is too early to measure the effect of this provision in Northern Ireland.

Court procedure for summary enforcement

Clause 9   *Option Y(UK) 2*

No provision is made in this respect   No provision is made in this respect

NEC PRINCIPLES

The main practical thrust of adjudication is getting to the decision of the Adjudicator and securing the recognition of that decision as binding in the meantime. Having contractually agreed to be bound by that provision and, where the Scheme is applicable, being under a duty in that respect, it is to be expected that the Parties will treat any decision of the Adjudicator as binding.

In practice, however, Parties sometimes – for what seems to them to be proper reasons – do not obtemper or comply with the decision of the Adjudicator. In these circumstances, it is necessary to have regard not so much to the contract as to the general law in order to enforce the interim binding nature of the Adjudicator's decision.

Potential UK human rights points

The enforcement of a decision involving the civil rights of a Party carries with it the requirement, in human rights terms, that the proper procedures have been followed. Accordingly, enforcement procedures potentially open up the whole panoply of human rights considerations at least where these are held to be applicable to adjudication.

England and Wales

The essential requirement

The HGCR Act 1996 c. 53 provides:

s. 108

(3)   The contract shall provide that the decision of the adjudicator is binding until the dispute is finally determined by legal proceedings, by arbitration (if the contract provides for arbitration or the parties otherwise agree to arbitration) or by agreement.

The provision

The Scheme for Construction Contracts (England and Wales) Regulations 1998 SI No 649 provides:

Paragraph 23

(2)   The decision of the adjudicator shall be binding on the parties, and they shall comply with it until the dispute is finally determined by legal proceedings, by arbitration (if the contract provides for arbitration or the parties otherwise agree to arbitration) or by agreement between the parties.

Commentary It has rapidly been established that in England and Wales – at least where the decision of the Adjudicator involves an award stated in monetary terms – if some the Party in whose favour the decision has been pronounced to issue a writ (usually in the Queen's Bench Division – often the Technology and Construction Court – of the High Court of Justice) and then to make an Application for Summary Judgment under CPR.

Scotland

The essential requirement

The HGCR Act 1996 c. 53 provides:

s. 108

(3)   The contract shall provide that the decision of the adjudicator is binding until the dispute is finally determined by legal proceedings, by arbitration (if the contract provides for arbitration or the parties otherwise agree to arbitration) or by agreement.

The provision

The Scheme for Construction Contracts (Scotland) Regulations 1998 SI No 687 provides:

Paragraph 23

(2)   The decision of the adjudicator shall be binding on the parties, and they shall comply with it until the dispute is finally determined by legal proceedings, by arbitration (if the contract provides for arbitration or the parties otherwise agree to arbitration) or by agreement between the parties.

Commentary It appears to be becoming established in Scotland that the appropriate method for dealing with such matters is by way of Judicial Review.

Northern Ireland

The essential requirement

The Construction Contracts (Northern Ireland) Order 1997 provides:

Article 7

(3)   The contract shall provide that the decision of the adjudicator is binding until the dispute is finally determined by legal proceedings, by arbitration (if the contract provides for arbitration or the parties otherwise agree to arbitration) or by agreement.

The provision

The Scheme for Construction Contracts in Northern Ireland Regulations (Northern Ireland) 1999 provides:

Paragraph 23

(2)   The decision of the adjudicator shall be binding on the parties, and they shall comply with it until the dispute is finally determined by legal proceedings, by arbitration (if the contract provides for arbitration or the parties otherwise agree to arbitration) or by agreement between the parties.

Commentary It is too early to establish what the best procedure in Northern Ireland is going to be.

Objections to jurisdiction in defence to enforcement proceedings

Clause 9   *Option Y(UK) 2*

No provision is made in this respect   No provision is made in this respect

NEC PRINCIPLES

As earlier noted, for a number of legal and practical reasons, where an objection to an adjudication arises (usually referred to as an objection to jurisdiction) then it may not be possible to have that objection to jurisdiction dealt with before the adjudication commences.

In these circumstances, the Party who is confident of their objection to jurisdiction has a choice – they can either ignore the adjudication or they can take part in the adjudication while carefully maintaining their objection to jurisdiction. Either way, at the end of the adjudication proceedings (if the decision goes against them) the Party with the objection to jurisdiction (if it has been maintained) may raise that objection to jurisdiction in defence to proceedings brought to enforce the decision of the Adjudicator.

Potential UK human rights points

The decisions which arise in this area are likely to be determinative in relation to the application of human rights legislation to adjudication. Provided, so the argument runs, the Party concerned can raise any human rights concerns either by way of defence in these proceedings or in any final determination then any breaches of human rights principles in the adjudication itself may be overlooked. Matters are not, however, as clear-cut as that and it may be that a number of important decisions will arise in this area.

England and Wales

The essential requirement

The HGCR Act 1996 c. 53 provides:

s. 108

(3)   The contract shall provide that the decision of the adjudicator is binding until the dispute is finally determined by legal proceedings, by arbitration (if the contract provides for arbitration or the parties otherwise agree to arbitration) or by agreement.

The provision

The Scheme for Construction Contracts (England and Wales) Regulations 1998 SI No 649 provides:

Paragraph 23

(2)   The decision of the adjudicator shall be binding on the parties, and they shall comply with it until the dispute is finally determined by legal proceedings, by arbitration (if the contract provides for arbitration or the parties otherwise agree to arbitration) or by agreement between the parties.

Commentary A number of decisions in the Technology and Construction Court in England and Wales have set the parameters of what does and does not constitute a valid objection to jurisdiction which may be raised in defence to enforcement proceedings.

Scotland

The essential requirement

The HGCR Act 1996 c. 53 provides:

s. 108

(3)   The contract shall provide that the decision of the adjudicator is binding until the dispute is finally determined by legal proceedings, by arbitration (if the contract provides for arbitration or the parties otherwise agree to arbitration) or by agreement.

The provision

The Scheme for Construction Contracts (Scotland) Regulations 1998 SI No 687 provides:

Paragraph 23

(2)   The decision of the adjudicator shall be binding on the parties, and they shall comply with it until the dispute is finally determined by legal proceedings, by arbitration (if the contract provides for arbitration or the parties otherwise agree to arbitration) or by agreement between the parties.

Commentary Differences in interpretation as regards adjudication have already arisen in Scotland but the English decisions on jurisdiction are likely to be of persuasive value.

Northern Ireland

The essential requirement

The Construction Contracts (Northern Ireland) Order 1997 provides:

Article 7

(3)   The contract shall provide that the decision of the adjudicator is binding until the dispute is finally determined by legal proceedings, by arbitration (if the contract provides for arbitration or the parties otherwise agree to arbitration) or by agreement.

The provision

The Scheme for Construction Contracts in Northern Ireland Regulations (Northern Ireland) 1999 provides:

Paragraph 23

(2)   The decision of the adjudicator shall be binding on the parties, and they shall comply with it until the dispute is finally determined by legal proceedings, by arbitration (if the contract provides for arbitration or the parties otherwise agree to arbitration) or by agreement between the parties.

Commentary The English decisions on objections to jurisdiction as a defence to enforcement are likely to be of persuasive value in Northern Ireland.

19. Final determination

Clause 9

Clause 93 makes provision for the decision of the Adjudicator to be reviewed by the tribunal where details of the tribunal have been inserted into the contract and the procedural requirements for referral complied with

Option Y(UK) 2

Clause 93 makes provision for the decision of the Adjudicator to be reviewed by the tribunal where details of the tribunal have been inserted into the contract and the procedural requirements for referral complied with

NEC PRINCIPLES

The main practical thrust of adjudication is getting to the decision of the Adjudicator and securing the recognition of that decision as binding in the meantime. Thereafter, provision can be made for the decision of the Adjudicator to be finally determined.

The NEC family of contracts (whether under Clause 9 standing alone or under Option Y(UK) 2) makes provision for a 'tribunal' but leaves it to the Parties to insert the details of just what that 'tribunal' is to be. The *'tribunal'* can, apparently, be Expert Determination, DRBs, Arbitration (recommended by the NEC) or indeed anything else which the Parties agree shall be the 'tribunal' and incorporate into their contract accordingly.

However, should – for example – an NEC contract be completed in a hurry and no details are inserted into the contract about the nature of any tribunal then it would appear to follow that (unless subsequently agreed by all the Parties) then *prima facie* there will be no tribunal and no avenue of appeal. Where a tribunal has been specified in the NEC contract then certain time limits and procedures are imposed in the course of reaching the tribunal.

The approach of the applicable Schemes is slightly different and appears to envisage only the agreement of the Parties, Arbitration (where that is provided for in the contract or agreed) or litigation.

Clearly, where the Parties to an NEC contract have agreed that the 'tribunal' shall be Arbitration and since Arbitration is, under the applicable Scheme, a permitted means of final determination, there would be no conflict between the contract and the applicable Scheme.

Furthermore, it has been suggested that it is not incompatible with the Schemes for the contract to make provision in relation to the Arbitration such as, for example, that the Arbitration shall not commence before Practical Completion of the Works.

Where the contract and the applicable Scheme are not in line, however, the position is more complex. Suppose, for example, that the Parties provide in their contract that a DRB shall be the tribunal to review any decision by an Adjudicator. Is that, perhaps under the heading of the agreement of the Parties, a competent 'final determination' of the dispute under the applicable Scheme or, failing true agreement between the Parties, is the only competent method of 'final determination' either Arbitration (if provided for or agreed) or litigation? No particular requirements are imposed under the Schemes for getting to the final determination.

Again, a view requires to be taken in this matter (complicated by the fact that this has in fact been expressed as an essential requirement of the legislation).

If the view is taken that the Parties have agreed or consider that the law requires the applicable Scheme to be implied wholesale, then logically it would appear to follow that whatever is provided for in the contract flies out of the window and, in the absence of agreement or Arbitration, all that remains is litigation in relation to which no procedural requirements are imposed.

It would also be possible to take a middle ground whereby the applicable Scheme was applied wholesale but that it required to be applied 'in accordance with any relevant terms of the contract' and that in this case, the terms of the contract providing for review by tribunal would be regarded as relevant and applied. In these circumstances the contract procedures for review and their procedural requirements would apply.

If the view is taken that all that requires to be implied from the applicable Scheme into the contract is that which is necessary to comply with the requirements of the UK legislation which are essential then (although these are expressed as essential) it could perhaps be argued that the essential requirement related only to the binding nature of the Adjudicator's decision and that there is no need to imply anything in relation to final determination procedures. In these circumstances the contract procedures for review and their procedural requirements would apply. This argument is even more critical if Option Y(UK) 2 is seen as compliant for, therefore, there is no reason not to recognise the contract procedures for review and their requirements.

The procedure for final determination/review under the contract

On the above basis, even where one of the Schemes was being applied, the contract procedures for final determination might apply as follows:

The time limit for the decision

By implication, the time limit for the decision will be 28 days from referral or as extended by the Parties.

Time limit for review/final determination by the tribunal

Clause 93.1 provides: 'If after the Adjudicator notifies his decision …, a Party is dissatisfied, that Party notifies the other Party of his intention to refer the matter which he disputes to the tribunal.'

Clause 93.1 goes on, in this respect, to provide: 'It [the dispute] is not referable to the tribunal unless the dissatisfied Party notifies his intention within four weeks of notification of the decision.'

Clause 93.1 further provides that 'The tribunal proceedings are not started before Completion of the whole of the works or earlier termination.'

This provision appears to envisage a two-stage process. There must first be a notification of intention to refer the dispute to the tribunal and then secondly, the tribunal considers the matter.

The second stage – the tribunal considering the matter – appears to be postponed under this Clause in that the Clause appears to suggest that – except in the case of earlier termination of the contract – the tribunal proceedings may not be started before Completion of the whole of the Works.

Accordingly, although the actual review by the tribunal is (validly, it is suggested) postponed until completion or termination, notice of intention to do so would require to be made within four weeks of the decision or the time for the decision (which would be within the 28 days or such extension as had in fact been allowed).

The procedure for final determination under the schemes

On this basis, the contract review procedures would be disregarded and any final determination would proceed under the Schemes only.

The Schemes to not make any specific procedural requirements in relation to the procedure for final determination which is therefore presumably open-ended (although bearing in mind that the decision of the Adjudicator will have had to be complied with in the interim).

The following considerations may apply:

The agreement of the Parties

This provision might have been inserted merely for the avoidance of doubt so as to make it clear that the Parties *can* agree to accept the decision of the Adjudicator and are not *obliged* to go forward for final determination.

On a narrow interpretation, only the true agreement of the Parties to accept the decision of the Adjudicator (perhaps as adjusted between them) would be regarded as a valid 'final determination'.

On a wider interpretation, it could be argued that the agreement of the Parties to abide by a review the decision by means of a DRB is nevertheless an agreement of the Parties amounting to a 'final determination'.

In effect, however, there would either be an 'agreement' in place or there would be no 'agreement'. No other procedural requirements will apply.

Arbitration

It is clear that it was not the intention of Parliament to make Arbitration compulsory.

The contract between the Parties (whether complying or not) may provide for adjudication and then Arbitration and even where the applicable Scheme has been implied in whole or in part it appears that that contractual Arbitration provision will be respected as a means of 'final determination'.

Even where the contract between the Parties does not contain an Arbitration Clause, it appears open to the Parties to agree to have the decision of the Adjudicator 'finally determined' by means of Arbitration.

There is no express provision in the Schemes as to the time or manner by which any Arbitration may be commenced. That may be provided in the contract Arbitration Clause or by the wholesale incorporation by agreement of a complete Arbitration procedure.

It appears to follow that a provision providing, for example, that there shall be no Arbitration (and therefore, in effect, no 'final determination') until Practical Completion of the Works would be valid.

In effect, however, either the Parties will have specified 'arbitration' as the tribunal or subsequently agreed to 'arbitration'. No further procedural requirements come from the Scheme in this respect although further procedural requirements might arise from procedures of any particular type of Arbitration specified.

Litigation

In general, many territories take the approach Parties cannot be denied access to the Courts and that any agreement seeking to exclude that right is valid on the grounds of public policy. Other territories, however, recognise a right on the part of the Parties to exclude the jurisdiction of the Courts.

It appears to follow that a provision providing, for example, that there shall be no Court proceedings (and therefore, in effect, no 'final determination') after a Final Certificate or Decision has been issued is more problematic but could be valid.

There is no express procedural provision in the Schemes as to the time or manner by which any litigation may be commenced. That may be provided by the rules of court themselves.

Potential UK human rights points

The position to be adopted by the UK Courts as regards human rights in adjudications is not yet settled. On one interpretation, many of the Convention Rights may not apply to adjudication on the grounds that there remains open to the Parties an avenue to the Parties to have any problem resolved by a 'final determination'. In those circumstances, the circumstances of any final determination will be crucial and any uncertainty surrounding them unfortunate in the extreme.

England and Wales

The essential requirement

The HGCR Act 1996 c. 53 provides:

s. 108

(3)   The contract shall provide that the decision of the adjudicator is binding until the dispute is finally determined by legal proceedings, by arbitration (if the contract provides for arbitration or the parties otherwise agree to arbitration) or by agreement.

The provision

The Scheme for Construction Contracts (England and Wales) Regulations 1998 SI No 649 provides:

Paragraph 23

(2)   The decision of the adjudicator shall be binding on the parties, and they shall comply with it until the dispute is finally determined by legal proceedings, by arbitration (if the contract provides for arbitration or the parties otherwise agree to arbitration) or by agreement between the parties.

Commentary   The cases of *Crouch* (Court of Appeal) and *Beauford* (House of Lords) may be of relevance in this respect.

Scotland

The essential requirement

The HGCR Act 1996 c. 53 provides:

s. 108

(3)   The contract shall provide that the decision of the adjudicator is binding until the dispute is finally determined by legal proceedings, by arbitration (if the contract provides for arbitration or the parties otherwise agree to arbitration) or by agreement.

The provision

The Scheme for Construction Contracts (Scotland) Regulations 1998 SI No 687 provides:

Paragraph 23

(2)   The decision of the adjudicator shall be binding on the parties, and they shall comply with it until the dispute is finally determined by legal proceedings, by arbitration (if the contract provides for arbitration or the parties otherwise agree to arbitration) or by agreement between the parties.

Commentary The English cases, particularly at House of Lords level, will be of persuasive value in Scotland.

Northern Ireland

The essential requirement

The Construction Contracts (Northern Ireland) Order 1997 provides:

Article 7

(3)   The contract shall provide that the decision of the adjudicator is binding until the dispute is finally determined by legal proceedings, by arbitration (if the contract provides for arbitration or the parties otherwise agree to arbitration) or by agreement.

The provision

The Scheme for Construction Contracts in Northern Ireland Regulations (Northern Ireland) 1999 provides:

Paragraph 23

(2)   The decision of the adjudicator shall be binding on the parties, and they shall comply with it until the dispute is finally determined by legal proceedings, by arbitration (if the contract provides for arbitration or the parties otherwise agree to arbitration) or by agreement between the parties.

Commentary The English decisions are likely to be of persuasive value in Northern Ireland.

The procedure of the tribunal

Clause 9	*Option Y(UK) 2*
Clause 93 makes provision for the powers of the tribunal to include the power to review and revise any decision of the Adjudicator and any action or inaction of the Project Manager or Supervisor related to the dispute and that a Party is not limited in the tribunal proceedings to the information, evidence or arguments put to the Adjudicator	Clause 93 makes provision for the powers of the tribunal to include the power to review and revise any decision of the Adjudicator and any action or inaction of the Project Manager or Supervisor related to the dispute and that a Party is not limited in the tribunal proceedings to the information, evidence or arguments put to the Adjudicator

NEC PRINCIPLES

The considerations relating to the procedure to be followed by the tribunal are likely to mirror the considerations relating to the tribunal itself.

The NEC family of contracts (whether under Clause 9 standing alone or under Option Y(UK) 2) makes express provision to the effect that the tribunal is a rehearing and not an appeal.

The applicable Schemes are silent as to the procedures which are to be adopted in relation to their final determinations. It is thought by some, however, that they also their intend final determinations to be a rehearing rather than an appeal.

Clearly, where the Parties to an NEC contract have agreed that the 'tribunal' shall be Arbitration and since Arbitration is, under the applicable Scheme, a permitted means of final determination, there would be no conflict between the contract and the applicable Scheme and its precise procedures are likely to be defined and laid down.

Where the contract and the applicable Scheme are not in line, however, the position is more complex. Suppose, for example, that the Parties provide in their contract that a DRB shall be the tribunal to review any decision by an Adjudicator and that Board is expressly directed to proceed not as an appeal but as a rehearing. Is that, perhaps under the heading of the agreement of the Parties, a competent 'final determination' of the dispute under the applicable Scheme or, failing true agreement between the Parties, is the only competent method of 'final determination' either Arbitration (if provided for or agreed) or litigation, in which case it would have to be inferred that it was not an appeal but a rehearing?

The Courts in particular have shown a reluctance to be Courts of first instance in highly technical matters.

If the approach of the NEC contract and the Schemes is in fact in line then it may be that not much will turn on this point. If differences do emerge, however, then again, a view requires to be taken in this matter (complicated by the fact that this has in fact been expressed as an essential requirement of the legislation).

If the view is taken that the Parties have agreed or consider that the law requires the applicable Scheme to be implied wholesale, then logically it would appear to follow that whatever is provided for in the contract flies out of the window and, in the absence of agreement or Arbitration, all that remains is litigation, in relation to which the Courts may or may not have regard to contractual provision for the procedure of the tribunal.

It would also be possible to take a middle ground whereby the applicable Scheme was applied wholesale but that it required to be applied 'in accordance with any relevant terms of the contract' and that in this case, the terms of the contract providing for review by tribunal would be regarded as relevant and applied. In these circumstances the contract procedures for review and their procedures would apply.

If the view is taken that all that requires to be implied from the applicable Scheme into the contract is that which is necessary to comply with the requirements of the UK legislation which are essential then (although these are expressed as essential) it could perhaps be argued that the essential requirement related only to the binding nature of the Adjudicator's decision and that there is no need to imply anything in relation to final determination procedures. In these circumstances the contract procedures for review and their procedural requirements would apply. This argument is even more critical if Option Y(UK) 2 is seen as compliant for, therefore, there is no reason not to recognise the contract procedures for review and their procedures.

Potential UK human rights points

The position to be adopted by the UK Courts as regards human rights in adjudications is not yet settled. On one interpretation, many of the Convention Rights may not apply to adjudication on the grounds that there remains open to the Parties an avenue to the Parties to have any problem resolved by a 'final determination'. In those circumstances, the procedures for any final determination will be crucial and any uncertainty surrounding them unfortunate in the extreme.

England and Wales

The essential requirement

The HGCR Act 1996 c. 53 provides:

s. 108

(3)   The contract shall provide that the decision of the adjudicator is binding until the dispute is finally determined by legal proceedings, by arbitration (if the contract provides for arbitration or the parties otherwise agree to arbitration) or by agreement.

The provision

The Scheme for Construction Contracts (England and Wales) Regulations 1998 SI No 649 provides:

No specific provision is made in the Scheme for the procedures to be followed in relation to the above final determination.

Scotland

The essential requirement

The HGCR Act 1996 c. 53 provides:

s. 108

(3)   The contract shall provide that the decision of the adjudicator is binding until the dispute is finally determined by legal proceedings, by arbitration (if the contract provides for arbitration or the parties otherwise agree to arbitration) or by agreement.

The provision

The Scheme for Construction Contracts (Scotland) Regulations 1998 SI No 687 provides:

No specific provision is made in the Scheme for the procedures to be followed in relation to the above final determination.

Northern Ireland

The essential requirement

The Construction Contracts (Northern Ireland) Order 1997 provides:

Article 7

(3)   The contract shall provide that the decision of the adjudicator is binding until the dispute is finally determined by legal proceedings, by arbitration (if the contract provides for arbitration or the parties otherwise agree to arbitration) or by agreement.

The provision

The Scheme for Construction Contracts in Northern Ireland Regulations (Northern Ireland) 1999 provides:

No specific provision is made in the Scheme for the procedures to be followed in relation to the above final determination.

The agreement of the Parties

Clause 9	*Option Y(UK) 2*
It is implied in this contract that the Parties may agree to accept the decision of the Adjudicator as a final determination either before during or after an adjudication	It is implied in this contract that the Parties may agree to accept the decision of the Adjudicator as a final determination either before, during or after an adjudication

NEC PRINCIPLES

The NEC family of contracts (whether under Clause 9 standing alone or under Option Y(UK) 2) implies that the Parties may at any time agree to accept the decision of the Adjudicator as the final determination of their dispute.

The applicable Schemes expressly make it clear that after the decision of the Adjudicator has been issued the Parties may agree to accept that decision by the Adjudicator as the final determination of the dispute between the Parties.

Clearly, therefore, there is a measure of agreement between the contracts and the Schemes in this respect.

Potential UK human rights points

Agreement or consent usually negates any human rights complaints.

England and Wales

The Scheme for Construction Contracts (England and Wales) Regulations 1998 SI No 649 provides:

Paragraph 23

(2)   The decision of the adjudicator shall be binding on the parties, and they shall comply with it until the dispute is finally determined by … agreement between the parties.

Scotland

The Scheme for Construction Contracts (Scotland) Regulations 1998 SI No 687 provides:

Paragraph 23

(2)   The decision of the adjudicator shall be binding on the parties, and they shall comply with it until the dispute is finally determined by … agreement between the parties.

Northern Ireland

The Scheme for Construction Contracts in Northern Ireland Regulations (Northern Ireland) 1999 provides:

Paragraph 23

(2)   The decision of the adjudicator shall be binding on the parties, and they shall comply with it until the dispute is finally determined by … agreement between the parties.

Arbitration

Clause 9	*Option Y(UK) 2*
It is implied in this contract that the Parties may agree upon arbitration as the tribunal for the final determination and indeed this is encouraged	It is implied in this contract that the Parties may agree upon arbitration as the tribunal for the final determination and indeed this is encouraged

NEC PRINCIPLES

The NEC family of contracts (whether under Clause 9 standing alone or under Option Y(UK) 2) implies that the Parties may provide for Arbitration as the tribunal for the final determination of their dispute and indeed encourages this.

The applicable Schemes expressly make it clear that after the decision of the Adjudicator has been issued the Parties may either have provided in their contract or, after the decision of the Adjudicator has been issued, subsequently agree that the dispute between the Parties shall be final determined by Arbitration.

Clearly, therefore, there is a measure of agreement between the contracts and the Schemes in this respect.

Potential UK human rights points

Adjudication and then Arbitration could be reviewed by the Courts so far as human rights complaints are concerned although as earlier noted, the stage which is recognised as being the final determination may be the critical stage in this respect.

England and Wales

The Scheme for Construction Contracts (England and Wales) Regulations 1998 SI No 649 provides:

Paragraph 23

(2)   The decision of the adjudicator shall be binding on the parties, and they shall comply with it until the dispute is finally determined by … arbitration (if the contract provides for arbitration or the Parties otherwise agree to arbitration.

Commentary The Parties may specify an Arbitration procedure such as the ICE Arbitration Procedures (England and Wales) or the Arbitration Act 1996.

Scotland

The Scheme for Construction Contracts (Scotland) Regulations 1998 SI No 687 provides:

Paragraph 23

(2)   The decision of the adjudicator shall be binding on the parties, and they shall comply with it until the dispute is finally determined by … arbitration (if the contract provides for arbitration or the Parties otherwise agree to arbitration.

Commentary The Parties may specify an Arbitration procedure such as the ICE Arbitration Procedures (Scotland) or the new Code for Arbitration in Scotland.

Northern Ireland

The Scheme for Construction Contracts in Northern Ireland Regulations (Northern Ireland) 1999 provides:

Paragraph 23

(2)   The decision of the adjudicator shall be binding on the parties, and they shall comply with it until the dispute is finally determined by … arbitration (if the contract provides for arbitration or the Parties otherwise agree to arbitration.

Commentary Various procedures and the Arbitration Act 1996 apply in Northern Ireland.

Litigation

Clause 9	*Option Y(UK) 2*
It is implied in this contract that the Parties may agree upon litigation as the tribunal for the final determination	It is implied in this contract that the Parties may agree upon litigation as the tribunal for the final determination

NEC PRINCIPLES

The NEC family of contracts (whether under Clause 9 standing alone or under Option Y(UK) 2) implies that the Parties may provide for litigation as the tribunal for the final determination of their dispute.

The applicable Schemes expressly make it clear that after the decision of the Adjudicator has been issued the Parties may have their dispute finally determined by litigation.

Clearly, therefore, there is a measure of agreement between the contracts and the Schemes in this respect.

Potential UK human rights points

Where litigation is selected as the means of final determination of the dispute then it may well be open to the Court at that time to pick up, consider and determine any human rights considerations.

England and Wales

The Scheme for Construction Contracts (England and Wales) Regulations 1998 SI No 649 provides:

Paragraph 23

(2)   The decision of the adjudicator shall be binding on the parties, and they shall comply with it until the dispute is finally determined by legal proceedings …

Commentary Presumably, the Technology and Construction Court would be a suitable venue to finally determine such disputes in England and Wales.

Scotland

The Scheme for Construction Contracts (Scotland) Regulations 1998 SI No 687 provides:

Paragraph 23

(2)   The decision of the adjudicator shall be binding on the parties, and they shall comply with it until the dispute is finally determined by legal proceedings ...

Commentary It is not entirely clear which of the Scottish Courts would be appropriate to finally determine such disputes in Scotland but the procedure might well be by Judicial Review with the Court selected being one which allows that procedure.

Northern Ireland

The Scheme for Construction Contracts in Northern Ireland Regulations (Northern Ireland) 1999 provides:

Paragraph 23

(2)   The decision of the adjudicator shall be binding on the parties, and they shall comply with it until the dispute is finally determined by legal proceedings ...

Commentary It is not yet clear which Court would be appropriate in Northern Ireland.

APPENDIX A
Judgments referred to in the text

1
(p.139)
The right of a Party to a complying 'construction contract' to refer a dispute arising under that contract to adjudication is mandatory and cannot be contracted out of.

> Christiani & Neilsen Ltd *v* The Lowry Centre Development Company Ltd, 29 June 2000; R G Carter Ltd *v* Edmund Nuttall Ltd, 21 June 2000.

2
(p.151)
The statutory right of adjudication applies only to 'construction contracts' entered into after 1 May 1998 (a jurisdiction question which a Court may examine).

> Christiani & Neilsen Ltd *v* The Lowry Centre Development Company Ltd, 29 June 2000.

3
(p.152)
The 'construction contract' must be in writing and in relation to the extended definition of 'writing' only where there is no denial of any of the alleged terms of the contract in previous adjudication, arbitration, or litigation proceedings will adjudication be available to a contract not otherwise in writing.

> Grovedeck Ltd *v* Capital Demolition Ltd, 24 February 2000.

4
(p.152)
But the provision requiring writing was an inclusive and not an exclusive provision, a precise recitation of the terms was not a requirement, and where the material exchanged between the Parties was comparatively great then the contract would be regarded as one in writing.

> RJT Consulting Engineers Ltd *v* DM Engineering Ltd, 9 May 2001.

5
(p.152)
The statutory right of adjudication does not apply to dwellings for occupation by a residential occupier, but when the works begin the buildings do not require to have that status provided that the operation can properly be described as principally operations on a dwelling.

> Samuel Thomas Construction Ltd *v* B & B, 28 January 2000.

6
(p.156)

Meaning of 'construction operations' and a 'construction contract'.

Palmers Ltd *v* ABB Power Construction Ltd, 6 August 1999; Nottingham Community Housing Association Ltd *v* Powerminster Ltd, 30 June 2000; KNS Industrial Services (Birmingham) Limited *v* Sindall Limited, 17 July 2000; ABB Power Construction Ltd *v* Norwest Holst Engineering Ltd; 1 August 2000; ABB Zantingh Ltd *v* Zedal Building Services Ltd, 12 December 2000; Stavely Industries plc *v* Odebrecht Oil & Gas Services Ltd, 28 January 2000; Fence Gate Ltd *v* James R Knowles Ltd, 31 May 2001.

7
(p. 161)

The definition of 'construction operations' and a 'construction contract'.

Homer Burgess Lid *v* Chirex (Annan) Ltd, 10 November 1999; Mitsui Babcock Energy Services Ltd, 13 June 2001.

8
(p.176)

The 'dispute' which may be referred to adjudication is all or part of whatever is in dispute at that time between the Parties. However, only a single dispute may be referred and if it is desired to refer more than one dispute then each must be made the subject of a separate reference.

Fastrack Contractors Ltd *v* Morrison Construction Ltd, 4 January 2000.

9
(p.176)

However, on the facts of a particular case the dispute in a subsequent adjudication may not in fact be the same as a dispute under a previous adjudication.

Holt Insulation Ltd *v* Colt Insulation Ltd, 13 March 2001.

10
(p.176)

An Adjudicator cannot adjudicate on more than one dispute under more than one contract without the consent of all the Parties.

Grovedeck Ltd *v* Capital Demolition Ltd, 24 February 2000.

11
(p.176)

Documents lodged following upon the Notice of Intention to Refer a Dispute for Adjudication do not cut down or enlarge upon the dispute referred for adjudication,

KNS Industrial Services (Birmingham) Ltd *v* Sindall Limited 17 July 2000.

12
(p.178)

Section 111 is intended to be a comprehensive code governing any rights of set off in a statutory adjudication. An effective Section 111 Notice must be served before any adjudication otherwise set off may not be considered in the adjudication or in subsequent proceedings to enforce the Adjudicator's Award.

VHE Construction plc *v* RBSTB Trust Co Ltd, 13 January 2000.

13
(p.178)

The absence of a valid Section 111 Notice may make the Application for Payment a debt capable of founding a Statutory Demand.

Re A Company (No. 1299 of 2001), 15 May 2001.

14
(p.182)

Section 111 is intended to be a comprehensive code governing any rights of set off. To be effective, a Section 111 Notice must be in writing and cannot precede the application for payment to which it is intended to apply.

Strathmore Building Services Ltd *v* Colin Scott Greig, 18 May 2000.

15
(p.182)

However, even in the absence of a Section 111 Notice, where the sums claimed were disputed, the Claimant still had to prove that the sums claimed were due.

S L Timber Systems Ltd *v* Carillion Construction Ltd, 27 June 2001.

16
(p.212)

A category of dispute may fall to be identified known as 'threshold jurisdictional disputes' – going to the ability at the outset to commence adjudication proceedings – matters which may be considered by the Court at the outset.

R G Carter Ltd *v* Edmund Nuttall Ltd, 21 June 2000.

17
(p.212)

Whether or not the Parties in question have entered into a construction contract may be a question for the Court or sometimes Arbitration.

Universal Music Operations Ltd *v* Flairnote Ltd & Ors, 24 August 2000; Cygnet Healthcare plc *v* Higgins City Ltd, 6 September 2000.

18
(p.212)

Whether or not a 'construction contract' exists is a question for the Court but once such a contract is in existence, the precise terms of that contract is a question for the Adjudicator.

Tim Butler Contractors Ltd *v* Merewood Homes Ltd, 12 April 2000.

19
(p.212)

Whether or not a settlement agreement has removed the right to adjudication is a question for the Court (and not a question for the Adjudicator).

Shepherd Construction *v* Mecright Ltd, 27 June 2000; Joseph Finney plc *v* Gordon Vickers and Gary Vickers, 7 March 2001.

20
(p.212)

The right to adjudication will survive the termination of the contract.

A & D Maintenance and Construction Ltd *v* Pagehurst Construction Services Ltd, 23 June 1999.

21
(p.212)

Concurrent legal proceedings do not amount to waiver or repudiation of the right to adjudication.

Herschel Engineering Ltd *v* Breen Properties Ltd, 28 July 2000.

22
(p.214)
A Court will seek to make a speedy Declaration in relation to an adjudication alleged to be invalid.

> Palmers Ltd *v* ABB Power Construction Ltd 6 August 1999; Sherwood & Casson Ltd *v* Mackenzie, 30 November 1999; The Atlas Ceiling & Partitions Company Ltd *v* Crowngate Estates (Cheltenham) Ltd, 18 February 2000.

23
(p.237)
So far as the appointment of the Adjudicator is concerned, it is competent for the Parties to include within the contract a provision that the Adjudicator shall be a person chosen by a Third Party from a list.

> John Mowlem & Co plc *v* Hydra-Tight Ltd, 6 June 2000.

24
(p.266)
The payment provisions of the construction contract is a question which is within the jurisdiction of the Adjudicator.

> LPL Electrical Services Ltd *v* Kershaw Mechanical Services, 2 February 2001.

25
(p.266)
The meaning within the terms of a Sub-contract may be a question for the Adjudicator.

> Watson Building Services Ltd, 13 March 2001.

26
(p.266)
The applicability of the payment terms of the contract is a question for the Adjudicator.

> Karl Construction (Scotland) Ltd *v* Sweeney Civil Engineering (Scotland) Ltd, 21 December 2000.

27
(p.266)
In principle, an Adjudicator must resign and cannot rule upon a dispute which has previously been the subject of a Decision in an adjudication (although on the facts the matter was not decided because the wrong court procedure had been used to raise such an issue).

> William Naylor *v* Greenacres Curling Ltd, 26 June 2001.

28
(p.267)
So far as concerns the ability of an Adjudicator to rule upon his or her own substantive jurisdiction and as to the scope of the adjudication, where that power is expressly given in a contract then on an Application for the Summary Enforcement of any Decision arrived at in that respect, the Court will not bring such a Decision under review.

> Farebrother Building Services Ltd *v* Frogmore Investments Ltd, 20 April 2001.

29
(p.267)
In relation to the dispute referred to him or her, an Adjudicator has the discretion to reach a decision about jurisdictional matters relating to that dispute in order to decide how to proceed with the adjudication but – unless the Parties so agree – any such decision arrived at is not binding upon the Parties and may be reviewed by a Court.

> Project Consultancy Group *v* Trustees of the Gray Trust, 16 July 1999.

30
(p.267)
A Party objecting to the jurisdiction of an Adjudicator may be considered to have the following options:
- Agree to widen the jurisdiction of the Adjudicator so as to refer any dispute about the jurisdiction of the Adjudicator to the Adjudicator
- Refer the dispute about jurisdiction to a different Adjudicator
- Seek a Declaration from the Court as to whether the Adjudicator had jurisdiction
- Reserve their position, participate in the adjudication, and then challenge on jurisdictional grounds any attempt to enforce the decision.

Fastrack Construction Ltd *v* Morrison Construction Ltd, 4 January 2000.

31
(p.267)
Where objection to the jurisdiction of the Adjudicator is taken, that objection must be carefully maintained or the Party concerned may later be estopped by representation and convention from later seeking to maintain that the Adjudicator had no jurisdiction.

Maymac Environmental Services Ltd *v* Faraday Building Services Ltd, 16 October 2000.

32
(p.268)
In relation to the dispute referred to him or her, an Adjudicator is obliged to reach a decision about jurisdictional matters relating to that dispute in order to decide how to proceed with the adjudication but – unless the Parties so agree – any such decision arrived at may be reviewed by a Court.

Homer Burgess Ltd *v* Chirex (Annan) Ltd 10 November 1999; Watson Building Services Ltd, 13 March 2001.

33
(p.268)
A Party objecting to the jurisdiction of an Adjudicator may be considered to have the following options:
- Agree to widen the jurisdiction of the Adjudicator so as to refer any dispute about the jurisdiction of the Adjudicator to the Adjudicator
- Refer the dispute about jurisdiction to a different Adjudicator
- Seek a Declaration from the Court as to whether the Adjudicator had jurisdiction
- Reserve their position, participate in the adjudication, and then challenge on jurisdictional grounds any attempt to enforce the decision.

Fastrack Construction Ltd *v* Morrison Construction Ltd; applied with approval in Watson Building Services Ltd, 13 March 2001.

34
(p.280)
Section 111 is intended to be a comprehensive code governing any rights of set off. An effective section 111 Notice must be served before any adjudication otherwise set off may not be

considered in the adjudication (or in subsequent proceedings to enforce the Adjudicator's Award)

VHE Construction plc *v* RBSTB Trust Co Ltd, 13 January 2000.

35
(p.280)
Claims arising from a repudiatory breach require to be mentioned in a Section 111 Notice before an Adjudicator will have jurisdiction to consider those Claims.

Northern Developments (Cumbria) Limited *v* J & J Nicol, 24 January 2000.

36
(p.280)
Abatements arising from circumstances outwith the ambit of the dispute referred to adjudication are not within the jurisdiction of the Adjudicator unless specifically referred to in a Section 111 Notice, but in relation to disputes within the ambit of the dispute referred for adjudication, an Adjudicator may consider abatement whether or not the question of that abatement had been raised in a Section 111 Notice.

Whiteways Contractors (Sussex) Ltd *v* Impressa Castelli Construction UK Ltd, 9 August 2000.

37
(p.280)
A 'dispute' can only arise once the subject matter of the claim, issue or other matter has been brought to the attention of the opposing party and that party has had an opportunity of considering and admitting, modifying or rejecting the claim or assertion.

Fastrack Contractors Ltd *v* Morrison Construction Ltd, 4 January 2000.

38
(p.280)
Care requires to be taken when specifying the dispute in a Notice of Adjudication, for a failure to do so properly may deprive the Adjudicator of the jurisdiction to hear that dispute.

Ken Griffin and John Tomlinson *v* Midas Homes Ltd, 21 July 2000.

39
(p.280)
The dispute referred to adjudication may involve payment of a sum of money or it may be declaratory of some other matter.

F W Cook *v* Shimizu (UK) Ltd, 4 February 2000.

40
(p.307)
As things stand at present, an Adjudicator does not require to observe the requirements of Article 6 of the European Human Rights Convention.

Elaney Contracts Ltd *v* The Vestry 30 August 2000; Austin Hall Building Ltd *v* Buckland Securities Ltd, 11 April 2001.

41
(p.307)
Adjudicators require to comply with the Rules of Natural Justice.

Discain Project Services Ltd *v* Opecprime Developments Ltd, 9 August 2000 and 11 April 2001; Woods Hardwick Ltd *v* Chiltern Air Conditioning Ltd, 2 October 2000; Glencot Development and Design Co Ltd *v* Ben Basrrett & Son (Contractors) Ltd, 13 February 2000.

42
(p.333)   Paragraph 20(1)
'The Adjudicator shall decide the matters in dispute and may make a decision on different aspects of the dispute at different times'. Note that this is an area where the adjudication procedures in Scotland differ from the rest of the UK. In Scotland, an Adjudicator is expressly given the (useful) power to make decisions on different aspects of the dispute at different times.

43
(p.333)   Where the only submission made to the Adjudicator by the Party concerned was that the monies reflecting any order for payment should be placed on deposit receipt in joint names, it was not an error of law going to the root of his jurisdiction for the Adjudicator to fail to consider every other alternative method of disposal before making a peremptory award.
Allied London & Scottish Properties plc v Riverbrae Construction Ltd, 12 July 1999.

44
(p.339)   So far as the costs of an adjudication are concerned, it is competent for the Parties to include within the contract a provision that (win or lose) the Referring Party will always be responsible for the costs and expenses of the adjudication (including those of the Adjudicator and the Party Receiving).
Bridgeway Construction Ltd v Tolent Construction Ltd, 11 April 2000.

45
(p.339)   Costs may, in certain circumstances, be awarded in an adjudication.
John Cothliff v Allan Build (North West) Ltd, 29 July 1999; Northern Developments (Cumbria) Ltd v J & J Nichol, 24 January 2000; Nolan Davis Ltd v Steven P Catton, 22 February 2000; Bridgeway Construction Ltd v Tolent Construction Ltd, 11 April 2000.

46
(p.344)   The correction by the Adjudicator of errors in the Decision after it had been delivered was initially not thought to exist.
Bloor Construction (UK) Ltd v Bowmer & Kirkland (London) Ltd, 5 April 2000.

47
(p.344)   But it was later decided that the 'slip rule' applied to adjudication provided that the correction was made within a reasonable time of the decision having been delivered.
Edmund Nuttall Ltd v Sevenoaks District Council, 14 April 2000.

48
(p.361)   An Application for Payment not met by a valid Section 111 Notice may form the basis for a Statutory Demand.
Re A Company (No. 1299 of 2001), 15 May 2001.

49
(p.361)
An Adjudicator's Award does constitute a debt which could form the basis of a Statutory Demand but it may be set aside in circumstances where a valid defence can be presented.

George Parke v The Fenton Gretton Partnership, 2 August 2000.

50
(p.361)
A category of dispute may fall to be identified known as 'internal jurisdictional disputes' – going to the conduct of adjudication proceedings – matters which ought to be considered by the Court in enforcement proceedings.

R G Carter Ltd v Edmund Nuttall Ltd, 21 June 2000.

51
(p.361)
The normal enforcement procedure in England and Wales is by Summary Judgment, the granting of which does not preempt any later decision by a court finally determining the dispute but instead merely reflects the fact that there is no defence to the interim binding decision of the Adjudicator being enforced.

Macob Civil Engineering Ltd v Morrison Construction Ltd, 12 February 1999.

52
(p.361)
In line with that approach, a Court may – where there is no prejudice – abridge the time periods involved and lift the stay which payment automatically creates to consider the award of costs.

Outwing Construction Ltd v H Randall & Son Ltd, 15 March 1999.

53
(p.361)
An error of fact or law on the part of the Adjudicator in interpreting the payment provisions of the construction contract, a question which is within the jurisdiction of the Adjudicator, will not prevent enforcement of the Adjudicator's Award.

LPL Electrical Services Ltd v Kershaw Mechanical Services, 2 February 2001.

54
(p.361)
Section 111 is intended to be a comprehensive code governing any rights of set off. An effective Section 111 Notice must be served before an adjudication otherwise set off may not be considered (in the adjudication itself) or in subsequent proceedings to enforce the Adjudicator's Award.

VHE Construction plc v RBSTB Trust Co Ltd, 13 January 2000.

55
(p.361)
The existence of an arbitration clause does not disable a Court from granting Summary Judgment in respect of an Adjudicator's Award.

Macob Civil Engineering Ltd v Morrison Construction Ltd, 12 February 1999; Absolute Rentals Ltd v Gencor Enterprises Ltd, 28 February 2000.

56
(p.361)
Where the Adjudicator has been properly appointed and is considering matters properly within his or her remit, a Court does

not have the power to open up and review the decision of the Adjudicator.

> A & D Maintenance and Construction Ltd *v* Pagehurst Construction Services Ltd, 23 June 1999; Nolan Davis Ltd *v* Steven P Catton, 22 February 2000.

57
(p.361)
The existence of a mere mistake on the part of the Adjudicator will not prevent the enforcement of the Adjudicator's Award.

> Macob Civil Engineering Ltd *v* Morrison Construction Ltd, 12 February 1999; Bouygues UK Ltd *v* Dahl Jensen UK Ltd, 31 July 2000.

58
(p.361)
If the Adjudicator has answered the right question in the wrong way, his or her decision will be binding; if the Adjudicator has answered the wrong question, his or her decision will be a nullity.

> Bouygues UK Ltd *v* Dahl Jensen UK Ltd, 31 July 2000.

59
(p.361)
Only where it can be established that there is a real prospect of success in challenging the jurisdiction of the Adjudicator is Summary Judgment likely to be avoided.

> Project Consultancy Group *v* Trustees of the Gray Trust, 16 July 1999.

60
(p.361)
A breach of the Rules of Natural Justice may, however, have that effect. A failure on the part of the Adjudicator to comply with the Rules of Natural Justice may, where compliance with those Rules might have produced a different decision, result in a Court declining to enforce the decision of the Adjudicator.

> Discain Project Services Ltd *v* Opecprime Developments Ltd, 11 April 2001; Woods Hardwick Ltd *v* Chiltern Air Conditioning Ltd, 2 October 2000; Glencot Development and Design Co Ltd *v* Ben Basrrett & Son (Contractors) Ltd, 13 February 2001.

61
(p.361)
The involvement of a compromise may have that effect.

> Lathom Construction Ltd *v* Brian Cross and Anne Cross, 29 October 1999.

62
(p.361)
So far as the review of Adjudicator's Decisions by the Courts are concerned, the following guiding principles may apply:

- A decision of an Adjudicator whose validity is challenged as to its factual or legal conclusions or as to procedural error remains a decision that is both enforceable and should be enforced.
- A decision that is erroneous, even if the error is disclosed by the reasons, will still not ordinarily be capable of being challenged and should, ordinarily, still be enforced.
- A decision may be challenged on the ground that the Adjudicator was not empowered by the Act to make the decision, because there was no underlying construction

contract between the parties or because he had gone outside his terms of reference.

• The adjudication is intended to be a speedy process in which mistakes will inevitably occur. Thus, the Court should guard against characterizing a mistaken answer to an issue, which is within an adjudicator's jurisdiction, as being an excess of jurisdiction. Furthermore, the Court should give a fair, natural and sensible interpretation to the decision in the light of the disputes that are the subject of the reference.

• An issue as to whether a construction contract ever came into existence, which is one challenging the jurisdiction of the Adjudicator, so long as it is reasonably and clearly raised, must be determined by the Court on the balance of probabilities with, if necessary, oral and documentary evidence.

Sherwood & Casson Ltd v Mackenzie, 30 November 1999.

63
(p.361) Where part of an Adjudicator's Decision is within his or her jurisdiction and part of an Adjudicator's Decision is outwith his or her jurisdiction then a Court may enforce only that part of the Decision which was within the Adjudicator's jurisdiction and decline to enforce that part which was not.

Ken Griffiths and John Tomlinson v Midas Homes Ltd, 21 July 2000.

64
(p.361) However, it is not open to the Parties to seek to dismantle the decision of an Adjudicator and divide that Decision into enforceable and unenforceable parts.

KNS Industrial Services (Birmingham) Ltd v Sindall Ltd 17 July 2000; Farebrother Building Services Ltd v Frogmore Investments Ltd, 20 April 2001.

65
(p.361) A perceived inability on the part of the Party concerned to later repay monies ordered by the Adjudicator to be paid in the interim is unlikely to prevent enforcement of the Adjudicator's Award and certainly not without full evidence to that effect.

Hershel Engineering Ltd v Breen Properties Ltd, 28 July 2000.

66
(p.361) Enforcement may not be delayed where a Company is simply in Administrative Receivership.

Rainford House Ltd (in Administrative Receivership) v Cadogan Ltd, 13 February 2001.

67
(p.361) But enforcement by way of Summary Judgment may not be appropriate where the Company concerned is actually insolvent.

Bouygues UK Ltd v Dahl Jensen UK Ltd, 31 July 2000.

68
(p.361)
An Adjudicator's Award may found a Statutory Demand.
Colt International Ltd *v* Holt Insulation Ltd, 2 November 2000.

69
(p.361)
Arrestment of the dependence in a litigation cannot be used to defeat the binding interim nature of an Adjudicator's Award.
Rentokil Ailsa Environmental Ltd *v* Eastend Civil Engineering Ltd, 31 March 1999.

70
(p.361)
However, arrestments properly put on do not fall to be recalled simply because of the interim decision of an Adjudicator that a lesser sum is due.
Stiell Ltd *v* Riema Control Systems Ltd, 23 June 2000.

71
(p.361)
An error on the part of the Adjudicator in relation to his or her jurisdiction has the effect of at least entitling a Court to decline to give the Adjudicator's Decision its normal interim binding effect.
Homer Burgess Ltd *v* Chirex (Annan) Ltd, 10 November 1999.

72
(p.361)
A distinction fell to be drawn between those Decisions of Adjudicators which were unsound but valid and those Decisions of Adjudicators which were invalid and 'procedural error' (i.e. a breach of the Rules of Natural Justice) may have the effect of placing an Adjudicator's Decision in the latter category.
Barr Ltd *v* Law Mining Ltd, 15 June 2001.

73
(p.361)
The Decisions of Adjudicators will be enforced unless that Decision is a nullity in the sense of the Adjudicator having acted *ultra vires* – for example, because the Adjudicator had no jurisdiction to determine the dispute referred; because the Adjudicator had acted unfairly in the procedure followed; or because the Adjudicator had erred in law in a manner which resulted in his failing to exercise his jurisdiction or acting beyond his jurisdiction.
Ballast plc *v* The Burrell Company (Construction Management) Ltd, 21 June 2001.

74
(p.361)
Although the Court 'felt uncomfortable', on the facts of this case the failure on the part of the Adjudicator to draw to the attention of the Parties the fact that she intended to substitute the statutory payment provisions for the contractual payment procedures did not amount to a ground for refusing to enforce the decision of the Adjudicator.
Karl Construction (Scotland) Ltd *v* Sweeney Civil Engineering (Scotland) Ltd, 21 December 2000.

75
(p.361)
A decision of the Adjudicator reviewed by the Court of jurisdictional grounds need not be set aside in its entirety by the Court (although it could be) but may as an alternative be remitted to the Adjudicator for adjustment.
Homer Burgess Ltd *v* Chirex (Annan) Ltd, 18 November 1999.

76
(p.361)
Or the Decision of the Adjudicator may on the application of the Parties be divided into enforceable parts and unenforceable parts.

Barr Ltd *v* Law Mining Ltd, 15 June 2001.

77
(p.361)
Where the Parties place an issue about the interpretation of terms within a Sub-contract before an Adjudicator in circumstances where the Parties agreed to be bound by the decision of the Adjudicator in that respect, it is not open to the Court to review that Decision.

Watson Building Services Ltd, 13 March 2001.

78
(p.361)
So far as the review of Adjudicator's Decisions by the Courts are concerned, the following guiding principles may apply:

- A decision of an Adjudicator whose validity is challenged as to its factual or legal conclusions or as to procedural error remains a decision that is both enforceable and should be enforced.
- A decision that is erroneous, even if the error is disclosed by the reasons, will still not ordinarily be capable of being challenged and should, ordinarily, still be enforced
- A decision may be challenged on the ground that the Adjudicator was not empowered by the Act to make the decision, because there was no underlying construction contract between the parties or because he had gone outside his terms of reference.
- The adjudication is intended to be a speedy process in which mistakes will inevitably occur. Thus, the Court should guard against characterizing a mistaken answer to an issue, which is within an adjudicator's jurisdiction, as being an excess of jurisdiction. Furthermore, the Court should give a fair, natural and sensible interpretation to the decision in the light of the disputes that are the subject of the reference.
- An issue as to whether a construction contract ever came into existence, which is one challenging the jurisdiction of the Adjudicator, so long as it is reasonably and clearly raised, must be determined by the Court on the balance of probabilities with, if necessary, oral and documentary evidence.

Sherwood & Casson Ltd *v* Mackenzie applied in Scotland by Watson Building Services Ltd, 13 March 2001.

Index